GREECE BY PREJUDICE

Also by Daphne Athas

THE FOURTH WORLD

THE WEATHER OF THE HEART

Greece

DAPHNE ATHAS

by Prejudice

J. B. LIPPINCOTT COMPANY
PHILADELPHIA AND NEW YORK

First Edition
Printed in the United States of America
Library of Congress Catalog Card Number 62-11334

Contents

GREECE BY PREJUDICE

2/63

I Arrival

1

The gray light of dawn came upon us. I refused to wake up. The morning train came to life around me. Still I slept. The train picked up speed through Greece. O *ílios,* the ancient sun, crept up over the morning mountains and began to pour into the train. Windows were opened. The morning moisture of still-clinging dew blew in with merry rays of the sun. People got up from their sitting-sleeping and washed their faces.

Suddenly I opened my eyes. I was sleeping with my feet in a Greek soldier's lap. Sophie was nowhere to be seen.

I bounded up. The soldier leaned over. He wanted to engage me in conversation. But I was sleep-proud. I glowered at him vengefully. I left him and slammed the door.

In another compartment I found Pano, Maria, and Sophie. These were three Greeks who had befriended me during the journey. Sophie I had met when I first boarded the train in London. Pano and Maria had got on in Germany, Pano a salesman with mechanical mice in his suitcase and Maria, returning to Crete from a season working in a German doll factory. We had drifted together during the long trek and were now bosom train companions.

They were eating oranges and bread. They offered me an orange. Gradually I came into existence. We began to laugh and talk.

Now the Greek sun glittered in. Noon was approaching. We hung out the window. There were poppies flying like red banners in the cracks between the rocks of the gray glittering morning mountains. All the dew had dried now. There was purple gorse spangling in the sun. The grass was thin-stubbled like tuffets. All Greece was piles of rocks. The weather grew hot. The train threw cinders and smoke at us. Above the sky was vivid blue. The sun caught the lights of our eyes.

The train stopped at a station.

Suddenly Pano, Sophie, and Maria screamed joyfully.

"What is it? What is it?"

They did not answer. They rushed out into the passageway and jumped out of the train. In the station was a man with a black mustache and a white apron. He stood over a charcoal grill. On the grill was a tray with slices of bread. On the grill were sticks with roasting pieces of meat. Between them they bought a dozen *souvlákia*. They also bought some goat cheese which is white and water-dribbling. Maria bought some more oranges and some small, runted apples.

The *souvlákia* were the prize. *Souvlákia* are roasted bits of lamb on pine sticks, a kind of miniature kebab. The way you eat it, you put it in your mouth sideways. You draw each piece of fatted lamb from the stick with your teeth. It tastes the sharp, ammoniac resin taste of the stick. When you have it in your mouth and are beginning to chew it, you take a mouthful of bread to eat with it. It tastes of charcoal, lamb, oil, resin and wheat. It dribbles on your lips. You wash it down with retsina, and then you take a piece of goat cheese. For dessert you eat those bad and bitter apples of Greece. Your lips curl and your teeth smart. You are transported into the East.

"Isn't it wonderful! Say it's wonderful!" said Sophie hopping in ecstasy. It was the first time she had had *souvlákia* for eight years. Tears came into her eyes.

"Wonderful! Wonderful!" I echoed.

Yet already, our separation imminent, we had become separated. Sophie and I talked fervently about nothing. Pano looked at me sentimentally. Maria gazed at Pano.

"Do you think you shall ever come swimming at Phaleron with me?" asked Sophie. Yet it was not mournful. It was an admission that I wouldn't. Already her thoughts were on her sister and her mother whom she had not seen for eight years.

The four of us stood in the windows burgeoning into that Greek breeze in the trail of the train. We were enjoined with the sun and the elements now. The bonds between us were failing.

"In half an hour we will be in Athena."

"In fifteen minutes in Athena!"

"Stand here. Do not let anybody else take this window. You will see Athena down there. Down there." (Pano pointed.)

"Like a thousand blocks and boxes standing in the sun as we curve around this mountain," said Sophie.

"And we will see the sea?" I asked.

"The sea. And Mount Lycabettus. And Hymettus."

"And the Acropolis? Can you see that from this train?"

"Yes. It stands a little way above the other buildings. Just in the middle. Stand here and look. Fifteen minutes and you will see Athena."

The whole train was a pulsing cry of joyful laughter. All the people got up and hung out the passageway windows. Their hair was flying in the sun. Their eyes were glittering and their mouths were laughing. They were eating nutlike peas called *stragália* which were sold in white paper bags at each station.

The train rattled slowly around the mountain.

Athens lies before us.

A gray, glittering mass of boxes spread loosely on the plateau between mountains. Beyond is the sea, blue and shimmering. From the center of the town rises the Acropolis. I see the faint, faraway columns holding up the roofless temple. It is definite, silent, matter-of-fact. It is not a matter of wonder at all.

The train snakes into the plateau from the mountain. The Parthenon comes nearer and nearer. It shines like the bleached bones of the ancients. Yet it is in present time. It is a temple for today. Unlike the Roman ruins which seem like gigantic wrecks of monumental ages past. In Greece it's the same temple the ancients knew.

It's the same sun, the same breath of wind. It's the same temple, a little denuded by various cartings-off.

It is easy. It is easy to watch it spreading higher and higher as the train descends. It shines silent and speechless. It is so definite that it needs no speech. One can afford to be frivolous in the light of it. I like my *souvlákia* stick still in my hand. I like the sound of my giggles, even the beat of my excited heart.

We turn into the suburbs. Donkeys pass. The houses are made of adobe. Greek men at the *kaphenía* look up from their coffee as the train passes. They wave to us. We wave back. We shout:

"We are in Athena! We are in Athena!"

II Athens

1

THE TRAIN STATION was cold and outside the street was white, hot, and blinding with sun. I had arrived in Greece after three days of journey by boat, car, and train from London. The first thing I had to do was to find Daddy.

I am American. Half American and half Greek. Daddy was born in the Peloponnesus, in Hora, home town of Nestor. He emigrated to Boston when he was sixteen. I had always known that I would go to Greece. But I did not know when, how, or in what circumstances.

I was in England in late winter, 1958. That winter Daddy went to visit Greece for the first time in forty years. In February he wrote: "Come down here. I am folding the flag of Greece." I finished up my job in London, bought the boat ticket, crossed the Channel, and followed the sun. I had fallen in with my Greek companions on the train and they were heralds to my adventure. Daddy had been in Athens a month and a half on this day.

The last I saw of Sophie she was stuffing herself and her baggage into a taxicab with Maria. She waved and the taxi spat off in a dust cloud. All taxis in Athens are Ford cars. The back windows are shaded by homemade lace. Sophie's proud head was silhouetted through the lace like a cameo. Then the sun reflected dizzily on the outside mirror and the curvature of the rear window glass, blinding all vision.

I asked a policeman the way to Emmanuel Benaki where Daddy had an office. He was wearing the summer helmet of the Athens police, a copy of the ancient Greek warrior's helmet. It was made of aluminum. If you stand too near a policeman you will burn spots in your clothes from the reflection of the sun on his helmet. This one welcomed me to Greece, pointed the way with loud gestures, and flaunted in a smile three dizzy, golden teeth.

Away from the station, the streets were deserted. I passed stuccoed walls and stuccoed houses in a poor square, and then walked upward following some trolley tracks. A few youths lounged by an empty *kaphenίon*. The shutters were closed. The wooden chairs and tables on the sidewalk were bare. The streets were breezeless and dusty. It was very hot. The smell of the streets was exotic. It was a Greek smell. I have never smelled it anywhere else. The smell was of donkeys, dust, gasoline, fried olive oil, and bay leaf. The light was also peculiar to Greece; it was white, expansive and blinding, broken sharply by the sharp shadows of a roof, a wall, an overhanging awning, or a scraggled olive tree poking its head over an adobe wall.

I felt in intrigue with the silence and desertion. Nobody knew I was in Athens but me! Flies buzzed, droning over spilt wine on empty *kaphenίon* tables. My footsteps echoed against the ramshackle white walls. I thought of all the Athenians asleep in their cool, dark halls, olive oil still shining on their lips, their consciousness inundated in the drowsy sonata of the flies. I was alive. I was brazen. I was rapt. I traced every vulgar sign painted in white and in red on the stucco walls. I looked at the shuttered kiosks which sell sunglasses, newspapers, gum, and orange beads like rosaries. ΚΑΜΕΛ. ΦΙΛΙΠ ΜΟΡΙΣ. American cigarettes. Greek cigarettes are better. Only five drachmas (15 cents) for Papastratos Pende, Ethnos, and Aroma.

I arrived at the office building where Daddy would have been any weekday. He was not there. I had my pack on my back. Nobody could understand me, and a small crowd gathered around the cigarette kiosk where I was trying to explain my life history. The word "*Français*" was shouted. I said "*Oui,*" and a girl of twelve or thirteen led me to the top of the building in a creaking cage elevator.

There was a sound of loud shouting behind a closed door. A man knocked and waved me to enter.

I entered.

Fifteen prosperous but obviously stunned people looked up. They were sitting on straight chairs all facing a woman at a desk. She was the leader, a woman with red hair and speckled arms, chic and commanding, with gray-gloved hands which held a typewritten report. I felt like saying: "Orson is in town. I have just come from Paxinou and I've got it, Confidential Report, that Redgrave is strictly for the Caryatids. We've got to move fast."

But they were waiting, and they were not amused, just goringly curious. It was a stockholders' meeting, I decided. This inspired me. My French was magnificent. So was my story.

"*Cleistó,*" said the woman. (The building is closed.) At my blank stare: "*Fermé. Fermé!*"

"But I have arrived from England this very minute!"

"You should not have arrived in Greece on a Sunday," insisted the woman. "That is wrong."

"I know that it is wrong, but what would you have had me do?" I was in that giddy state, like a drunken, honey-rich bee, frenzied with excitement so that even the most mundane fact seemed fantastic. And the most fantastic events were really happening in an utterly mundane way. The worst of it was I was enjoying them. I had not a care now, whether I found Daddy or not. I simply wanted to continue my French speeches in this stockholders' meeting, intoxicated by the rhapsodical absurdity of it. I embroidered my story. I put in cedillas and petits points. I spoke with serious inspiration. I told them that I had hitchhiked and therefore I had not been able to guarantee that I should not arrive in Greece on a Sunday. The more far-fetched my story became, the more eagerly they believed it. They hung breathlessly on my bad accent. The whole meeting began to go to pot. One man asked me to sit down. Another offered me a cigarette.

"No, thank you, I must not sit down. I am interrupting your business," I said.

"Not at all," said the leader-woman. "Greece welcomes you, even if in this condition. But *ti na kánome?* What can we do? Business always beckons. Ha! I have an idea!" Her face lighted up. She clapped her hands. A man came running out to do her bidding. "The *teléphono* book. There will give you the names. If you cannot do anything. If you cannot find anything, then rest assured, there is a hotel right down the street. It is called the Rodos." She got up, I followed her to the window where she gave me the directions to the Rodos, pointing with her gray gloves. "Don't pay more than thirty drachmas. You know?" She pointed to her head with her forefinger, squinting up her eyes and twisting her forefinger to her temple like a screw.

"Thank you very much. I wouldn't think—"

"Remember, don't ever come to Greece again on a Sunday."

Glittering like a diamond, I offered my most grandiloquent thanks. Then I exited.

In the anteroom I perused the telephone book with no success. I gave up. I would find Daddy tomorrow. Right now I must go to the Acropolis, and for the night I would enlist in the Rodos Hotel.

II I left my bag with a concierge woman who lived with her family of children in the basement of the office building. From the door I sighted the Acropolis rising above the city below. I headed for it. I did not have a map. I did not have any Greek money either. This is an unconventional way to travel an unknown city, treating it like terrain. Furthermore the Acropolis disappeared from my sight as I descended into the Plaka, the artisans' section. Emmanuel Benaki was a foothill of Mount Lycabettus; I could see the Acropolis easily from its height. Now I had to keep its direction in my mind.

In the Plaka were butcher shops, candle shops, metal shops, canning shops, shoe shops, china shops, baker shops, and left-over smells of *baklavá*, leather, grease, olive oil, frankincense, honey, alcohol, fruit, dust, sweat, charcoal, and wine. I pushed through it, hopping willfully over old donkey droppings. It was almost three-thirty. A haunchy flea-bitten cat pondered at me from the doorway of a shop then scuttled into an alleyway. Somebody was singing strange music in a nearby street. On top of an artisan's shop, a girl with brown hair and brown lips opened a shutter. An old woman came out of a house and poured water from a pail into the gutter.

People were beginning to wake up from siesta. At four everybody would dress up to the hilt and go *perípato,* to parade. But now they were only beginning to yawn and stretch. The sun was high. The streets rose and turned into dirt walkways. I kept wondering if I was going in the right direction. I could not see the Acropolis yet. I passed a small square. A eucalyptus tree hung over a small white stone which indicated that Byron had lived there.

I did not stop to wonder why I was rushing pell-mell to the ruins of the Acropolis, moneyless, mapless, sleepless, hotel-less, and Daddy-less. I carved the Parthenon in soap in the fourth grade. I spelled it at the age of seven. I had never been myself without the Parthenon and that was because I had heard of it. That was the whiteness of my obsession that afternoon. I had lived a long while with the dregs of romanticism. They had taken life and carbonated. They were dizzyingly splendid and shook up as I chanted and ran, ran past Byron's former existence place. I looked forward to, I waited for the explosion of myself as if I were a bottle of champagne.

I was the product of twenty-five centuries of wonder, of layered culture whose inception, the temple to Athena, still lives in the city of her name. I was like a crustacean still alive. I could not have the pure story, for I read of it through impurities of history. I was born with all the horns and curlicues of history. Yet I am not myself without my history. I am not myself without the Parthenon. This is a pathetic and awesome view of oneself. A thousand million people have lived and died in these twenty-five hundred years which have elapsed between me and this temple, and here was I, running with their brimful spill-overs of culture, sayings, propaganda, and beliefs in regard to it. Ostensibly I should have been too bowed by these burdens of blood and culture even to run, let alone to have traveled a continent to get to it. But I was not. As far as I was concerned Athena's temple was sitting there waiting for me. I was not concerned with my debt to Mahaffy, Bulfinch, Homer, Dilys Powell, Lord Byron, Hesiod, Edith Hamilton, the British Museum, or the Turks. I shucked off the mounds of culture's gifts. I turned over the pyramid of culture and set myself at its top ecstatically ignorant. 'Nothing can be seen except through the individual first,' I thought. 'Athena was arrogant in taking hold of her city's mind. But here she has got hold of mine too. The Parthenon is mine first, Praxiteles' later, Demosthenes' still later, history's later, the world's even later.'

I was under the Acropolis. I could not see it. It was all slum houses, poverty houses built on the slope. Everything was stone. Stone, whitewashed houses. Stone walkways. Stone stepways. Stone walls. Stones in the dirt paths. Stone wells with water trickling from pumps.

An old woman in black sat in a stone doorway. She held in her hand a carding stick of wool. Her rough fingers went pick, pick, pick, as she took pinches of the sheep's wool and twisted it into string. The stick of wool looked like cotton candy. She smiled out of her wrinkled lips and nodded. Then she shifted her stick in her hand. Inside her house was a packed dirt floor. An oily, serene, cool, tomb-like atmosphere. It smelled of garlic and myrrh.

Since I could not see the Acropolis, but only knew from the steep rise that I was on its foundation, I continued upward and counterclockwise. The houses above obscured the view. I mounted rickety, crooked stone steps. I bore to the right on dirt paths, and then mounted other flights of stairs. Grass and bitter hunches of acacia trees spread shade. Here and there stood a cypress. Donkeys, goats, chickens, and ducks passed me in conversation.

At last I came to a wide roadway white with limestone dust. Above me soared the bastion on which stand the temples. Below lay the Agora, like a blanket messy with toys. Rubbish of columns, statues, pieces of uncovered floors. All the disinterred stones were stacked in piles. Only the Theseion stood, looking very hollow and melancholy, darkened with time. It also had an air of surprise, for it seemed to be made of orifices of mouths and eyes startledly agape. A resurrection of an ancient stoa stood opposite it, housing a new museum.

The roadway led straight to St. Paul's rock. I rushed to it. I climbed upon it. It is like a gray stone table top. Breezes lolly there hotly and gently. It was sudden eminent freedom. Below lay all Piraeus, all Athens to the sea. The landscape is the droop and slope of green-gray mountains against the gray plain. Silhouetted capes. The sea was a reflecting strip beyond, spitting the brilliant reflection of the sun in its blue. There were a few tiny pillow clouds scudding across the heavens, mere frivolities in the fathomless blue. Athens stretched out, a million glistening, boxy, gray hives scattered on the tan Attic plain. Each house was distinguishable and separate in the light.

Across sat the Parthenon, the Erechtheion, and the Temple of Nike luminating, bonelike, shedding the rays of the sun, half tan, half pink, half gray, on the wild crowned rock nose of the world. They secured all vision. The jagged fragments of the rock columns cast a blinding spell both delicate and fierce. Yet they seemed shockingly familiar. They were not dead. The sun, the air, the moon, and the rain had bleached them fresh each day. Bones they are, but present-time bones.

I felt the thrill of heat in the air from the sun and the dry breeze. The perfume is not city perfume. It has the wild lightness of country. Burning throbbing grasses are in it, and wild herbs. Athens was silent below. There was a still up-pouring of heat from its limy plain, blending with the breeze from the sea. I felt the air and I smelled it. There was that thing that they always speak of when they speak of Greece, the blinding luminosity and clarity of the air and sun on every object. Luminous were the edges of every pale rock, of every stubble of grass, of every crevice in the citadel. All objects and landscapes stare and shimmer. The heat is dry. The edges of everything are formidably clear. It prevents wonder, yet makes everything possible. The light is high, and so fierce that it transcends fierceness and enters the realm of tangible delicacy. The heat itself seems delicate. Only the dust raised by hoofs, feet, and automobile tires below obscures it.

This has an interesting effect. You have the impression of existence in a transcendent, abstract atmosphere in which all objects present a static face, no matter where you stand. This is a kind of proof of an ideal absolute, only dreamed of in moist or lush countries. It is as if your wistful dreams of an absolute truth, an absolute good, or an absolute beauty have their seams turned out suddenly. You are presented with the fact of this in material form.

Suddenly a cloud of dust rises from an automobile below. Dust clinging, dust rising. It is motion. It is proof of motion. Does it break the stasis? By all visible counts, yes. It indicates that an animal is alive on earth, a human being.

Yet, such is the power of silence above the city, and of the temples, the inexorable face of sky and stone, so unutterably light, so clear, that a rake or a rasp of dust cast by a human tire upon the hillside seems like a tiny point in a millennium. One jet of dust, like a tiny voice on the soundtrack of ages.

I wanted to raise my arms for joy for this vast presentation of an infinite material absolute. But this was my first experience with Greece. I thought it would be petty.

The staring silence of the face of the Parthenon, lucid and white against the span-blue infinity of the sky, is the most austere spectacle of joy one could ever imagine. You are encompassed in it, the abstract manifestation of an immutable face of land and an immutable temple under infinite sun and infinite sky. You cannot take the temples away from the Acropolis. And the Acropolis is, in fact, pure nature. A face of mountain and a stretch of sky. Columns. But the mountain is dauntless, aged, dusty, gigantic tan rock, treeless, grassless, even birdless. The sun is all the arias of the Parthenon. It has none of its own, only what it reflects in its silence.

And the arias of the Greek sky are illimitable, with its dusks, its sunsets, its night stars, its moon, its flaming dawns, its scudding noons, its merciless, knifelike afternoons. These are what make the Parthenon breathe.

Every day that mountain has sat there since the beginning of this very earth. Every day that mountain has lived in the space of the sun's beginning and rising. Twenty million years after man was man upon this earth, a temple was placed on this city's citadel. That temple, having lived through many other hundreds and thousands of years, caused this Acropolis to be known above other mountains and other temples poised on roofs. The relation of this Acropolis to nature is so naked that it can only be described as existing in nature. But it has no longer the aura of pomp to the majesty of Athena, or the decorative delights of paint once used to gild its figures. Weather, time, the Turks, and explosions have stripped them all away. They are now the pure bones of man's simplest aspirations naked under the sky.

Suddenly a fly buzzed in a tuft of switch grass. It found me. It beat its wings bluely in my direction. This helpless activity spilling and throbbing in the silence of the sun shattered my blankness. I looked at the dust on my heels, and I loved myself sheerly for my mortality. I envisioned myself with fondness for every trial, tribulation, even for my ultimate death on this planet. Having three-quarters allied myself with indestructibility, this did not seem heinous at all.

I became frivolous. Suddenly I kicked a pebble off St. Paul's rock down into the Agora.

Did Paul really speak here? Did he have to raise his voice mightily to have it carry far down below where my pebble has gone? Or did he have a foghorn trumpet? Poor old Paul, hair dropping in the wind, throwing out his words of Jesus on an empty-eared mob in the Agora. Did they bounce like my pebble and echo back?

On top the Acropolis is all rock. Not a bloom or a bud of grass. It seems huge, rock, marble, lime, an abstract field all shapes, all white, all blacks, except for the panorama of blue sky and the fields of cedars and city buildings swimming below. Only the Greeks, laughing gaily and brilliantly understand that such austere abstraction is nothing to their mortality and their life.

The Caryatid women are far-gone, crazy fragments of womanhood. That the weather has chewed off their noses only adds to their dignity. There is only one Caryatid that has an undamaged nose, and she is stained a rusty color, darker than the rest of them, as if she, the youngest one, had been preserved in an unwholesome place, while the others, noseless, are wrecked but free. They are all slightly solidified in their straight-standing and their straight-holding. Their serenity in holding up a building is formidable. Their wisdom and their austerity are admirable. Even after these thousands of years, chipped, they contain no evidence of having lived through hell.

I went around the temple to see the tree of Athena. It is a fake tree. A little olive tree, planted, they say, from a branch of the original, ancient olive which Athena herself planted in this place. It sits in a little well surrounded by large block stones covered by crazy Turkish writing. They paid their homage as well. I metamorphosed the tree into Athena herself. She was living, rustling. It looked like life itself. The wind whistled and snorted sneezily, whetting her wild, silvery leaves. The wind was monstrous, tricky and mammoth up here. So great Athena is still alive. She does not have to look at us disdainfully through the immutable beauty of the fashioned bones and columns that the ancient Greeks built for her. She has her amulet in that tree. It is a life amulet from the branch of an olive sprung to root by man's not so grand design and not so grand skill.

Still, that Parthenon always looms. Whatever direction I took it haunted me. I could not get away from its columns, arrogant in their humility and their clarity. I could not get away from the great roar of the wind moaning through them. I could not get away from its beauty.

The Parthenon is too solemn to break. Even seeing the roof of sky, one could not conceive of an explosion able to wreck her placement. Even seeing her bits and pieces scattered luckless and preserved in the British Museum, one could not be able to conceive of her not whole.

I could understand how the Turks hid powder kegs in her.

Suddenly from a little bastion overhanging Athens, away from the sea, there was a shout. The blue and white flag of Greece was struggling up the pole. It was haggling with the wind about who was stronger, Greece or centuries. It spanked and flapped in the wind.

There! That was Aristophanes writing!

III The Rodos Hotel had a marble entranceway and a neon sign, but once you got beyond the front, its halls were archaic corridors bordered by the slatted doors to the rooms. There was one bathroom to each floor, beautifully tiled and stinking horribly. There were plugless bathtubs and no hot water system. The rooms were white plaster. Each room contained an iron bed which sagged in the middle. The windows had long French blinds, and when you closed them, you were in cool darkness.

The manager was a fat, pink-faced, smooth, drooling man. I decided not to argue with him about price. I would let Daddy sink his Greek bargaining fangs into him in the morning. I asked for a bath and found out the tea-kettle, no-plug system, which I accepted because I had to. But as they brought the water to a simmering boil, I demanded a pail, and with the aid of it, kettle, and faucet (but with no plug) I finally created water the right temperature for washing.

The next morning the bright sunshine sprang like a tiger through the window slats. I got up and went to the Emmanuel Benaki office.

Daddy was not there.

A dyed henna-blonde let me in. This was Voula. She sat at an empty polished desk looking very busy, but smoking an Aroma cigarette. She had two gold teeth and, I found out later, was a social climber.

"*O patéras mou*," I said. "Athas."

"Eeeeeh! *Ti* Daphne!" She held up her hands and arose, as if she had been awaiting me a long time.

"Where is he?"

But she understood no English. We pointed and signaled. We shook hands. We grunted and stuttered. We laughed. From all this I concluded that he would be back in a half-hour.

On the desk I spotted his typewriter.

I signaled her for permission to use it. She assented. She was full-blown with curiosity which she could not conceal. She followed my movements greedily, noting everything about me, how long my hair was, what kind of shoes I wore, and what color my fingernails were painted.

"I am here," I wrote on the typewriter. "Will be back in 10 minutes. I am staying at thc Rodos Hotel. It is a dump, but all right. I don't think I should pay more than 30 drachs, but I think he said 42. I hope you can bargain him down. Are all Greeks as curious as Voula? D."

"Yirízete?" Voula asked anxiously when she saw that I planned to leave.

I pointed to the street, made a circle, and then pointed to where we were standing.

"Kalá. Kalá."

"Good-by."

"Good-by."

It was full morning. People milled and jostled on the sidewalks. Mostly men. I had to elbow my way. That very day the Mayor of Athens sued Parliament because the government began digging up Syntagma without his permission. The sidewalks were made of cheap limestone and each slab was worn down like a tip-basin. This made everybody walk like crabs or giraffes with no sense of balance. Also there were potholes every ten feet, like animal traps.

The crowds must be seen to be believed. A street is to a Greek what a stage is to actors. It is a place for performance. It is a place for shuffling, milling, flirting, selling, for staring, shouting, greeting, lolling, posing, arguing, bargaining, gesturing, and blaspheming. It breathes life and fire. It is a din. It is so crowded that the excess crowds have to spill off the curb. No one minds the policemen. There is no system to the walking. Nobody keeps to the right. Nobody to the left. You are jostled. You are pushed. You are kicked. You kick back. Somebody moves aside so that you can pass. Groups of lollers clog the way. They have no business. They are merely chattering. The spirit of the streets is not to go somewhere, merely to be there. Any other attitude is alien. Everything blocks progress. Lottery vendors with thousands of tickets on strips crackling in the breeze. They shout their wares with mighty voices. Sponge sellers. They carry around their waists on a string a thousand sponges. The sponge skirt is bigger than the man. What if he got caught in a rain? Would he be dragged down? Now people crush his sponges to get past him, and he barks his sponges in a gravel voice.

Suddenly, by a kiosk I saw Daddy. He looked like Pope Pius with a beret. He has icy blue eyes and a beaked eagle nose. He held a newspaper under his arm. He looked very prosperous because of the newspaper, because of the knifelike press of his trousers, and because his shoes were sparkled to a polished sheen. A man in a dusty gray suit bumped into him. Daddy lifted the newspaper in his hand. He raised it on high. Like a policeman his voice rang out: "*Aristerá! Aristerá!* To the left. To the left." The man was not offended by this tone. He was amused. He grinned sheepishly and moved off.

"Daddy!" I shouted. "Hey Daddy!"

He looked up. He saw me. He moved forward.

"Well, what do you say! What do you say! When did you get here?"

"Yesterday."

"You don't say. You don't say!"

IV Seeing Daddy in the street like this, I suddenly felt like a traveler. But also I felt like a returner. I was a tourist and a comer-home all simultaneously. It was a double-barreled effect.

When I was seven years old, Daddy tried to teach my brothers and sisters and me Greek. He tried to teach us manners at the same time. We learned manners, but we did not learn Greek. We learned how to go to the door, how to open it, how to say how-do-you-do when there was no one there, how to say "Come in," and how to introduce one thin-air piece of imagination to another. At the same time we succeeded in learning in Greek, "Thank you, Please pass me the sugar, Please pass me the butter, and Good night." We learned the alphabet too, but who could remember what order *phi, chi, psi,* and *xi* came in? Especially when some came before *mi* and *ni* and others after. In college we studied ancient Greek, but not only did we just get to Aesop, no sooner had we finished screwing our minds and tongues into that fake old crazy pronunciation that some British neo-classicist claimed was the way the ancients pronounced than our "Please pass me the butter" pronunciation had gone down the drain, and most of our proficiency, brain, and desire to learn Greek had vanished along with it. But after all, we were Americans, so what did we care? We didn't even believe we had Greek blood in our veins. It might as well have been Pepsi-Cola.

Who could conceive that there was a totem of relatives and ancestors stringing all the way back behind an ocean and a mountain, down back through a crumbling Ottoman Empire, a crystallized Byzantine mess, a Holy Roman Empire, an Alexandrian Empire, a classical democracy, back, back to the heroic, superstitious time when Cousin Nestor lived to the age of at least 200? It is easy enough to think back to the *Mayflower*, even back to William the Conqueror. Daddy was used to that. Mother was a New England Yankee, descendant of a Revolutionary War general, Joseph Spencer. But as he said at a Harvard Club luncheon after the *Mayflower* had been discussed: "And I am descended from Zeus." What could they do? They had to clap. But remember it was the Harvard Club. Otherwise, in America today, Zeus wouldn't make the impression of a peanut.

As a saving grace, Daddy thinks most of the world is fools. He is always telling people how to do things. When they rush along doing them their own way, he dismisses them, sniffing, as fools.

He believes in John Dewey, in slow experiment, in trial and error, in everlasting learning, in new generations coming and old generations dying. He believes in the new, the everlasting new. One moment is different from the next moment, he says. One moment's problems and desires give way to the solution of those problems and the granting of those desires, but within that next moment and the granting of those desires, there arise new desires. Thesis, antithesis, and a synthesis which immediately demands its antithesis. That is how the world goes on.

The world is relative to him. He does not state where he will go beyond the grave. But in this life he wields sarcasm like a wit. He turns people over like turtles. Sometimes he laughs at the way their fins whack helplessly in the air. Other times he picks them up and turns them back over on their legs to walk away because he is sorry for them.

Along with being a philosopher, Daddy is also a con artist. But he is interested in conning not so much for the results as for the performance. This is a Greek trait. This is why the Greeks are better at the liturgy of business than the net profits.

"Daddy, listen," I said. "I am staying at the Rodos Hotel. Not only do they have no plugs for the bathtub, but they are making me pay forty-two drachs for a room which stinks!"

Daddy's eyes lighted with enthusiasm. He suddenly envisaged his opportunity.

"Let us go right over there," he said.

"Now?"

"Yes."

He flapped his newspaper under his arm. We walked briskly. He shouted "*Aristerá! Aristerá!*" to all who got in our way.

"Were there bugs in your room?"

"Yes, two cockroaches."

"Ignorance. They are no better than animals. Poor cusses, what can you expect? Every cutthroat, thief, robber, liar, and thug from every village in Greece is in Athens right this minute."

We walked up the marble steps of the Rodos. The manager was standing at his counter. As he spotted us he puffed and preened greasily.

"He just graduated from a donkey, and now he wants to throw out the red carpet," Daddy said loudly. "Don't look at him. Watch this. This is going to be good."

A maid was crossing the lobby with a pail and a mop. She wore her hair like Anna Magnani, but her lipstick was impeccable. Daddy waylaid her, ostentatiously ignoring the manager.

"*Yásou,* Eleni."

"*Yásou.*"

She didn't know what was up. But quickly she spotted the signs of a demonstration. She set down her pail which slopped soapily at the rim.

"Where do you come from?" he asked in Greek.

"*Kríti.*" Pleasure rose in her face.

"What is your name?"

"It's not Eleni."

"What is it then?"

"Aphrodite."

"Ah! Aphrodite! That is an excellent Greek name. Do you realize that you are the goddess of Love?"

She flushed to the forehead.

"Aphrodite was an ancient Greek goddess, the most beautiful of all goddesses, let alone mortals," he explained. "How many people are in your family?"

"Nine. But *o patéras mou* is dead."

"How much money do you make at home in Crete? Do they raise grapes in your villages? Olives? How much money does the manager of this hotel give you?"

She answered all of these questions like a shot. She was growing flashing and exuberant in the attention. Daddy translated loudly to me.

"She makes thirty drachs in one day. Tch. Tch. Terrible. Figure that out. It costs thirty drachs for one pound of lamb. See what poor cusses. And the manager grows fat."

The manager was not able to resist these loud English exclamations. He came hurrying over. He was wringing his hands oilily, and a fat oozing smile was on his face. Daddy turned to him with exaggerated pleasure.

"Ah! So you are the manager of this hotel!"

"Constantine Aristides. Glad to meet you," and so on in Greek. He began a recitation full of flattery to me, wiping the ground and trying to usher Daddy toward the counter away from the maid. He began offering, with servile droolings, weekly rates for me at bargain prices.

Daddy ignored him.

"How many times do you mop out each room, Aphrodite?"

"Once a week."

A crowd was beginning to gather in the lobby to stare.

"You said there were two cockroaches?" he asked me.

I nodded.

At last Daddy turned to the manager. He began a peroration in very flowery Greek:

"I would hate to cast aspersions on your fine hotel, but we cannot deny that in front of all these excellent people the maid has testified that she mops the floors of each room once a week. Now we all know the habits of the Greeks, but for worldly men like you and me, we cannot hide the fact that only in an ignorant country would once a week be adequate for the washing of a floor. Why, in America any hotel who washed its floors once a week would be closed up by the Federal Board of Sanitation, or would be rented out only to goats and donkeys."

The manager grew white. His lips twitched like a mouse's over his teeth. He uttered feebly that to be sure, there was a great difference between America and Greece. Nevertheless—

Daddy pretended that he had heard nothing.

"What is your sister's name, Aphrodite?"

"Eleni!"

"Eleni!" uttered Daddy in transports. "Then I was right! Do you know that for Eleni's sake the entire Greek army fought ten years in Troy?"

"The Turks?"

"Now you've got us into this," I whispered to Daddy, "you'd better get us out. You've got the manager so mad that he won't let me stay here even if I can't find another hotel room in the whole of Athens, let alone beating him down on the price."

The manager took this opportunity to bark at Aphrodite to get the hell back to work.

Daddy sent her off with loud jokes and beautiful good-bys. She waved at him with her mop over the banister.

Then he turned back to the manager full of charm. "Now what we wanted to discuss was not weekly rates, but simply the rates for last night, as my daughter does not think she wants to sleep in a room with two cockroaches and eighteen *kounoúpia*."

"There are no *kounoúpia* in that room!" swore the manager.

"What are gnoopies?" I demanded.

"Mosquitoes." Daddy beneficently swept over this denial with the lordly air of one who will not be bothered to contradict one who is obviously lying. "Then how much do we owe you, Kyrie Constantine Aristides?"

The manager had to be coaxed to give the price. Finally, entreated he said:

"Forty-five."

"Ach!" said Daddy, smiling. "Twenty."

"Thirty-five."

"All right. Thirty," said Daddy, patting him on the back. "Bravo."

"May I ask you, Kyrie," said the manager, "who you are?"

"I am Athas."

"That is your name. But who are you? Of what nation?

"I am *Éllinas*."

"You are not *Éllinas*. You can't be *Éllinas*. What what country? What country, Kyrie?"

"I have to insist that I am *Éllinas*."

"You do not talk like a Greek. You do not smell like a Greek."

"As for the smell, that is the American influence," said Daddy. "But as for my Greek, it is better than yours. You talk pig Greek, sir, and that means it's full of Latin barbarities. If Socrates were to come to Athens this minute, he could understand you, but you would not understand a word of what he said. He would understand me better and would recognize me as a true Greek. That is because I speak Greek, not Latin. As for me, I would understand Socrates, for I understand the Greek tongue. Of course, I too have graduated from the donkey, but that is not what makes me a true Greek. You understand?"

v For three weeks Daddy and I resided in Athens. I moved to the Solonion Hotel in the Plaka, and began writing. We ate in restaurants and walked the streets.

At the Ideal Restaurant I looked at the Greeks eating.

"Do you think the Greeks are much changed? Are these the ancients?" I asked Daddy.

"They must have changed somewhat. They are probably mixed with Jews, Phoenicians, Turks, Carthaginians, and so forth. Who can say?" But he liked the thought. "See them crossing themselves." He pointed to three country girls and their father and mother at a nearby table. "Country bumpkins. See the mustache on the man. Relic of the days of fighting against the Turks. Still superstitious. They cross themselves to eat."

"But the ancients didn't cross themselves."

"They made other signs to the gods. It's all superstition."

I thought of golden Greeks. The people at the tables in the Ideal were gold all right, but they were not shining. The color of these people was like rocks and sand, like sun-riven grass, like figs faintly bleached and ripe. I saw why no Greek ever shone gold. It was the proof of their mortality. Only the sun shone. The sun shone so wildly in Athens that people could not shine or they would be immortal. These Greeks were the effects of the sun. They were toasted. They were elusive. They were a blend. The figure was there, but the color was the olive and the rock and the sand. Purity could not be a consideration. One could live and one could die, but the color would go on forever. The Greeks were spawned as the dragon's teeth. Natural and perpetuative. The true Greek was brown, with either blue or brown eyes. Their eyes did not shine either. They were vacant sea shells. They existed to be looked into. When looked into it seemed that these eyes were far away, but the more I looked, the more I was dissolved into those eyes. The Greek eyes are takers, not givers. They put around you, embrace, and finally you are inundated as if you had gone swimming.

Exploring Athens at the center was a dizzy experience. But it had its impure side, for I had my mind hanging out at every corner, greedy, and not wanting to waste a drop. I had the predisposition to like it. I had taken great pains. I had followed the sun south a thousand miles for the sight of oranges, platonically imitating their Apollo, a thousand orange little suns bobbing and bouncing, ripening across the mountains on the plateaus of Greece. I had studied *Greek Made Easy* by George Divry, a good book, *demotikí*, but respectable. I had a well-formed personality. And I had Daddy with his dispositions full of wonder and debunkery.

But it was monkeys who commanded my attention. They were used to advertise the lottery and they sat in store windows in cages filled with lottery tickets. There was one monkey to every block. The entire population of Athens clogged the streets. I saw one monkey point to a woman who had a gold tooth. He opened his own mouth and pointed to his own tooth. It was gold. He lifted his feet and jumped onto the wire grille shrieking: "Hee, hee hee." A man with squeaking two-tone shoes explained to me that this was a true Greek monkey who had been raised by some gypsies outside Salonika.

I became a monkey myself to the Greeks. I could not pass incognito. I was a "foreigner." "What is your name? How old are you? Why are you in Grecce? Are you married? How many children do you have? Boys or girls? What do you think of Greece?" total strangers asked me. Women felt the material of my clothes. I was even chucked under the chin.

"*Che sarà sarà,*" sang a flirting man. When that did not work, he burst into "A *rivedérci, Roma.*" He bent all his abilities on this flirtation. "*Comment allez-vous, mademoiselle?*" he asked. Then in an imploring voice: "How you doing, baby?" He insisted on my eye. He preened himself. "*Germanída,* eh? *Fräulein, Fräulein, sprechen sie Deutsch,* eh?"

"No, I speak English," I said.

"Oh! Oh!" Triumph made him clasp his hands. He bounced to the sky. "Where you come from dar-r-ling?"

"I come from the United States of America, and you should not be talking to me in such a grand street full of such grand people because you don't know what you're saying, and if I were really hep, I'd give you the sign of the evil eye, but how can I when you would misunderstand, when you think I'm such a foreign monkey, and I think you're such a foreign monkey and we are so charmed with each other?"

Inasmuch as he did not understand a single word (on purpose I had made it go fast—I was even out of breath), it worked. But as discouragement, it worked the opposite. He followed me by yawning shop workers as they raised the tin corrugated fronts of their shops. He followed me under balloons waving gaily above kiosks. He followed me across drilling construction works in the middle of Omonia. Across the paths of yellow and blue buses piling up in traffic and cramming pedestrians out of the street. He followed me under the arms of waving policemen, through flooding crosswalks of people, under the marquees of three movies, where Lex Barker was playing in *Tarzan,* and ΡΟΜΠΕΡΓ ΤΕ-Ϊ-ΛΟΡ and ΙΝΓΡΙΝΤ ΜΠΕΡΓΜΑΝ stared over us. I walked fast. I butted eight people out of the way and was stepped on by two. The eight I butted, he butted also. Finally in an arcade near the Syntagma I stopped. I thought a long time in silence, looking at him. Then I said in the best Greek I was able to muster:

"I thank you for all your invitations."

"Yes . . ."

"But the simple fact is that I do not want to go out with you. I do not want you to follow me. I have one request which I would be flattered if you would receive."

"Yes?"

"You turn that way . . . see?" I pointed. "I will go this way, you see?"

"Ah, *despinís, signómi.*" He took off his hat. He bent his head. "I am sorry. I hope you do not take offense at what I have done." He offered his hand. "I did not mean to offend you. Again, I offer my apologies."

With a bow, he walked back to Omonia Square.

One morning Daddy and I were in the office. It was early by Greek time, nine-thirty. We were alone, for Voula had not arrived yet.

The telephone rang. Daddy picked it up.

"*Mpros.*"

On the other end a raucous voice asked for Kyrios Stratopoulos.

"He is not here," said Daddy.

"I am Andreas P. Miliopoulos, Private Secretary to the Council for the Secretary to the Minister of Interior," said the man. "When will Stratopoulos be back?"

"I don't know."

"You don't know?"

"Perhaps in half an hour," said Daddy.

"Perhaps! Who are you?"

"I am P. C. Athas," said Daddy. "P. C. Athas, President of the National Association of the Bootblacks of America." And he hung up.

Outside in the street there was a crowd. I counted them: 657 people blocked the sidewalk, fastened on a sight in the store window.

"What is it? What is it?" I asked Daddy.

"The ice-cream machine," said Daddy. "The one from Sweden."

The ice-cream machine burped and ground. A shiny scoop shovel whirled like a dervish. A sparkling metal hand held out a flat-bottomed ice-cream cone. It inserted the cone in a hole in the machine. The machine grunted. Then it emitted a blob of pink ice cream. Everyone clapped. The man next to me began singing. He jounced up and down in time to the machine in the song of the double-edged love from the movie *Stella.*

"You know Piccadilly George," said Daddy as we pushed our way through the mob. "He decided to put up three ice-cream machines in Omonia Square. But he wanted American machines. He paid twelve thousand dollars and waited six months. And when they arrived he discovered that they could not be hitched up to the Greek electric current."

Piccadilly George owned the Piccadilly Café right opposite the University on Panepistimiou. He was a Milwaukee Greek, and the Piccadilly Café was large, fashionable in the style of 1910, sporting marble-topped tables and a balcony. It had elegance, like Fortnum and Mason. It was patronized by students from the University, by the foreigners, the elite, and the fashionable.

All the Greek retirees living on social security from America congregated in the Piccadilly. Daddy did too. It was his headquarters. He berated it: "Fifty years behind the times." But he always went there. It was one of the five cafés in Athens which served American coffee.

We went to the bar of the Piccadilly and ordered coffee. Daddy hovered like an eagle over the boy to see that he did it right. "Warm the cups first. Warm the cups," he ordered. When the coffee came to us cold, Daddy sent it back. Ostentatiously he led the way to a marble-topped table. We sat down. "Get Farouk," he said conspiratorially to a passing waiter.

Farouk was the main waiter in the Piccadilly. He was a refugee Greek from Egypt; he had been a waiter in Alexandria before coming to Athens. He had also worked part of his life in a restaurant in Piccadilly Circus. He was fat. His face was jaundiced, pouched, sweaty, gleaming and floating beneath a nest of greasy pomaded hair. His eyes were liquid and sinister black. He looked as if his sullenness and secretiveness were merely a mask, as if he would suddenly burst out laughing at the role he was playing. But what was formidable about him was that the mask was the real thing. He was the warden who ate red peppers in the glaring sun watching a prisoner having his tongue cut out in a French movie about Devil's Island. He was the Machiavelli of the plot of the murder, if not of Queen Elizabeth, at least of Frederika and Paul.

He came at Daddy's command, thick-breathed, half muttering, his eyes piercing derision.

"What do you want?" he asked in Greek. He spoke and understood English, but no one had ever heard him speak it.

"Hot coffee," said Daddy. "Coffee that is hot," he added to make it clear. "The boys—" and Daddy made a gesture to indicate that the boys behind the counter were hopeless.

Farouk's weird fatness jiggled for a moment and then was silent. He was only five foot five. He was wanted dead or alive by Interpol, but the only person who could have really stood up to him was Humphrey Bogart, and he was dead.

Without a word, he shifted the cloth on his arm and left us. Around us the overtone was a mad, jingling clatter of glasses on the marble tables, the chink of silver, and a gay, voluminous cacophony of men's voices.

"That is Farouk?" I whispered.

"Never call him Farouk to his face. No one knows his real name, but he will not allow Farouk in his presence."

We waited.

"I have taught Farouk how to heat the cups," whispered Daddy. "I have taught him to fill them with hot water, slosh the water around the cup, and only then, only then pour the coffee in."

At that moment Farouk approached our table. Daddy was silent. Farouk sported a tray lifted in the palm of his hand over his shoulder. He banked in like an airplane. There were glasses of water upon the tray as well as coffee. The water, sparkling and winking in its glass, catapulted to its brim, and then Farouk brought it to a perfect landing on the marble table top where it joyfully welled from lip to lip of the glass. But not one drop spilled. Farouk's performance contained an intricate excitement in exact contrapuntal motion to the sullen vindictiveness of his demeanor. It was like watching a tennis match at Wimbledon. He lifted the water and the coffee off the tray and placed them on the table.

For a moment he waited, the sneer on his face darkening. We lifted the coffee to our mouths.

Just as we were about to announce triumphantly, congratulatory, that the coffee was hot, Farouk turned. His expression was a crescendo of insolence in which boredom bobbed, like a boat adrift in the sea. We stuffed the messages back into our mouths and watched him waddle off.

"That man is a Greek?" I asked. "It is impossible." There was a clicking sound above the clatter of the café as the man at the next table played with his orange Turkish beads.

"The Carthaginian element has entered into him," confided Daddy. . . . "Phoenician, Jewish, perhaps even Berber, from long generations in Africa. Yet he likes to conceive of himself as Greek. Well, all the better. *Stin hygeiá tou!*" he drank his health, but secretly, so that Farouk could not see or hear.

III To Hora

1

Daddy was always prone to let events take their course. He did not look up any relatives.

One day as he stood by a sewing-machine shop in Stadiou, he got into conversation with another man. In the course of the talk, the man asked Daddy where he came from, and Daddy replied: "Hora in the Peloponnesus." It turned out that the man was the neighbor of one of Daddy's young cousins who that very moment lived in Athens.

The next day a man came to find Daddy in the Piccadilly. He was a young man, short but very muscular, with a black mustache and a rapidly balding head. He was very nervous; his face flushed red, and he held his hat in his hand. He darted up to Daddy.

"You—you are our *théo!*" He almost dissolved into tears that moment.

Daddy did not know him from a hole in the ground. But the young man was in no shape to be asked, as he was staring at Daddy as if he were a ghost, not an uncle, and crossing himself and uttering *Panagías*.

"Sit down and have some ice cream." Daddy pulled out a chair for him. But the young man would not take it. He mopped his face with his handkerchief.

"I am Andreas. Andreas Athanasopoulos, son of Ioannis . . . son of Barba Ioannis . . . you know!"

"Ioannis! Of course! Ioannis. He is alive?"

"*Dóxasi o Theós!* You are the spitting image of him! Of course, different . . . that is . . . you have coat, shoes, . . . I mean you are a big man, that is, rich, you know! . . . *Dóxasi o Theós* . . . Excuse me, Theo. You have asked about my father. Why yes, only two days ago I had a letter from him. Now they are almost ready to harvest the grapes . . . excuse me. You must . . . I don't know what . . . We had no idea that you were . . . Do you remember, Theo, in 1944 you sent a box . . . during the war? . . . And after that . . . But I don't know what I am saying . . . forgive me . . . I never imagined that you were . . . that is to say . . . that I would ever see you."

"Sit down. Sit down. Waiter! Hey, you there! Tell Farouk to bring one dish of ice cream."

Andreas lived with his wife and his tiny daughter in Neos Kosmos below the Olympian Zeus. He owned a small coffee shop which was barely making its way. Besides his wife, his second brother lived with him. This brother was a carpenter, and it was on his salary that the family depended. Andreas' father, Barba Ioannis, was Daddy's first cousin. Barba Ioannis had spawned four children upon his first wife, who thereupon died, and five children on his second. Andreas was the oldest of the second batch, and therefore important in family relations.

This meeting was the first of the snowballing operation. Daddy was even more important than heretofore suspected. He was the only senior member, male, of the family besides Barba Ioannis. The only person of Daddy's immediate family in existence was one sister, a widow, with five daughters and only one son. They lived in Hora.

Everyone immediately began to lay claim.

One week later Andreas led a delegation of seven into the Piccadilly to pay court. The committee consisted of his brother, his wife, and assorted men who turned out to be some distant relatives. They paraded into the Piccadilly and stood before Daddy's table. They told of wartime, of Hora, of sister, cousins and nephews, of family scandals, of hardships, of near starvation, and of all the children that had been born. Forty years of news.

Then they waited. They sighed. They philosophized about the difficulties of making a bare living in this hard world. They invited Daddy to their homes. Whatever crusts of bread they had were perforce his. They asked his advice on their businesses. Andreas had need of 3,000 drachmas for instance.

"What you think you see, you do not see," said Daddy, jabbing his forefinger at them archly. "You think, for one thing, that you see a rich American. You think, for another thing, that you see Panacea. What you see is one *ptohós* (poor) gentleman. That is I. One *ptohós* gentleman who has lived high on the hog, who has lived in the lap of luxury, who has lived through tantamount vicissitudes, who has been wiped out by banking mishaps and world depressions. *Dóxasi o Theós!*" He crossed himself, mocking. "Yet one who has an idea. Has two ideas, in fact. The first one is that we should eat. We should eat like pagans, right this minute! So come with me! Let us go to the Ideal and make ourselves a meal right this minute, and there I will expound to you my second idea." He led them like a Pied Piper into the street. "You know why Greece is backward? You know why Greece, which is filled with the most intelligent people on earth, is backward? Because these people, with all their native brains, are ignorant. It is the young people, the young Greeks, you, all my nephews, who will be the saving of Greece. But you have to have ideas. Ideas make machines. Ideas make progress. Come let us eat and talk of the ideas that men can have."

The ideas Daddy told them were, viz., what they ought to do: (1) Greeks could not compete in the world market of oranges because they did not sort their oranges out in standard sizes. Therefore they ought to standardize their orange sizes and crate in boxes. (2) Greeks do not have refrigerators. But they also do not use the methods they have at hand for keeping foods. They should use jars and bottles and preserve vegetables and meats in olive oil. All progress should start on a village level. God does not help those who do not help themselves.

Daddy paid for the eight macaroni dinners. (This much was dispensed.) They all waxed eloquent.

"Why did you not let us know you were here, Theo?" And then, "How long have you been in Greece?"

"When are you coming to Hora?"

"What a disgrace, Theo! Is this the way you do things in America?"

"Let us all go to Hora. Now. During the harvest of the grapes. We will bring Theo home at last. Theo, do you not remember? It is beautiful. We will live out in the fields, and dance and sing."

"You will come to Hora. Won't you, Theo?"

"Everybody will be waiting."

"Theo, Theo, what do you say?"

"Of course. Of course. I had just been waiting for the season of the grapes."

It is not to beware of Greeks bearing gifts. It is to beware of Greeks who do not. All returning Greeks bring wristwatches and trunkloads of clothes to distribute to relatives. Daddy brought nothing, and was proud of it, was proud of having dispensed a macaroni dinner to them all, and believed that his advice was worth far more than presents.

His return to Hora was being set in motion. Yet the whole procedure smacked of intrigue and of capture. Unknowns sniffed at each other, like animals. Great expectations and great explorations.

"But I will go in my own time and in my own way," he said.

By coincidence an event occurred which finally decided Daddy to take the step. He met, at a party given by some crooked Greek lawyers, the militant lady Despinis Maria Ekonomopoulou. She was a scion of Hora. She owned many lands, both olive groves and grape vineyards. She had had in her employ for twenty years Barba Ioannis and the entire family of Athanasopoulos, on a share-cropping basis. She had as her servant Martha, Andreas' sister. She owned a house in Athens, and spent a few months in the capital every year. She laid, as her claim to fame, the fact that her brother had been the chief of police of Athens before and during the occupation of

Greece by the Germans. He had been killed in a melodramatic way by the Greek Communists only a few hours before the British had landed in Piraeus to find and quell the Greek revolution.

The lady was about sixty-five years old. She had a yellowish complexion and dirty blue eyes which popped out like marbles. She dyed her hair a henna color, but it always had roots of gray because it grew so fast. She was of bulklike proportions with two great breasts which she fitted into à-la-mode Greek cupcake-full brassières. She paraded them around proudly, like fabulous medallions. Her waist was like an olive trunk, and her hips like hard goat cheese. Her Greek was very good, but her teeth and eyes were bad. She had never married and blamed her dead parents for this. She was a crustacean, an indomitable, a tyrant, a cheat, a hypocrite, and a flirt.

She made Daddy sit down at once next to her. "You must come down to Hora. You must come down," she said, breathing and swaying with prodigious enthusiasm. "We will stay in the vineyards this summer, when they pick the grapes. We will go swimming at Petrahori. We will eat outside at the campfire at night. I invite you. It is my cottage, right in the vineyard. You must come. I will have them make you a *kalíva,* and we will stay down there three weeks of the summer season. You must come. It will be very amusing."

"Miss Maria Ekonomopoulou, you are the smartest woman I have ever seen," said Daddy.

"Kyrie Athas, you are the greatest flatterer."

Daddy went to Hora in August. But I did not go with him. I was up to my ears in work. Besides this I had a friend aboard the *S.S. Roosevelt* which was in at Piraeus. We were living it up in museums, night clubs and sidewalk cafés.

"I will smell out the situation in Hora," said Daddy.

"If you can wangle it right, I would like to come down in a couple of weeks," I said. "All I want is just one room somewhere. Because I have to finish this work and get it off. But I wish you would keep conning to the minimum."

"I will fix it up, don't worry. You mind your P's, but let me attent to my own Omicrons."

II "When are you coming?" Daddy wrote me in late August.

I wrote back: "Are you sure it's all right? I don't care what you con for yourself, but I feel very obligationy. You know Greeks."

"Forget conning and obligations. They are leaving the vineyards now. They have gathered all the grapes. Now the figs are ripe. I can stay on in the cottage. You can stay here too. Every day I borrow tomatoes and buy eggs for from one to two drachs. If you don't come there will be a large wastage of figs. They are dropping off the tree. Don't worry about Maria, or relatives or anything. As far as Maria goes, she says to come. Where are you?"

"Is there room to work?" I wrote.

Daddy wrote back: "Life is trial and error; if you don't like where you are, then try another place. Life is not stationary (comes from *stasis*, static). No idea or place or concept is stasis. Bad habits come from considering that ideas are static. Barba Ioannis has the habit of tying his donkey right next to my *kalíva*. I got him to remove it three times and he does so very obligingly, but with underground jealousy. He is convinced to this day that I do not like his donkey; but I do not mind his donkey. What I do not like is his donkey's fleas."

Two days later I had one more letter from him:

"They have gone now, and I am sleeping in the cottage. The water at Petrahori is magnificent, especially in the morning. You can eat as many grapes as you want. You can lie on the beach and eat grapes and go swimming. No one goes here. Once a year they wash the goats and themselves in sea water. When you get to Hora, go to the house of Miss Maria Ekonomopoulou. It is in the little alleyway behind the bus station. If I am here, she will get Ioannis, her head workman, to take you down here. You get the bus to Hora from the SPAP station. You will have to leave early, at 7:30, but the bus is better than the *automotrice* because you don't have to change."

III I leaned back against the drone of the bus. It was a fat, old, lumbering, sweating, smelling drone. I was half spilled toward the edge of the mountain. It was steep and exciting.

We were rising from the Argolian plain. It was a curve and sweep in successive U's against the back, not of one mountain, but a range. I was held only by my seat and the quivering, hot, flapping metal of the bus which was burdened with a tonnage of people inside and a tonnage of luggage canvas-strapped on its top. The very weight of the bus seemed a liability at first. But it became an asset after I had let go my muscles and allowed it to do the straining. I was surrounded by dark-rimmed, chattering people, eating, dozing, and laughing. Some sucked lemons to keep from being sick with dizziness. I leaned out the window. My arm was poised on the brilliant iron bar. The sun was brilliant. The air grew lighter and lighter. I was going steadily up and up like plodding flea tracks on an elephant's back. But I had no concern for where I was going. I did not look upward. I looked off and over at the Argolian plain, watching it in all its multifold aspects. At last it seemed that I was not of any caravan going anywhere. I was disembodied and possessed of a vision.

For two hours, pictures of the towns of Nauplia and Argos, and the gulf lying breathtakingly blue in the basin below me. It was a moving picture of the same scene always. So that I got, not a melody unrolling quantitatively before me as in Tchaikovsky or Brahms, but the qualitative exploration of one note, always the same note, but different in timbre, in rhythm, in harmonics, as in Stravinsky. It led nowhere in itself, but it was mesmerizing in its suspense.

Yet something was moving. That was the curious part. It was not the vision, but it was myself. The tipping and spilling of my body sideways and backward poised over the edge of mountain gave me this sensation of disembodiment. It allowed all my attention to fall upon the plain beneath. It gave to me the power of the bus. Effortless, while the bus sweated and panted and struck upon its myriad gears for different slants of the climb, I was as sagged and relaxed as if I were on a magic carpet. My disembodiment had the added joy of having a powerful slave work my muscles while I was given over to the spell. The mountain fell winking tan below me. There was the beckoning shadow of a cloud crossing the plain. Way below lay the snapping, blue, shocking water of the Mediterranean.

But the very movement of me forced the recognition of the place where I was (the mountain) and the road by which I hung to (the mountain). So I saw suddenly the entire hypnotic vision of the Argolian plain through the red flash of a spring poppy. It was like an open mouth of astonishment. I was arranged in the silent spectacle of austere beauty and at the same time surprised by the lick of the clever red tongue laughing against the breeze. A slim cypress tree stood against the edge of the road. The view was immediately rearranged and completely changed by that one lick of dignified, green fir. I had to focus and refocus my eye. Far and near were brought together. Yet I could not see far and not have seen it from near. Two honeybees suddenly visited the poppy in a clump of gorse by the roadside. I was startled in the brilliantine air. It had a thrum of summer insects in its heat and sudden sunny carousings of a breath of wind which licked my face and hair just traveled up over the vines of Dionysus. The sense of heat and summer space and traveling breezes. A cloud dusted me on the mountainside, the poppy and grass quivered, the very breath of the air sighed, the whole mountain place became bluely purple, and yet before me still lay that Argolian plain brilliant in the sunshine, untouched, immutable, trimmed by the banner-blue sky and the aquamarine sea.

IV Hora. I like to say it. I say it over and over and smile, because it signifies both the comedown and the immutability of Greek civilization. Hora. It means nothing. It means land or region, sometimes just town. It must be strange to be born in a town whose name is Town. The nameless quality of this name is simultaneously pretentious and unpretentious. It pits nothing against the ancients, but in fact, it is more truly the site of ancient Pylos than Pylos of the present time. But because of its quality of abstraction, it does not pin its significance upon either Hermes or Nestor. It allows the significance of ages to stare upon it, yet with a *soupçon* of pride it seems to say: 'I am the Town, the present Town, the living Town. I am the present generations of the antecedents of Nestor and the slaves of Nestor who have not moved nor died from the glare of the ancients' brilliance, nor forgotten the songs and superstitions, who have lived through Venetians, Turks, and

Christianity, who still call their ancient gods by the names of saints, and who laugh in the summertime.'

We did not reach the Western coast until seven.

It was sunset. The land dipped downward from the road to the sea. It was fringed with olives, lanced with cypresses and trussed with nestling white-plastered houses of villages. These houses' roofs were curved in terra cotta tiles like ears which were listening to the quiet bleat of the sea. The orange eye of the sinking sun dyed the sea a golden braid. The coast curved in and out making crescent beaches. The sea was golden too, and the sky above a faint and languorous blue. The windows of the bus were open. Everything smelled of sea, bay leaf, dust, and thyme.

In the village of Agorelitsa they were making wine. Flies buzzed around hogsheads left in the dirt road. There was the powerful, acrid smell of wine everywhere. We turned out of the village. There was a plain below. Beyond rose a mountain upon which Hora sat, like an eagle. It was a rising scatterage of whitewashed houses, set-edged into the mountain. Like a sentinel the church of Agios Ioannis sat before it, endowed with a fragile silhouette of a cross.

In the dusky, night-coming air, the lights of Hora came on. They twinkled over the basin. Everything was silent except for the grinding of the motor-bus. It began to crawl wormlike across the basin. It crossed a bridge over a dry stream. One hundred and fifty Germans were ambushed at this stream by Greek fighters during the war. We made our meandering way up the mountainside under Hora. The low gear growled. Everyone was silent in expectation.

The driver switched on the headlights. A yellow sign in Greek said: SITE OF ANCIENT PYLOS. The bus began to toot loudly to signal that it had arrived in home port. Like an ancient vessel returning to home harbor. People in the bus got up. People in the town came out on the street to hail them, "Why are you so late? What adventures did you have?" There was a great commotion. People waved: friends, arrivals, acquaintances. Insatiable curiosity. Shouts. Halloos. Men hung out of the coffee shop. The bus creaked, guttering, around the block and came to a lurching halt outside the coffee shop.

I got out of the bus quickly. I picked up my knapsack as the man threw it down from the rack atop the bus, and skidded away from all the people who wanted to take me under their wing. It was night now. All was dark. In the lights of the coffee shop I saw a boy. He was about twelve years old and wore a school uniform cap which looked like a cop's.

"Hey, Yannaki!"

"*Oriste.*" He was very respectful, but his face was atremble with curiosity.

"*Pou eíne spíti tis despinís* Maria Ekonomopoulou?"

His eyes brightened. He beckoned me.

He led me through a back alley behind the coffee shop. There were stone walls and gaunt crooked whitewashed houses each side of the dirt road. He walked ahead of me. Two donkeys passed loaded with faggots. Their hoofs clopped on the stones. The street was very narrow. The faggots brushed me. I looked up. I could see only the faint outlines of the whitewashed walls overhanging the street.

We came to a gate in a mud-brick wall. It creaked as he opened it. I followed him into a footpath leading through a dark garden. The air was filled with the sour-sweet perfume of lemon trees, orange trees, pomegranate and apple trees. I ducked my head under a trellis of grapevines until at last we came to the foot of a rickety stairway. Above there were lights.

The boy called.

"*Oríste!*" came the sound of a woman's voice above.

There was a rush of footsteps. I looked around to thank the boy, but he was gone.

v "Ah, *ti* Daphne!"

This was uttered with a clap of hands. They pronounced my name with a broad *a* and the Delta with a *th* sound.

I started up the stairs. As I climbed, three pairs of feet were revealed. There was a fat pair, a man's pair, and a Cuban-heeled pair. The fat feet belonged to Martha. The man's feet belonged to Ioannis. The Cuban-heeled pair belonged to Maria. I recognized her at once: her sallow face with seams down the cheeks, and the large eyes, now greedy with curiosity.

"*Haírete,*" I said.

For the first time in Greece I had to rely on the Greek language. They did not know a word of English. It turned out very poorly. I forgot everything, and their words were a jumble of meaningless sounds to me through which once in a while I caught the poetic refrain of a word I could recognize.

"*Exadélphi sou!*" screeched Maria, pointing to Martha and to me. "My cousin. My cousin, Martha!"

Martha was young and squat as a duck, yet paradoxically she had the swimming elegance of a swan. Her eyes were liquid and dark. Her head was flung back, and her hair was coiled around her head in the ancient Greek way. She had a startled look on her face as if she could not believe that an American was in the same room as she was, let alone her own blood cousin.

"*Kathísate. Kathísate!*"

I was whirled through a narrow passageway and set upon a straight-backed chair. The electric light shone nakedly in the room. It was a dining room, but it had a metal bed in it covered with a dark red rug. A calendar hung upon the wall. The table was covered with oilcloth.

It was not merely the fact that I could not speak that created this strange, febrile situation. It was that I was a member of them, and yet as strange to them as a Martian. Ordinary manners were of no avail. It demanded some ceremony of which I was entirely ignorant. They wanted to touch me, to feel me, as one would some animal or unknown creature from another planet.

"*Aftós eíne o* Ioannis! Ioannis!" yelled Maria in her high-pitched voice.

We shook hands. He was a gristly man of medium height with steaming strength. His eyes were pale green and had a paradoxical quality of vacancy and fierceness. A jet-black mustache tipped his lips, but when his sullen mouth smiled, it was a bright blaze of joy.

A meal was set before me. A bowl of tomatoes dripping in olive oil and peppered with *orígani* and bits of *márathon* (fennel). Martha also brought me a glass of retsina, and sat down beside me, stretching her arm over the back of my chair. They all watched me avidly while I ate and drank.

At last I sat up.

"*Pou eíne o patéras mou?*" I asked in book Greek.

They told me where Daddy was. But I could not understand. Their words began to fly about my head like swallows.

Maria shook her head and shouted words at me. Ioannis shouted at her to shut up. Martha put her hands over her face in despair. Then she tore them off and stretched out her arms as if to tear away the implacable barrier of language and reach me.

Ioannis walked over. He set one foot on the rung of Martha's chair. He leaned his head toward me.

"*Kámpo,*" he said.

I shook my head.

"*Chtíma,*" he said.

I shook my head.

"*Staphília,*" he said and nibbled at some imaginary fruit.

"Grapes? Grapes?" I asked.

"*Nai! Nai!* Gr-r-r-apes!" Then, shyly: "Far-r-m."

"Farm!" In triumph I clapped my hands.

"Kilometers *októ.*" He held up eight fingers.

"*Nai. Nai!*"

"*Páme.*"

I shook my head.

"Go."

"Go. Yes. Go. Let's go right now!"

He shook his head.

"Go," I repeated.

"*Argá.*"

I shook my head.

"*Argá,*" he repeated. He pointed to his watch, which said nine-thirty. "*Ennéa kai triánda tóra.* Far-r-m *déka kai triánda.*" He pointed to ten-thirty.

"Never mind. How will we go?"

He shook his head.

There was a silence.

"*Páme. Motosiklétta. Egó kai seis.*" He pointed to himself and then to me.

I looked dubious.

"*Óli! Óli!*" He waved his pointed finger to all of us.

"*Nai. Nai,*" I said.

But how could four fit on a motorcycle?

Ioannis' manner was of triumph. Behind his efforts which had ended in this triumph lay a fierce philosophical dominion. 'I take you, and you know it,' he seemed to be saying with his eyes. 'You are mine because no one else can begin to speak to you.' He puffed himself up like a huge peacock and strode out of the room.

Martha and Maria made preparations. They gathered rugs together. They fetched a sack of what looked like meal. They led me down the steps to the dirt street.

Everything was dark. The lights of the shops faded. We descended on a street leading down the mountain.

The moon rose in the sky and illuminated the dirt street. We stopped by a church. From far away came the roar of a motor. A headlight beamed. Ioannis bulldozed up to us sitting astride the motorcycle like a storm trooper and skidded the machine to a halt. Stones spat.

There was a sidecar to the motorcycle. Martha laid in the rugs. Pulling and pushing she and Ioannis shoved Maria aboard and settled her on the rugs like a load of baggage. She sat up, very dignified, and allowed Martha room to sit at her feet.

I straddled the seat of the motorcycle behind Ioannis. There was a gasp of surprise. This is bad in Greece. Women always ride sidesaddle, though this usually applies to donkeys.

Ioannis made a joke and pinched my leg secretly. I pulled away from him prudishly, startled.

"I ought to slap your face," I said out loud, because he could not understand a word.

He continued his flirtation by taking off with a wild cry. He pumped the motor and we were speeding down the mountain from Hora toward the sea. Stones flicked and spat from the back wheel. The moonlight was magic. The roar was deafening. We tore by some olive groves whispering in the night. We rose to the crest of another mountain. We turned hairpin curves. Martha shrieked entreaties for him to drive slower.

"Nestora! Nestora!" he shouted. There was a large, round mound, whitewashed by the moon. Below lay the Aegean, black under the moon. Far off the lights of Pylos twinkled in a semicircle. The mountain of Navarino rose luminous out of the sea. There was a ravishing smell in the air, bay leaf and wild oranges. The road was white and clear in the moonlight.

Maria's fat jiggled wantonly over the bumps and stones. Every now and then she groaned. We sped past a lone *kaphenion.* We crossed a bridge.

"*Potámi! Potámi!*" shouted Ioannis, indicating the river below.

We descended onto a flat plain. At last he turned the motor to a low growl, and we turned off the road into a cart path under confidential olive trees.

We were in a vineyard. The night sky was open and vast above us. In the moonlight the cottage where Daddy was shone.

Maria and Martha alighted from the car. Maria groaned.

"Kyrie Athas! Kyrie Athas!" shouted Ioannis.

Daddy came out of the unlighted cottage in pajamas. He stood in the open door yawning with great surprise in the moonlight.

"So you finally got here," he said.

IV In the Vineyard

1

THE NEXT MORNING I slept till noon. My bed was in the second story of the cottage. I was awakened by the sounds of voices below, and the hiss and whine of the pump-stove. Someone was making coffee. A donkey brayed and snuffed. Children were playing outside. I could hear their chattering and running footsteps on the ground, and intermittently the sound of a woman scolding them. I turned over to go back to sleep. Light, bright and sunshiny, filtered through the eaves and cracks in the roof.

It was a crude cottage. But there was something gaunt and grand about the dusty beams vaulted over my head. Unplaned cedar. There was no roofing at all, only the terra cotta tiles laid one over another upon bamboo strips. It was like sleeping in the loft of a barn. It had the amateurishness, the vulnerability, the beauty, and the joy of the man-made. I thought: 'Who made this roof? How much time did it take? How many calluses on the hands? How many songs were sung?' All the while the sun poked through, making fingers of brilliant light on the wooden floor. The floor was rotten, full of splinters. Dust and leaves lay upon it, blown through the windows during the summer. There was an old potato in a corner. It had a great bite in it where a field rat had eaten of it.

Daddy called.

"Who are those people?" I shouted.

"Relatives. Relatives."

"Who else?"

"Donkeys. Workers."

I did not want to burst my cocoon, even though I knew that outside was a different world, a blast, a huge, panoramic song of sun.

"Make them go away."

I might be entranced by their primeval labors, but I did not want to put up with their primeval curiosity. The chattering continued, and footsteps trailed off.

When I awoke again, they were all gone. Like a sneak thief I arose and dressed.

The stairway was only a ladder leading down from an aperture in the floor. Downstairs the floor was earthen, wavy and uneven, packed hard by generations of footsteps. Under the ladder was a huge metal oil barrel on which stood the kerosene Primus. The furniture was rude, a table, covered with oilcloth, two straight chairs, and a settee covered with a Spartan rug. From the ceiling hung a wicker basket on a rope. The bread was kept inside so the rats could not get at it. But the place was swarming with flies. On the whitewashed wall, hanging from a nail, I saw Daddy's flyswatter.

There was no running water. There was no bathroom. There was not even an outhouse. People used the fields outside, and grape leaves for toilet paper.

I went outside with my toothbrush. The sun was fierce and blinding. For seconds I could see nothing. From the doorway the grape fields stretched out full-leaved and flat and dusty, beyond their prime. Far off a small mountain rose toward the sea, and the whitewashed village of Petrahori glistened on its side. To the left was the inlet of Pylos harbor. The sun sparkled on its waters. Three rock islands rose from the sea. Navarino. Beyond on the other side of the harbor lay modern Pylos, its houses barely discernible.

Daddy was sitting in a camp chair with fluted aluminum arms. He was reading *Democracy and Education* by John Dewey. The sun outlined the flies which were large, lazy, indolent, and multitudinous, buzzing about the grass. Their blue gauze wings were silhouetted.

"I forgot my toothpaste," I said.

Daddy brought me his Colgate's from his *kalíva.* As I pulled the water up from the well, he took a bowl and went into the vineyard. He picked two types of grapes, the green type and the purple type. He also picked eight figs from the fig tree.

I washed them in the water from the well, and we sat down to eat.

The first thing we discussed was how we would eat. Maria and Martha had left us coffee, macaroni, dried fish, a loaf of molding dark bread, and cheese. We could buy eggs from the field worker Fotis who was still harvesting a mile away. And we could buy canned fish and meat at Petrahori.

"Also, Maria has promised us a *kotópoulo.*" said Daddy.

"What's a *kotópoulo?*"

"It's a chicken. They bake it with rice or macaroni, and it will last us two or three days."

"Hallelujah!"

Behind the cottage the fields stretched flat for a quarter of a mile. Then there rose steeply a mountain upon which stood the village of Koryphasion. Behind was a loop of mountains glistening purple. Nestor's palace stood upon the headland above us. We were living in the fields of Nestor's slaves.

The air was tenuous, experimental, exciting, as it is anywhere in autumn. But it had a dry, hot, light, yet vast quality, created by the sun of high noon. Above was the cry of a hawk. Now and then the sound of far-off laughter. Some peasant in the fields.

Summer was over, yet the destruction and death had not been accomplished yet. Everything was still hanging on the vines. The grapes that had been left still hung, overripe, purple, and green, in clusters. Tomatoes were still growing and would continue to grow until December. The fig tree was laden with purple figs, and the ground below was sodden and moist with the dropped, rotten figs, squashed under foot. The leaves of the fig tree were thick. They cast an unbearably brilliant contrast of darkness of shadow upon us while the sun stood in the sky, hot, still, and brilliant.

II That morning we had a visitor.

We heard hoof treads, very slow. A donkey appeared around the side of the cottage, led by an old woman in black.

"*Kali iméra*," she said to Daddy.

She was small, neat, and olive-colored, with perfect teeth. She wore a black *mandíli*. Her face was solemn. She set her blue eyes upon me with hard curiosity. She looked me up and down. It was as if she did not believe what she saw, or as if she did not know what to make of what she saw. She wanted either to approve of me completely, or disapprove of me completely. But she had no basis on which to approve or disapprove. All of this set her into a kind of embarrassment which configured strangely with the narrow-set, dogmatic, solemn, granite countenance.

"Who is that?" I asked sharply.

"It's my sister," answered Daddy.

I heard the hawk cry once again.

"Daphne," she said experimentally.

"What shall I say to her?"

She began walking toward me.

"Say good morning."

"*Kali iméra*," I said, stretching out my hand.

She stopped in her tracks. The stolidity left her face. It broke up into perfect paroxysms of grief. She smiled an anguished smile. She broke into a pouring stream of words.

"I cannot speak to her. She cannot speak to me!" I knew what she was saying, by instinct. "What a tragedy! It is a tragedy! One of my own family!" She turned to Daddy, accusing: "What have you done! Why does she not know Greek?" And then back to me. "Ah! *Ti* Daphne! *Ti* Daphne! You do not even know what I say! Oh, how you look like your mother! She looks like her mother. But she does not understand a word I say. What can I do? What can I do?"

"What's she saying?" I demanded.

"Nonsense."

"What's she crying for?"

"She's just an ignorant cuss. She doesn't know any better."

"What's she going to do?"

These exchanges in English suddenly elicited her wild alarm at the lack of communication. She wished to break across. To break it with her arms. She threw herself upon me, tears streaming down her face. She kissed me on both cheeks.

I felt disconnected from her.

"What is she slavering for? What is she crying for?"

"Custom. Custom."

"You're laughing."

"Now you see. Now you see Greece."

Her sudden commotion of grief began to amaze her as much as it did me. She stepped back. She wiped her eyes.

But having created that gesture, she continued to stare at me, almost in awe. She continued sniffing and crying. She addressed Daddy in broken words. She made elegies to me as if I were dead. In her language I was dead. Or deaf and dumb, dead to the world. She saw the English language as a fake, a hollow appearance of language. She did not believe in it. It was wrong, hollow, deniable. And yet an affront.

"Go now," said Daddy to her in Greek. "Stop that nonsense and go make some coffee."

She went toward the donkey. She brought out bread, wrapped in a white-and-blue dish cloth. She presented it to him. Then she raised her arms in a gesture of defiance and of hopelessness. It was an eloquent gesture. Her black-sleeved arms were silhouetted against the sky.

III We stayed in the cottage for two weeks.

The days were long. We were bidden and commanded by the rise of the sun and the set of it. We never knew the time correctly because Daddy's watch was always wrong. A bus passed from Pylos to Hora twice during the day, once at 6:30 in the morning, and then at two in the afternoon. Daddy went to Hora once in all those two weeks. It was an all-day expedition, for he took the early morning bus and did not return until three in the afternoon.

At night when the sun set, we watched it from the grass yard which separated the cottage from the vineyard. It emblazoned the earth. It was all the grander, all the more Byzantine because it was September. Its fiery red light perpetrated rings of scarlet around the billowing clouds. As it sank lower, it washed gentle pinks against blue-green, and finally brushed the mountains purple and dusty silver. The very silence of it spoke.

Being stuck alone with nature in this way, so much its effect, we paradoxically became its most objective appreciators. When the sun was going down, not only did we join in its thrilling death agonies, but we knew specifically what we had to look forward to.

The sunset was a kinetic thing. Not one moment remained the same as the moment before it.

Nights came at about 8 P.M. We moved the aluminum-armed camp chair in. We lit the kerosene lamp, and the hut trembled with light. Besides the kerosene lamp we had two little oil lamps or *kandília*. They were exactly like the ancient oil lamps of the Greeks, except that the container was of metal and had a handle to hang it on the wall. A wick of a string of raw wool rose out of the oil, coiled like a snake. We had to trim it every evening to keep the flame bright. On the whitewashed walls, the *kandília* reflected and flickered. We were surrounded by pockets of light and the dim recesses of the room were barely visible. Outside it grew cool and the night damp fell. But inside, the hut was warm. We always ate before night fell. Otherwise we could not have seen enough to cook or to wash dishes.

Daddy went to his *kalíva* to sleep. I read. Upstairs I heard the flopping sound of the owls upon the eaves, and then that conspiratorial, wise, intimate "Coo Coo Coo" began. The owl would come no nearer to the light and warmth than the eaves, but he made his home as near as possible, he in his station of dark, I in my station of light. Each night the rat played ball with the potato upstairs. I heard it rolling. He crunched. It slid scuddingly out of his mouth and rolled. He became intensely silent. I could imagine him holding his breath against his whiskers, a fearsome intensity in his eyes, waiting with bated breath to see if awful human damage would result. If the noise was too loud, I clapped my hands and stamped my feet angrily, laughing at the fear I would arouse in him. For an hour he was silent afterward, hiding out.

All this primitiveness had a different aspect from primitiveness in America. I could never imagine for one moment that I was not in

Greece. The rat was a Greek rat. The owl was a Hellenic owl. The moon was fierce and prophetic because it was Greek. The vineyards burned in the sun in the morning, and all the ages of Greece burned out as the dew dried in the hot sun, bringing new morning.

Every day I rose, ran out to the vineyard, picked some grapes and washed them at the well. I sat in the sun eating them, shading my eyes from the sun, allowing the sun to burn me to wakefulness. Sometimes I made Turkish coffee in the special tiny Greek pot which held two cups. After that I returned to my room and worked on my writing. At noon, astonished with the sun, I emerged. Daddy and I foraged around and cooked meals with leftovers, and with tomatoes he had stolen from the neighboring fields.

Nature is more immediately infinite than people. It shouts fierce blessings on you in the autumn and gives you harvests and hallelujah colors, and reveals no hints of its cruel possibilities for winter. It is never to be conquered by love. It is beyond such humanities and inanities. Therefore you find yourself grappling with it at every moment, even though you lie indolently sopping it up in sun-time.

The mouse is nuisance. The rat is evil. The flies are robot and multitudinous. The owl is prophetic but inhuman. The wolf is ruthless. Suddenly the flames of the merciless sky have lighted you. You can partake of the hubris of nature. You grow merciless too. It is an absolutely wild feeling. It is grand. It is heartless, great. You are being conquered slowly, surely, by the riches of Greek autumn nature. You have no thought yet for its wily turn against you. You are yet a part of its blessing, eater of the fruits that it turns out. You see no sense in appeasement. You have not become superstitious. It does not make sense to you. You are new-born of nature. You approached nature, perhaps, with dread, for you saw it peopleless. Now you are infected with its very simple lack of humanity. You see any morality as inane in regard to it. You cannot conquer it in an embrace, even though you are part of it. It has not given you its utmost challenge yet. It has not even hinted it.

But in it you find as much to live for as in society. You are at once slowed down, having only to answer for your own thoughts, and no other human thoughts. Nature is thoughtless. It gives you only its thoughtless manifestations. Slowly, slowly, as the clock hand turns. But at the same time as your reactions slow to its, you are filled with an all-abiding, all-encompassing fierce ecstasy of amorality, and love beyond human love. Every human emotion is a ruse . . . irritation at the rat, frustration at the rotten fig, satisfaction at the afternoon shade. You are fooled at your emotions' flaming. All your reactions go infinitely wild and wide, because there is no other human being to exercise upon and no radiating answer.

You become a flagrant imitation of nature, and you cannot estimate whether you are imitating or merely reflecting. It does not matter. You are filled with nature. And you want nothing else.

IV Daddy carried a walking stick. He twirled it smartly up in the air and flicked it down touching the ground lightly. He wore his blue beret and his corduroy jacket.

I wore sneakers.

We carried our bathing suits and towels under our arms.

We walked through the fields toward the village of Petrahori. We followed little paths on the boundaries of the vineyards. Grasshoppers of the flying type picked up from the vine leaves and whistled across our path to light on tomato vines. There was a thrum of insects in the dry grass.

"Which are these? *Staphília* or *staphída?*" I asked.

"*Staphília,*" answered Daddy. "*Staphília* is grapes. *Staphída* is currants. When we come back we must remember to pick some tomatoes. The lady told me we could pick as many as we wanted."

"Cucumber too," I added.

Strangely enough, it was very difficult to find our way through the vineyards, even though the little mountain of Petrahori rose before us as a guide. This was because all the vineyards were of different geometrical shapes. If we embarked on a wrong path, it led us farther and farther from the direction we wanted to go. It was impossible to cut through the fields, for it meant tangling with the shoulder-high vines.

On the way we passed two cottages. These belonged to the tenants of other fields. A mound of raisins lay in the yard of one of them drying in the sun. And a donkey was tied to a plane tree by the door. A dog barked. The peasants of these houses greeted us as we passed along our way.

At last we came out to a dirt road bordered by groves of olive trees. This road led straight to the portals of Petrahori.

"Look there." Daddy pointed with his cane. "That is the house of Lykourgos."

Lykourgos was spading in the yard. He came to greet us with his hoe. He had the straight features of an ancient statue. His head was twined with bleached brown curls. But his face was very mobile.

"*Haírete! Haírete!*"

"How are you, Lykourgos!" shouted Daddy.

Lykourgos' wife sat in a straight chair with her legs spread wide apart. She looked much older than he because one front tooth was missing. She was fat and puckery and had a squint in her eye.

"Hey, woman," shouted Lykourgos. "Get up and get glasses of water."

She rose and brought two glasses of water gleaming, dripping and bespeckled with water drops.

"*Kathísate. Kathísate,*" she bid us. "*Pou páte?*"

She stared at me avidly.

"Swimming."

This produced a sensational reaction. Of surprise, of envy, and of laughter.

"I wish I could go too," said the woman unashamedly.

"Come along."

"Oh no. What can I do? I have to work. I have to cook the supper. I have to finish the cleaning."

"Well, some afternoon, come," said Daddy.

She nodded and glittered, smiling.

"See this house," said Daddy. "When I was nine years old, I was here. Your father and I," he said to Lykourgos. "We went swimming. It was too late for me to walk all the way back to Hora. So here I stayed. Up there. I slept up there." He pointed with the stick. "I remember your grandfather, the old man. He was a doctor."

Lykourgos was very proud of his grandfather's being a doctor. He nodded and smiled.

After we left Daddy explained to me in English that Lykourgos' old grandfather was really a hog butcher and practiced his Aesculapian talents on people.

We passed along the road, under the olive trees. We came to the house of the family of Manoulis. A thousand activities were going on in the yard. Wine-making had started. Next to the house there was a slanted cement platform which ended in a small trough. At the end of this trough was a bucket. Grapes, stems, leaves, all were packed into huge burlap bags. The man of the family placed the bag on the platform. Then he took off his shoes and socks. He pulled up his trouser legs. He jumped upon the burlap bag of grapes and began his foot-dance. Slowly, gracefully, up and down he trod his feet into the mashing grapes. The bag oozed and drooled. Red juice squashed out of the bag and dribbled down the cement platform, down the trough into the pail. At each heavy step the bag squeezed succulently. Seconds later the rush of grape juice tinkled into the pail.

Everyone broke into laughter.

Greeks were the first to be cognizant of the ridiculousness of this act of wine-making. As a matter of course, the man spent the day squeezing his bags of grapes. He looked like a prize-fighter practicing his footwork with the ropes. But slower. His arms were akimbo.

"*Yásou!*" he hollered. "Watch!" He slapped one ankle vivaciously. He grinned sheepishly but hugely, like a clown. He began to perform. His footsteps mashed grandiosely, his ear all attuned to the sudden swashes of the juice in the pail.

His wife suddenly thrust her hand toward him. It stopped in midair with two fingers pointed toward his eyes. It was exactly like the V for Victory sign, but pointed *at* someone. It was the sign of the Evil Eye. But today it was a joke. She upbraided him for making a performing fool of himself, yet she herself laughed at the performance.

"What are you doing?" asked Daddy, to bait him.

"What does it look like I'm doing? Making love to my wife?" he asked.

An old grandmother burst into a fit of hysteria and sat down on a stone to wipe her eyes. All the children turned around. The wife threw up her arms with a gesture of anger.

"Look what a husband I have!" she screeched to Daddy. "You call that a man to make insulting remarks to his wife?"

Daddy, smiling, said: "He is not speaking of you, in fact, quite the opposite. Your husband is subtle. He is the only man in Petrahori who would dare to make this remark, for the very reason that it is so ridiculous that no one could take it seriously. Besides, look. Your husband is a master of mime! Look at him. Doesn't he prove it? Maybe he is making fun of every married couple in Petrahori! You should be honored to be a master-figure in such an eloquent burlesque!"

The wife immediately became very respectful. She was in fact, a merry girl. She was carrying a dirty, grinning baby in her arms and she came over to inspect me. She had black, dashing hair and eloquent dark eyes. She was rough and at the same time she was gentle.

"Who is this?" she asked. She breathed and smiled in my face, taking my elbow in her hand.

"*Aftí eíne kóri mou,*" said Daddy.

"*Tha páme bánio,*" I said.

"*Panagía mou!*" She clasped her hands likc a worshiper. She brimmed with laughter. "Listen to the girl. How long has she been here?"

In Greece even the worst Greek uttered by a stranger is the occasion for admiration. The psychology of an under-dog nation. The slave becomes enamored of that altitudinous person who manifests such democracy as appreciation of their language. Yet to the Greek, it is also unbelievable. There is something ludicrous in it. They do not want to smile, but they cannot help it.

"Eeeeh! *Panagía mou!* How she speaks! Speak! Speak!" she urged me. "Speak some more."

"*Páme mazí mas.* Come with us."

She dissolved into rapturous laughter. She praised. She stared. She worshiped. Then she said to Daddy:

"How can I go? You see how I have to work . . . and with such a husband! What can we do? We are not rich like you!"

"Bah!" said Daddy.

"Well, we are not Americans. I have no bathing suit. Besides, I am too fat. I would bust the seams of all bathing suits. Let me see yours," she said to me.

It was black nylon. She oohed and ahed. She held it up.

"You can see me in such a bathing suit! Is it American bathing suit?"

"*Londíno*," said Daddy.

"No, it's not. I got it in Athens and I only paid three dollars and . . . ," I began in English.

But she had been conquered by the fact that it was bought in London. It went up a hundred drachs' in her estimation.

"Ah, *Panagía mou*. I would like to go. But we do not go swimming now. The summer is over. *I thálassa* is cold now. You will catch a cold. Besides that, if you really want to know the truth, it is not a good thing to go swimming even in summer. You are clutched by the salt water. It makes you thin, and eventually you die."

"To swim is very healthy," said Daddy. "What you say you say because you are ignorant. Everybody ought to go swimming at least once a day. That is the most healthy thing in the world. If people do not go swimming at least once a day, they will sicken, and their lives will be shortened by at least twenty years. American doctors will testify to that. You do not know it, but it is true. Greece has not made that discovery yet."

"Ah? Is that so?" She nodded very seriously. She was doubtful, but she was skeptical of her doubts. "I love to swim," she admitted uncertainly. "Maybe I will go with you one afternoon, even though everyone in the village will think I am crazy. For only goats and horses go now; people wash them in the sea."

"That is why Greek goats are so healthy and live so long," said Daddy.

We waved good-by and started along the road.

"When will you come back?" asked the wife.

"In a couple of hours when we have finished our swim," said Daddy.

"You will come by here and greet us, yes? Promise? We have some grapes to give you. Also, you must taste the wine that is finished. Promise. Promise!"

We climbed up the rock face to the main street of the village. A few steps had been cut into the rocks in one place, but the rest was a climb.

"Why did you tell her my bathing suit came from London?" I asked Daddy.

"It makes her feel eighteen times better. Now she can go and tell all her friends that she actually had a bathing suit from London in her hands."

"I disapprove of lying," I said.

"Would you deprive her of the feeling that she is a beeg shot?" asked Daddy.

Petrahori smelled of the stench of wine-making. Hogsheads stood in the street. There were emptied buckets of grape dross collecting flies in the street. The whole town rose upward on the mountain. The main street went upward, up, up. We stopped to pant. The sun was a blinding glare. Flocks of chickens halted, screamed and ran in front of us. A donkey laden with baskets of grapes wheezed and groaned going down the stone street. Its hoofs clopped and dislodged stones which ricketed down in front of it. Dogs barked. People stared down upon us through their drying clothes on the upstairs porches. They hailed greetings.

"Say the name of this town," said Daddy.

"Petrahori."

"What does that mean?"

"Village of stone," said I, charmed.

"This town was Communist during the war. Hora people despise Petrahori. They say it is a village of thugs and thieves. They say these people steal them blind. Ha ha."

"Were they Communists?"

"I don't know. There was probably a schoolteacher here who got the others to be Communists. They are rough people here, but they are as good as anywhere else. But most Horaites still call them Communists. Some of these people are still imprisoned on an island in the Aegean somewhere where they keep the Communists."

At the top of the town lay a bull tied to a big fig tree. It rustled and looked at us out of sleep with its insane eyes. Three dogs suddenly barked. Rotten figs had fallen in the street and lay bleeding. Swarms of flies surrounded us.

The last house in the town lay almost at the top of the little mountain. We rose above it. Suddenly we were at the top.

Below lay the sea. A gentle grade of sand, gorse, *márathon*, lilacs, and asphodel led down. The beach was a perfect crescent shape with two stone promontories, like arms enclosing it. We were very hot. The breeze from the sea licked at us, warm and mild. I wanted to rush down at once. But we took a circuitous route through blackberry bushes. Sand filled our shoes. Bees buzzed upon a thousand flowers. The breeze was sleepy and sandy. It was very silent. The low waves of the Mediterranean bleated against the beach.

Navarino seemed very near, near enough to swim to. In the opposite direction the coast of Greece swept as far as the eye could see. It was a series of crescent beaches, like white bosoms of sand heaved in arms of raw, petrified lava. The village of Roumanou, not far distant, glistened very white and orange, a tree-armed village with red tiled roofs, thrumming with September flies and braying with hungry donkeys.

That summer and every summer all the people of Hora, Gargalianos, and Pylos came to camp for a month on the beach of Roumanou. They brought tents, or lived in *kalíves*. A *kaphenion* was set up in a tent during the month of August. *Bouzoúki* players and Egyptian singers were imported and every night there was singing and dancing and drinking. Ouzo, raki, coffee, and laughter. Old peasant ladies took baths in hot sand to improve the blood flow through hardened arteries. Old men picked seashells. Children splashed in the sand and water. Farm workers labored in the fields and then dipped in the sea before evening. They lived a communal life, like gypsies, roistering, gossiping, brawling, eating over campfires of grapevine sticks or charcoal.

We picked some grapes from a vineyard just before we climbed down the rocks to the beach. Running down from the mountain was an underground stream of fresh water. It made a pool in the sand, and there we washed the grapes.

We hid behind caverns of rocks and put on our bathing suits, and then we lay in the sand. The sun was brilliant and hard.

"I'm going in!" I shouted.

Daddy did European gymnastics. I went swimming.

A lava rock stood out in the water. I swam to it. Far out, behind the protecting arm of rock, lay Navarino. It glistened through the drops of water on my eyelashes. The water was warm, but it cooled me from the sun.

I wanted to dive. But the lava rock is so sharp and ragged that it will pick the tiniest thread off a piece of cloth. I climbed it carefully. I hardly put any weight on my feet. I stood.

The water was clear to the bottom. I saw every rock. I saw waving green sea grass. I saw the reflection of the bright terror of sun. I saw white bleached pebbles waving. I saw a starfish.

I rose. I hit the fragile air, tenuous, sun-laden. Everything was so still I thought that I could hear all the way to America. I lowered my head. I sprang. Underneath the sea ramified all its echoes, danking votive whispers and fishes tinkling from time immemorial. But it was bright. Holy bright. The sun plumbed the glass of water above and spread radiance all below. A fish giggled at my knee, and my hands waved whitely before me.

I came up and swam. And then I came to lie on the beach again, and I ate the glistening grapes. The air was splendid and sun-still. Daddy did knee bends. A dog barked. Suddenly I heard a donkey bray, and I laughed. I looked at the sea and away from the sea, up the rise of the beach, up the vineyard fields, away past the head of Petrahori to the mountains above.

V

What is the difference in mountains? I asked myself. Surely an Alp is as immutable as a Taygetus, or a Rocky as undying as an Ida. Yet gods have been born on Olympus and have played on Parnassus. They have not been born on McKinley or on Everest. These mountains are too formidable. They are pure juice, or call it pure spirit. The spirit is dangerous. It smells and tastes of the enemy. It is the place to conquer, not to enjoy. And it must be conquered, for it has gone out of the domain of the natural or the imagined into the supranatural. It has become personified.

Once a man has conquered his senses and his manhood and entered into a domain which is pure god, he has to depend on science. His body is nothing on Everest, and yet he must consider it or die. He has pitted himself against god. Beholding the god he is little. He is a tiny nothing creeping in the face of power. His pulsating ego (squeaking I, I, I) against the god, and knowing the ego of the god, one splendid, death-shattering 'I' can blind and obliterate him. This situation is Danger. It requires obeisance or defiance.

Scientists having mastered so many of life's physical restrictions defy, and thus mountain-climb. But when they get higher and higher, to the very hollow kernel of the god's heart which lies naked in unbreathable air and frozen in the cataclysmic deep-freezing sky, offering nothing but pure frozen beauty and nurturing nothing but death, what do they do? Wrapped in quilts and oxygen masks, armed with ice-picks and ropes, furnished with nothing but biscuits and cans, their hands bemittened, and their eyes begoggled, they begin to count their heartbeats to know that they are alive. And they begin to move their fingers to see if they have been leprosied off by the god.

When a man who has conquered Everest shall not say: "I counted my body's heartbeats and checked the condition of my fingers and my toes," as if one needed an effort to do it, instead of its being a natural thing to know; or shall not say: "At Camp II, X's fingers were slightly frostbitten, Y's leg was found to be fractured, and therefore Z, it was decided, should make the last lap of the assault on the summit," then we shall know that he was not a scientist and that the mountain was not a god.

If a man dies on a mountain it is never the mountain's fault. It is always the man's. A man takes it on faith that Everest and the Matterhorn are dangerous, and if he does not, he is a fool. If he is a fool, he shall find out by dying.

In the Greek mountains there is a separation. Olympus was always Olympus, the mountain. Zeus was Zeus, distinct, the god who lived there. The Greek mountain does not affright with the nonsensation which can create death. The Greek mountain is all around you, but far away, half mirage, even while you look at it. It reflects rather than exists. It reflects orange at dawn, gilted silver at the rising of the sun, blue in the shimmering noontime, gray, green, gilt, and tan in the early afternoon, dusty tan and hot limy gray in the peak of the afternoon, white when the afternoon clouds scud by, dark green, cold blue when the sun begins to fall, orange and dark, throaty purple at sunset, and red and shadowy green when the sun goes into the sea and only the memories of the day exist like wraiths upon its sides. When an eagle or a cloud hides the sun in the parade of sky's living things, a shadow crosses the hump of mountains. It is like a god's passing by. Somewhere there is a little snickering breeze laughing around a rock like a taunt. A poppy blows. But you are aware. You are caught by the specters of these gods. You wish you could see them. You would like to catch one maybe, and hold it with its heart beating like a bird's. If you could catch it, you would hold it up like a prize fish and think: 'See, I have caught the heartbeat of four thousand years!' But you don't need trophies in Greece. Gods' hearts like wildflowers are better unpicked. That way they are forever ranging and playing about you.

The Greek mountains, being playgrounds, do not threaten the size of you. They rise and fall, breathing the face of Greece and causing her islands. But they never cluster in one area so that they swamp you or cut off your breath. They make you a vision instead.

One tiny cloud moving across the sky changes the weight and weightlessness of the picture, varies the relationship of near and far, fixes you in a state of delighted trance, perhaps like opium. The vision is there before you, testifying nothing, yet enticing and unutterably beautiful. The lightness of the air bespeaks in you a buoyancy and a titillation simultaneously, so that no matter how drowsy and hypnotic the vision is of the distance, you see it in fragile immediacy, and these two qualities at once place you, finite and infinite, in the aura of the gods. The beach is what you lie on. The mountain is what you see. But the god is who you converse with.

In such a condition, and in recognition suddenly that this mountain has been spoken of as the dwelling of such-and-such a god and enshrined in the literature of three thousand years, say, you can suddenly flick off this immutability with a gargantuan, yet entirely natural, sense of your own mortality. That is, it does not seem arrogant. It is pure delight that begins to enlarge you. The air of delight is lighter than helium. You have no idea how inflated you become, because as you grow larger, and larger, you grow at the same time clearer and clearer. The enlargement is, in fact, clarity. And it seems, stepping as you are upon the rock of the earth's beginnings, that your mortality is as important and as clear to you and as grand as the rock of the mountain which goes back to the time before the gods were born. That you will die may seem possible, feasible, or probable, but it does not seem important. It is delight and clarity that has put you into this mood. In talking to the gods, you have got a reflection from them. For a time you can play with them, or be one of them. You can join with them, nameless as they are. If you smell the grapevine you could say that it was Dionysus, but all this naming, charting, or pigeon-holing would be unimportant to you in this state. Your mortality no longer swaddles you, it enthrones you. You can play with the gold of yourself as if it were sand. But you are convinced that it is gold, and that is the important thing. Norman Vincent Peale would say you were living to the height of your capabilities. What it is for you, you do not know. The question is automatically rejected by the state.

It is the enlargement of your mortality that creates delight. There is no sense or danger of bursting. In the converse of gods and the breath of gods, so unutterably light that it enters into you and makes your mortality light, you have opened and become glorified.

VI

It was noon. The sound of the motorcycle buzzed like an insect from far away, but it grew louder as it turned in to the track to the cottage. It bounced and ground over the tufts of coarse grass and roared to a halt in front of the door.

It was Martha and Ioannis bringing two loaves of bread, two jugs of wine, tomatoes, eggs, a rope, a kerosene lamp and the news.

"*Haírete! Haírete!*" shouted Daddy.

I rushed down from upstairs.

We had a great and joyous meeting in the yardway.

"Theo, Theo, how are you!"

"Fine. And how are the birds in Hora?" Etc. Etc.

"Theo, you are always blasphemous. I thought a week in the country would have cured you."

"And you, niece, are always busy, if not with your hands, then with your tongue. How does it go, Ioannis? *Ti néa?*"

We made preparations for dinner. Daddy and I decided on macaroni, and we poured some in a pot of water and began boiling it.

"What, no oil, Theo? Ugh!"

"We are eating American today. Try it."

Martha cut tomatoes, Ioannis poured the wine. And I tore pieces from the loaf of bread.

We sat down to eat.

"*Kalós írthate!*" shouted Ioannis, raising his glass.

"*Kalós evríkame!*" said Daddy. And we all drank.

Greek idiocy unfolds very slowly like a ball of yarn, and its skein is made up of intrigue and innuendo. You cannot elicit it, but you can help it along just by waiting and listening.

"How is your *théa?*" asked Daddy of Martha. "She came down to visit us one day."

"Eh! Thea Panayota! Eh!" Martha splayed out her hands, looked up to the ceiling and shrugged magnificently. Then slyly she looked at Daddy. "What did you say to her, Theo? What did you say to make her so mad? She has been going around the town spreading the most awful lies. Why, between the two of them—"

"What two?" asked Daddy avidly.

"Thea and my *kyrá,* Maria . . . You are only fortunate, Theo, that you are living out here with the *koukouváyes;* you do not have to hear the noise of those two. But Thea has always been a jealous woman. *Zilévi. Zilévi.* Why, she is even jealous of me."

"And Maria," said Ioannis with wickedness in his green eyes, "Maria is crazy." He pointed his forefinger to his temple and screwed it around meaningfully.

The story was this:

Thea Panayota, returning from her visit to us, began whispering in her daughters' ears:

"Why, my own brother, does he not stay at my house? It is only right. After all, he is my brother. What does he do? He accepts the invitation of the *palaio-skíla*, bad old bitch-dog Maria, to stay down on the vineyard. He sits down there the whole summer eating her chickens, salads, grapes, everything. Does she set a better table than I do? Who is she, that he abandons his own family and stays with her? It is a disgrace! How dare he insult me! *Palaio-gynaíka*, rotten woman! Prima donna! Struts around in this town claiming her people were granted by God himself to sit on the throne of Hora. Old maid. Says she is forty-one years old when everybody knows she is not a day less than sixty-five. Claims she wears Paris mode clothes and has Kyria Toula sew for her day in and day out. Well, I am not fooled by these carryings-on. Well I know her reputation. How many times has she cavorted in those upstairs rooms, locking Martha out the whole night? And he with all his elegance and book-learning. Men are fools, and he is the biggest fool of all. They are not pulling any wool over my eyes."

The daughters relayed these complaints to their husbands.

And the husbands relayed the complaints to Maria's brother, Kyrios Nikos.

Kyrios Nikos was known to the town as *to Paidí* (the Child). This was because he had entered his second childhood. He picked his nose and snoozed in the coffee shops. He gargled with retsina, spat constantly, and would never wash his hands or face or feet. Before dinner he tipped retsina out of his wine glass on to his hands and washed them in wine, but this was the extent of his cleanliness. He never cut his toenails, and they were so long that he could hardly get his boots on, and they hurt him so much that he could hardly walk. He did nothing all day but stumble illiterately from house to coffee house, to the fish shop, and back to the house again. In summer he rode, honking up and down like a bag of bones on his mare, to see that the Athanasopouloses were performing their duties. All the rest of the time he slept.

When *to Paidí* heard these stories from the daughters' husbands, he opened his bloodshot eyes, drooled, and coughed. Then he pushed himself up from his seat in the coffee shop, spat, and left. As he entered the portal gate of his house, he stumbled over the horse's water bucket. It had not been hung on its hook. Swearing, coughing, and grumbling in fury he mounted the stairs.

"Maria!"

"Yes, Nikos, *adelphé mou*. What is it?

"Kyrios Athas is making a fool of you all over town!"

Maria was aghast.

"Who?" she asked. "Who has been talking?"

Tangling with Maria was like tangling with a hornets' nest. And besides, Nikos had spent himself stumbling over the bucket and making his first accusation. Breathing heavily he sat down in his chair. He rolled his eyes gloomily and talked in a hoarse growl.

"You should curb your womanish enthusiasms. You are disgracing the house of Ekonomopoulos. What would Captain Stelios have said? And who is this Kyrios Athas anyway? A crafty man. Plays on your woman's weaknesses. You think he is interested in you? If you think your maidenly beauty could attract even a fly, you are more a fool than I think you are. The only thing Kyrios Athas is interested in is food. Witness: Every time he has eaten at the house he has had a second helping. Meat too. He took three helpings of cauliflower on Ohi Day. Now I may never have been as brilliant as Captain Stelios, but I am not too old to observe these things. From this day on Kyrios Athas is not welcome in this house. I say it. I, Nikos Ekonomopoulos."

"*Adelphé mou*, Nikos," Maria said with a voice full of glue, "you are beside yourself. All from some gossip put out, no doubt, by that witch Panayota. Now everybody knows that she was pregnant before she was ever married, and every one of her daughters too. And you take her seriously! You are getting senile, *adelphé mou*. I think you should take a nap."

"I don't want a nap. Bring me some wine and some soup."

He sat. He washed his hands with retsina from the glass. He gargled the retsina in his mouth, washing it through his rotten stubs of teeth. He picked his nose and ears with his long fingernails, and then he began slurping up the soup.

Later in the evening Maria turned on her favorite goat, Martha. "Worthless and inefficient dog," she began. "I am sick and tired of hearing the elegiac things that you are continually parading about your Theo. He is no better than he should be, and if he thinks I don't know what he is up to, he is a fool. He had the gall to ask for a *kotópoulo*, but he is not going to get it."

"But *kyrá mou*, he did not ask. It was you that offered it to him."

"Go get that water and keep your mouth shut. You never do anything until I ask you three times, and here you have left the water until the last thing. I told you before that you were to get three buckets up here for morning. You know as well as I do that we have to boil eggs and potatoes in the morning."

"But *kyrá—*"

"And never mention that Theo of yours to me again. Or Thea Panayota, or any of your troublesome tribe!"

Martha told me her story when we went out to pick *chórta* after dinner.

Chórta are wild greens which grow in the fields and the olive groves. Picking them is the woman's job. Women like picking *chórta* because it means they can get out of the house and go a-roaming. They do it with a spirit of discovery and of competition. Some of the greens are bitter, like dandelion greens. Others are tough. The choicest greens of all are called "*ovriés*." This is a wild, slim, fey plant which grows in the spring and is related to asparagus. It is very hard to spot and you have to pick hundreds of them to get anything at all. During the occupation of Greece by the Germans the poorest peasants lived on boiled *chórta*. Their eyes popped out, their faces were bone thin, their faces were yellow, and their bellies distended. Daddy's oldest sister had survived the Germans, survived the Communists, and finally died of malnutrition from eating nothing but *chórta*.

At first Martha and I did not talk. The sky was blazingly vacant. The sun and the retsina sent me reeling. The silence of the fields hummed and echoed with nothingness.

She cut, grinding with her knife into the earth in a circular motion. She pulled out the *chórta* with a flick of the wrist and threw them into a burlap bag.

"I want to do something," I said.

She turned around, pleased.

"You hold the bag. You can't do anything because you don't know how. It doesn't matter anyhow. But you hold the bag if you want to."

She went on in silence, cutting. At last she sat down, and I sat down in front of her.

"You are my cousin," she said, leaning over and picking up my hand. She looked at it and compared it to hers. "*Christós kai Panagía mou.* Think of that. You are my cousin. My father, Barba Ioannis, is your father's first cousin. Isn't that a miracle? Did you ever know a Martha existed across the ocean?

"In 1944 when I was knee-high to a toad, your father sent us a box. Inside was a pair of children's shoes. Inside the shoes was a picture of you. Isn't it strange? I never thought I would see you as long as I lived. Nor Theo. Suddenly you are in Elláda. What a miracle! Ah, *Panagía mou. Panagía mou.*"

Now I could no more understand what she was saying than I had been able to understand Daddy's sister. But the *ambiance* was different. Thea Panayota had invoked a tragedy and throttled all hope of communicating. But Martha divined that my process of understanding contained both guesswork and divination. She said:

"Here I am talking to you. How do I know what you understand? Perhaps you understand nothing." She looked at me piercingly. "But yet you understand something. I look at your face. Do you know that I loved you the minute I set eyes on you? Yes, you understand something. Soon you will begin to understand more and more, until, finally, you will understand all that there is to know."

This measure of stupidity, stubbornness, and faith in blood-love had its effect. That is the reason that I can put down this conversation now.

"You have *kalí tíchi,* a good fate. But I, sometimes I think I have *kakí tíchi.* What tears I have wept! My father has been a poor man all his life. All his life he had to work hard for Maria and Nikos, picking grapes and beating the olive trees. Now we have a new house, out of the mud bricks provided by Nikos and Maria. But when I was nine years old, during the war, we did not have enough to eat. My father came to me and he cried. He said he did know what to do. Maria had come to him . . . her cellar was stuffed with oil and wine, and every day she had enough money to buy bread from the *foúrnos*. She made my father an offer. She would take me, she said, and it would be better for all. And when I was of an age she would provide my *príka,* and I would marry the man she chose for me with my parents' consent. This was a promise. So this is how I became a psycho-paidí, a soul-child. What an erroneous conception! At nine years old, when I was smelling in all the cracks and corners of Maria's house, she said to me: "Now I am your mother, and Nikos is your father." But my soul belonged to my mother and father. It shuddered. It could never rest in Maria. A mother? *Ohi! Ohi! Poté!*"

She put her hand on her breast and rolled her eyes to the tops of the sockets so that only the whites showed.

"I could have loved Maria too, but she is an erratic woman. Her main motive in life is greed. God knows it is not up to me to criticize that woman, but what I have suffered from her. *Den phantázese!* Scoldings! Blows! Beatings! Kickings! When I was ten years old, in a fit of temper she kicked me down the stairs. I rolled from the very top to the very bottom. I should not tell anyone, but you are my cousin in blood. It is fitting to tell a cousin, *étsi den eíne?* We are of the same blood. Eh?

"Fifteen years I have lived like this. Fifteen years a slave. I cannot go out of the house without asking her. I have no money. She gives me ten drachmas at Easter and ten at New Year's. Sometimes, when the spirit of rebellion is on me, I think: 'I will leave.' But I promised my father. No. No. Where should I go? What should I do? I am not *morphoméni* like you. I am ignorant. Even in Athena what should I do?

"Now there is Ioannis. He wants to marry me. For four years we have waited. One day Maria says yes. The next day she says no. *Yerásame. Yerásame.* We grow old, and yet we are not married. All because she does not want to give up the dowry. My fate hangs upon her greed. In Greece we are immoralists. Women are like horses, bought and sold. But I say nothing of this. Ioannis is a good man. He could get ten thousand drachmas for some rich girl in Athena, but he waits for me. And we grow old. Oh *Theé, Theé!* Why have I such a miserable fate? What can I do?"

Her hand kneaded the burlap sack. She began to rock to and fro, sobbing. Such utter hopelessness was anachronistic at the height of the afternoon. The bees buzzed monotonously in the vines around us, and the sky was vacant and glazed above.

I wanted to laugh. Imagine the stillness, broken only by these sobs. It was in these very vineyards that five thousand years ago Nestor's slaves complained, laughed and sobbed. The burden was intolerable. Five thousand years of a stranger universe cast heavy in my lap. A speck of suffering in miles of teeming vineyards. Unspeakable poetry and ludicrous farce. She had climbed over the mundanity into the world of personalities, emotions, and fate. But I was caught immovable. Hypnotized into a Hesiodic lethargy.

What was the use of all these people? Why had they lived? Why had they suffered? Why had they even laughed? They had all died in the end.

They had given their place to her, and to me. And now she sang their old song, decrying the fates. I was traveling in the history of my own blood.

She looked at me imploring.

With great effort I sat up very straight. I said:

"There must be something to be done. Something can be done."

She rustled. She stirred from this gentle orgy of suffering. She sighed. She took in a faltering breath.

"*Páme. Prépi na mazépsome chórta.* The sun will go down and we will not have finished our work."

For protest to be sufficient, that was the final farce. I had offered nothing concrete. It was perfectly obvious that she did not even believe in the efficacy of my protest. Nor did she want, nor did she believe in a panacea. To her it was not centuries' suffering. But I was new, and I was kin, and she had put her blood in me, and me in a god's place to throw her life upon. It wanted only the meagerest answer. Go to Delphi. Never mind if the Pythia utters a riddle, a degradation, or a protest.

I was relieved when her cries subdued to sighs. But everything became strangely unsatisfactory. The sun still glared as fierce and meaningless as before. The protest against suffering grew monumental when suffering was mitigated.

What is the historical significance of one grief? There was something wrong in the acceptance of any burden, even the burden of the universe's meaninglessness. Margaret Fuller was bloated in her ravaged and foolish egotism when she decided that she would accept the universe. But Carlyle was a degraded god, rubbing his hands in rueful triumph when he begadded she'd better.

VII Two days later Ioannis and Martha returned, again on the pretext of cutting *chórta.* Daddy and I, in the anomalous position of being both guests and masters of our own household, were like magnets. While Thea Panayota, the daughters, the daughters' husbands, Maria, and Nikos squabbled over the issue of us in the town above, Ioannis and Martha were irresistibly drawn.

This time the mood was sharp and ebullient, belying everything that had gone before. But it was not a simple care of quick-change artistry. The framework of grief, ordainment, and fate had been superscribed; that is why everyone in Greece abandons himself to the present so joyously.

This time Martha cooked. Macaroni again, but dressed in olive oil. She was like a bird, who, not admitting it, keeps her eyes on everything at once. The wine tasted like ammonia because of the resin, but it cut the grease.

When we had feasted everyone burped luxuriously. Our legs slipped out indolently. Our eyes were fascinated by the patterns and configuration of the sun and shadows of high noon, and our minds evolved majestic, imaginative patterns of their own.

"You think we are indulging ourselves?" asked Ioannis. "We are as nothing compared to the *papádes* of Greece. Wheeeee!" He put two fingers to his mouth, whistled, and churned his left hand in concentric circles to illustrate the hyperbole. "Listen to this story."

"My father wanted me to be a pope, but I was *koutós,* too dumb, so I went to the school of psalmody in Saloniki. . . ." In this story a pope is a priest, or a *papás.* ". . . There, being with the *papádes,* I lost my religion completely. Believe in God? Christ and *Panagía!* They believe in Girls, in Food, and in Graft. But *télos pándon.* When I finished the school, I returned to Hora and became the A-Number-One psalmist at big Agios Ioannis. The pope was Papa

Papadouklas. He was very old, near eighty, and fat. He had two chins and his neck wagged. He had a wart the size of a grape on his jaw, just below his ear, and they called him 'The Frog' because of it. He was a good-natured thing, very amiable and sweet, just the opposite of the way he looked. Every morning when we came in to practice he would say: 'How are you, *paidákia mou?* Are you in good voice today? Are you going to give us a good mass? Be sure you live good and eat plenty, and don't go out with women, or you won't have a voice and you will fail the Church and God.' '*Nai, nai, papoúli mou,*' we always answered. 'You know we will always be good boys, Papouli.' Beneath his thick, porous, coarse flapping skin, his black meringue eyes winked when he said this.

"I was older than the other two psalmists, so I grew more or less into his confidence. Once or twice he would single out some girl in the congregation and say greedily: 'You see that one? See the beautiful breast? Also, see the ankles. Ah-ha,' he would sigh. 'She is so religious.' In other words, you understand, I could never figure out whether he was really a lecher, or what he was in fact.

"One summer, the Bishop came on his yearly round. He was about sixty-five, and though he was moderately stout, it was just as a man should be at that age. When he came to the church to inspect, he sat around listlessly. His eyes wandered about, and he paid no attention to Papa Papadouklas, who jiggled up and down trying to give a good impression. Papouli swung the perfume censer out five times more than necessary and rang his bell ten times instead of five. Also he had us sing an especially long mass, and his voice creaked and groaned because he sang his part so loudly, trying to make an impression on the Bishop. But the Bishop was a cold fish. He was completely bored with Papouli's attempts. In fact, he was just about to give up and go on to Kalamata when something happened.

"One Sunday a woman came up and introduced herself to Papouli. This woman was a *xéni,* a stranger, from Athena. One could see at once that she was not like our women around here. She was painted. Her eyes were covered with black mascara, and she wore lipstick. She had lived in Hora a year. She lived alone in that house just below the post office, the one that used to belong to Nicolaïdes.

She claimed to be a widow. Her reputation was worse than nothing, but whether she lived up to it or not . . . who knew? *Télos pándon.*

"The Bishop sprang up and joined the conversation. In the course of it, the Athenian woman invited Papouli and the Bishop to a feast of roast chicken. They accepted. Papouli, noting the effect of this woman on the Bishop, was delighted, and without consulting his own wishes at all, he said he thought it would be nice if they had more to join in the company . . . for instance, he knew that the Athenian woman had a friend.

"Indeed! The friend would be coming in two weeks from Athena. The friend was a Turkish woman, a belly dancer, who danced practically nude in every town from Istanbul to Athena. Papouli was overjoyed. So was the Bishop. Of course, they did not discuss it in those terms. For instance, no one admitted either that the second woman was a Turk or a belly dancer. It was accepted that she was a fine, upstanding woman, just like the Athenian woman. Papouli became so carried away by the free gift of these women and the roast chicken dropping by accident into his lap, that he suggested that they make it a real outing, that they go by donkey up to the church of the Little Cypress, Agia Katerina, over the hill, about fifteen kilometers from Hora near the town of Metamorphosis. There they would have leisure. The sun would shine, and they would have the benefits and joys of nature. The Athenian woman agreed, and the date was set.

"Now I knew the Athenian woman myself . . . I need not tell you how . . . and I suspected that she had mischief in her head. While I was with her, however, I made out as if I enjoyed her plots. And she told me about them in the coyest fashion, flapping her heavy eyelids at me, yet never admitting what she was up to.

"Papouli grew more and more excited as the days went by. But at the same time, he grew more and more nervous.

" 'I think she is a nice woman, don't you?" he asked me. 'Of course I am not one bit deluded. I know what the people think of her. But there is no reason why we should be as provincial as most Horaites. You saw yourself, how impressed the Bishop was. Now I intend that everything shall go well, and that she shall sing, and drink wine, and have the best feast in the world. We want to give the Bishop a good time, you know. Yet our conduct must be exemplary. We don't want to give him a bad opinion of us.' He dug his elbow into my side and winked. 'If the Bishop wants to avail himself of other delights than dining and drinking, why that is his privilege. Good luck to him. Ha ha ha ha!' At last he said to me, the day before the date set for the feast: 'Yannaki, you know I am a little afraid.'

" 'Why, Papouli? Why? There is nothing to be afraid of. You know it was the Bishop himself that was so entranced with the idea of going on this feast.'

" 'I know. It's true. You saw for yourself. You saw how interested he was.'

" 'Why of course he was.'

" 'Yet, I would not like him to think . . .' He sank his chin down into his black robe and blinked his eyes, just like a frog. 'I . . . ,' he started. But he did not go on. 'After all, it is up to me to see that the Bishop has a good time.'

" 'Yes,' I said. 'Of course, Papouli. And anyway, you don't have to be worried about yourself.'

"His eyes opened and he glared at me fiercely. I saw that he did not like my implications.

" 'Why not?' he demanded.

" 'Papouli *mou*,' I said falteringly, but covering it up with a laugh of bravado, 'after all, no one, even a bishop of sixty-five, would have any suspicions of a man of eighty years old.'

" 'I would like you to know,' he said almost angrily, 'that for a man of twenty-six years old, I do not think you know much of the world. And it is too bad, too, for I was just about to invite you to come along on the feast.'

"That cut me hard, for the thing had blown up to such tremendous proportions now that there was nothing I wanted to do more than to go. I could see that he was very angry. He was split down the middle, you see. At the same time that he wanted to appear a very paragon of virtue, he did not want his virtue to have the appearance of standing upon a failure of virility on his part. He was trying to prove two different things: that he was a paragon of virtue, and that he was a paragon of eighty-year-old virility. I decided to play on these weaknesses in spite of the fact that now I was beginning to be sorry for the old mule.

" 'Papouli *mou*,' I said. 'I would have appreciated your invitation very much. In fact there was nothing I would rather have done. Yet, you know, it is better this way. There should be only one man for every woman, and one woman for every man, and had I gone, I should have had to stand idly by, not only as a witness, but more than that . . . as a duenna. For, you know, with these prima donnas, not to speak of the metropolitans of the Church . . . I should have been the only existing representative of chastity. Now you know you would have hated me in the end, having to put up with me as your guardian angel.'

"He wanted to laugh, but he tried not to. 'Nonsense. Nonsense,' he fumed, waggling his head with pleasure at the flattery. 'We are talking about a lot of nonsense. It's not as if we are going to conduct a Babylonian orgy. I take issue with you calling these women prima donnas. They are good Christians and respectable women to boot. Modern, yes. After all, we are not back in the days of Kolokotronis. Look at the American women. It is ignorant to call them loose, fast, or immoral just because they are independent.' The thought of how modern and liberal he was made him feel very good. He began to talk in a highfalutin, *morphoménos* way. "And I insist that you do come too. But don't give yourself any airs, *paidáki mou.* I am asking you because it will look better to the Bishop. It will make it evident that we are good hosts, just trying to return all the favors we have received from the bishopric, and to send him away feeling pleased with himself. Ah ha ha ha!'

"Through the whole week before the outing Papouli became more and more enthusiastic. He giggled at sudden hours of the day. He took to eating more than usual. He was in a perfect flutter of activity, waddling and groaning his way around the town. Everyone remarked on how pepped up and energetic he was, and he said that it was all because of his inspiration from the visit of the Bishop. That one week he performed two house-blessings and one funeral. He extracted a chicken apiece for the house-blessings, and two chickens and thirty drachmas for the funeral, which was good pay considering that it was Kyria Stavrilis who had kicked the bucket. She was a very penny-pinching woman and had commanded her children, just before giving up the ghost, not to pay more than twenty-five drachs for her funeral. If Papadouklas would not do it for that, then have Papa Fotis do it. But the children had not obeyed. They wanted to keep up their standing in the town, so they forked up the extra five plus the two chickens which Papouli hinted would do in place of the additional fifteen drachs which he said he ought to charge them.

"He kept these four chickens in a little pen in his yard and bought special feed for them, whispering and giggling how he was fattening them up, and hinting that he hoped the two prima donnas (he did not call them by that name, however) were doing the same to themselves. You see, he broke down his pretense of virtue very early, and was continually winking, bobbing, and drooling saliva down the sides of his mouth in his expectation of what delights lay before him. He had already decided on the Turkish belly dancer for himself. The Athenian woman he was donating to the Bishop.

"At last the fine day arrived. Papouli borrowed a donkey. With his own, that made two donkeys. I brought my motorcycle, two big kegs of wine, and a bottle of ouzo. Papouli also brought some ouzo. He had spent the entire day before catching and tying the chickens, hiring a woman to roast some lamb which he put into a bag, and filling two *kaláthia* with olives, figs, dates, nuts, and bread. It took hours for these preparations, as he had to haul his huge bulk up and down the stairs, to the *vrísi*, and to the kitchen house. It took him hours to dress himself too, for he decided to wash, and he found that his beard had some lice in it. He heated the water and put it into the tub that they wash olives in, and then found out, when he had got in, that not only all the water, but also his mounds of fat overflowed the sides. He got stuck in the tub, and there was not a drop of water left in it to wash himself with. Well, you will say that I am exaggerating, but I went to see him, and he was in this predicament. He was so irate at the luckless fate of his life that there were tears in his eyes. He finally gave up on the lice. He said that he had lived with them all his life, and he had gotten fond of them too, but he begged me not to tell the Turkish woman. I promised I wouldn't, and I told him to hurry up and to go to bed early, for we were all to meet at the church at five the next morning.

"He arrived not more than ten minutes late. He was pomaded, and he wore his best black cassock, and had unearthed a beautiful golden cross which swung and whished around his neck, fitting neatly into a little fold of his gown where it began to protrude over his gargantuan belly. The Bishop was there, and I offered to let him ride in the sidecar. I had it fixed up with three Spartan rugs and my mother's best blanket so that it would be comfortable. The Bishop accepted as if it were his rightful due. He was a very proud man, even haughty, and he was used to sitting in the best places and eating the best food. In his worldliness he would not have thought of offering either the ancient Papadouklas or the women a better place than he had. He got in at once, before the women had arrived, and he commenced to bring out a Havana cigar which he bit the end off and spat at Papouli's feet. He then pulled out a golden cigarette lighter and lit it, smoking in great wreathing puffs. Papouli was heaving and moaning in ecstasy, huffing like a walrus, telling all the things that he had brought. 'Oh, ouf, ach, *poh*, *poh*, *poh*, the insomnia last night! the dreams! The Lord and Panagia send their blessings on us and give us a fine day!' I could see that the Bishop was amused. He looked at me meaningfully from under his well-combed eyebrows and bestowed congratulations on Papouli for putting himself to such great trouble for his humble superior.

"Finally the women arrived. Oh, *Panagía!* You should have seen them. The Athenian woman had a purple hat with streams of purple ribbons hanging from it whipping in the wind. She wore real nylon stockings and high heels . . . at least three and a half inches, with the heels made of steel, she said, the latest thing. She scraped her thighs with her hands, like this, showing her knees which were very large and had a dimple in them apiece.

" 'Oh-hoo!' she laughed when she saw Papouli grunt with pleasure and jump up and down with ecstasy. 'I forgot where I was, it's so early in the morning. I didn't mean to provoke you. You must forgive me, Papouli. Isn't that right, Bishop *mou*?'

"The Bishop immediately guffawed, just like a camel. So the day started off with a bang. Everyone could see the direction at once. It was as obvious and transparent as a baby shark in the sea that the Athenian woman and the Turkish woman were going to tease Papouli to death, and the Bishop fell in with their plans at once. For the first time since he had been in Hora, his eyes lighted up with pleasure.

"If the Athenian woman was a sight to behold, the Turkish belly dancer was even better. She acted like a skittish naiad, as if she were sylphlike and ethereally thin. In reality she was almost as fat as Papouli. She was bouncing and buttocky, and yet for all her fat she was as lithe as a butterfly. So that to see her move just one step provided licentious thrills. Her hair had been dyed henna and platinum blond, but she had forgotten to dye her eyebrows too, so they were jet black and gave her a most striking look. She wore tendril-thin ballet slippers, golden pale in color. So that with her pale blond hair and her pale blond shoes she looked like a painted figure that somebody had made a mistake on, as if she were unpainted at both ends. She wore a feather-gauzy dress of silk, with red, shimmering streaks in it, exactly like those new candy-striped toothpaste advertisements in Athena now. The dress was low, and her breasts were very full and very white. They flapped full-bodied and enticing like milky cream-puffs. Her neck was fat and it crinkled into little rings like a sugar-covered doughnut. *Télos pándon.* She was good enough to eat and Papouli went crazy with enthusiasm and excitement.

"In his first burst of pleasure he offered her his donkey, which she accepted. I backed it up against the adobe wall. Papouli offered her his hand while she climbed on to it. She dumped herself, like a shimmering mass of jelly, on to the saddle. He took one of her little feet and put it tenderly through his old rusty stirrup. You could see the place in her jelly-fish buttock where the wooden back of the saddle pressed against it.

"This left Papouli and the Athenian woman one donkey between them. Neither could walk, she because of her steel heels, and he because he was so old and fat. There was the back seat on the motorcycle, but that would mean that the Athenian woman would have to put her arms around me if she took it. As for Papouli, I trusted him better on the other donkey than on the motorcycle, for the back tire was bad. So we decided that the Athenian woman should sit in back on the motorcycle and Papouli ride on the other donkey.

"You should have seen us on our journey! *Ti yélia!* I, the motor cavalcade, leading the way, with the Bishop enthroned on the blankets in the sidecar, his blue and gold cassock fluttering, his cigar emitting great puffs of smoke. The Athenian woman, her nylon-stockinged legs hanging out in the breeze, screaming with laughter and hanging on to me for dear life. Followed by the two donkeys straining under their loads, the Turkish belly dancer and Papouli flopping and shivering in their fat. We had to stop twice. Once for water at that sacred spring halfway between Hora and Metamorphosis, and once to allow the Bishop to perform some natural duties behind a big acacia tree. On the whole journey the Turkish belly dancer spoke in a very soft voice to Papouli, and I could see that he was very enamored of her.

"At last we arrived at the church of the Little Cypress. Around the back there was a large garden bounded by forsythia and rhododendron. There we dismounted. I had to help Papouli and the Turkish woman, for, after sitting so long, their flesh had melted into the rhythm of riding, and they could scarcely make a move. We tied the donkeys to the branches of an olive tree, and spread the rugs and blankets in the garden. I dug a hole and made a fire of sticks; then we made a spit and set to roasting the four chickens. The Bishop broke out one bottle of ouzo and everyone began to drink immediately, sitting upon the blanket, gazing up into the clouds and the hot sky above, and nibbling on the olives and the nuts that Papouli had brought. If I say so myself, Kyrie Athas, I never tasted a better meal than those four chickens and the roasted lamb. Papouli had also brought some tomatoes and some tangerines, oranges, and two grapefruit. We were already slightly *methisméni* when we began to eat. The women had dropped their pretense of being elegant darlings once the food was brought out, and set to cooking just as if they had been housewives and mothers. Bravo to them, I say. The Athenian one took off her steel shoes and rolled her stockings down and went about barefoot, twisting the chickens' necks with her strong, bare arm, her purple hat fluttering in the breeze.

"Yet it was the food, rather than the drinking, that made them first begin to drop all pretenses. The Athenian woman, for some reason, seemed to have a satisfactory and utterly opaque understanding with the Bishop. Loosened by the ouzo, he began to stroke her bare ankles with his hand as she stood by the fire, and he began to laugh roisterously and joke with her.

" 'Oh Bishop *mou*, what are you doing? You will have me in such a state that I will not know what I want, you or the chicken!'

" 'Look at them. Look at them!' laughed the Bishop, pointing to the Turkish belly dancer and Papouli at the same time as he pinched the Athenian woman's bottom. 'Papouli *mou*, if I may call you that. You had better watch out for that one. She will catch you, and then what will you do?'

" 'I can think of no greater pleasure,' said Papouli, stretching his greasy, thick lips in a licking greedy smile. He had half a chicken leg in his mouth and, interrupted in his labors, he had no time to pay attention to the Turkish woman. A great burp stopped him from swallowing the rest of the chicken whole. However, following the example of the Bishop, he too reached out, changing his chicken to the other hand, and began to caress the thigh of the Turkish woman. 'My little Yannoula,' he crooned. 'You are so big and so beautiful!'

" 'Watch out, Papouli *mou*,' warned Yannoula, with the first hint of sharpness in her voice. 'Do not begin what you cannot finish! Besides, you would want to clean your hands before you begin touching your little Yannoula, isn't that so? Wipe them, Papouli *mou, chrisé*, on the grass there at your feet.'

"These words of warning seemed to arouse Papouli, and really turned him away from the chicken to the thought of Yannoula. He let the chicken go, wiped his hands, and sat around, making a perfectly hideous smile at the Turkish woman, clenching his fists. Finally he sat up straight and beat his quivering breast, shouting in a low, loud tone: 'Oh, if I were not a pope, my little Yannoula. If my hands were really to touch you, you would feel the horns of a bull and the strength of a lion. Believe me, you would say: "What is that roaring pope? What may I do that I can get under him once again!" '

"This brought the house down. The Bishop laughed until he had to wipe his eyes on the edge of his cassock. Papouli was so pleased with his behavior that he drained off two glasses of retsina at one go.

"It inspired new ebullience on the part of everyone, for they thought that they must have much more to deal with than they had anticipated. Immediately everyone started with renewed energy to prompt what they wanted to happen. And in everyone's eyes Papouli gained new stature, and made them want to test him.

" 'Be careful, Papouli *mou*,' warned the Bishop. 'Don't drink too much. You know what the Dionysian vines do.'

" 'Were they not the last resort of the dying pagan religion?' boasted Papouli. 'They were the only things that put guts into the old religion until Christianity came in to show the error of their ways.'

" 'What are you comparing yourself to, then, Papouli?' asked the Bishop, again wiping his eyes. 'And a pope!' He laughed between convulsions. 'What a mistake! What a mistake!'

" 'I am a better Christian than you, *Doxasi o Theós*, Bishop. I would not take the matter so lightheartedly.'

" 'I meant nothing, Papouli *mou*. Drink as much as you can then. I only ask you not to limit your pleasures. I am thinking of your own good,' said the Bishop very cleverly. At the same time he poked me in the ribs with his elbows, and said in a loud whisper so that Papouli could hear: 'Yannaki, see that he does not drink too much . . . if not for his own benefit, at least for the Turkish woman's. It will not do for her to be disappointed. Unless you have a vested interest,' he said cruelly, watching the expression on Papouli's face. Papouli at once turned a glare of suspicion and jealousy upon me.

" 'Bishop,' I said, 'much as I respect you, I think you go too far. After all, Papouli is a *papoúli*, and he is talking only hypothetically, not of what he will or can do. *Etsi den eíne*, Yannoula?'

" 'Oooooh, my pope, my precious little pope,' she gurgled, swinging her gauzy feminine raptures into his face. 'I do not care for all this talk. They have no right to tease us, do they?'

"Papouli put one hand tentatively on her knee and drew it upward to the huge inner part of her thigh, watching his fingers under her transparent dress, and then began to shiver.

"All this talk and fooling had put the Bishop into an impossible situation, so between two oranges he got up, cleared his mouth, spat the retsina on the ground, and pulled the Athenian woman up with his hairy hand. They disappeared like two swallows into the church, he already kneading the flesh of her shoulders and neck with his greedy hands. They did not come out again for an hour.

"In the meantime, their disappearance left Papouli in a state of wretched and suffocating dismay. He turned to me and said:

" 'Ioanni *mou,* I do not like the implications. The Bishop, he is full of barbs.'

" 'Pay no attention to him, Papouli. He was just greedy. You will see, when he comes out again he will be very satisfied. After all, though he is a worldly man, he does not know any better than that. And remember what you told me. I should think you would be congratulating yourself. After all, could there ever have been a more successful feast than this?'

"This satisfied Papouli. At once he began to finish the chicken leg that he had put down for Yannoula's thigh, and he began drinking more and more retsina.

"When the Bishop came out, it was just as I said. He was very satisfied. He sprayed his benignity on all, and then lay down on the Spartan rugs with the Athenian woman, and they fell into a doze. Watching him, Papouli also became sleepy.

" 'Come, *koúkla mou, angeloudáki mou,*' he said to the Turkish belly dancer. 'Let us go to sleep too. I didn't have a wink last night.' He scooped her up against his fat robe as tight as he could, squeezing her and kissing her with great smacks under her pink ear, and then, tracing little patterns with his big white hands on her breasts and squeezing them so they danced, he fell into a snoring sleep.

"I was smoking a cigarette at this minute, looking at the Turkish woman. She arched her eyes in a little cat-glance, looking down almost tenderly at Papouli, and then glanced back at me with a most quizzical expression. Her expression said: 'You have seen nothing yet. . . . I intend to get back at him. You will see. . . . Although . . .'

"I immediately turned around away from her and continued smoking my cigarette, and when I looked at her again she was asleep. So I went to sleep too.

"When we awoke, the moon was shining. We set to, building the fire, cooking again, to have another feast on the remains, and we began again, drinking wine exclusively this time so that the atmosphere that began to invade us seemed a muted one, but of the same thing that had gone on that afternoon.

"All except for Papouli. He was very wide awake, but subdued, it seemed. As if he were both more serious about his intentions toward the Turkish belly dancer, and more serious about his chastity as a pope. Everyone became electrified by the wine and the clearness of the moon.

"Before we knew it, Yannoula, the belly dancer, had risen softly to her feet.

" 'Sing for me, Yannaki,' she said.

"I began to sing in a very low voice. I sang, maliciously, the song of Stavroula, the water-carrier, who was in love with a man whom she could not move to love for her. The Turkish woman took off her shoes and danced in the bare grass. She clapped her hands softly and talked with closed eyes. It was as if she were talking to herself, improvising upon the song that I was singing, and making it apply to herself and the ancient pope:

'Poor Yannoula . . . the dancer . . .

'He said he would show me the roaring pope
  but he only shows me the cassock.
He said he would show me the horns of the bull
  but he only shows me his ears.
He said his kisses would be like tall waterfalls on Taygetus
  but he only drools.
He said his passion would be fire and snow,
  but the only thing I feel is the wind from his snores.

'And yet . . . and yet . . .

'I still love my Papouli
I still have my imagination.
My breasts burn and my throat is dry
And I wait, and I wait, and I wait . . .

'Where is my Papouli?
Is he behind the braid of his necklace?
Is he beneath the cross on his breast?
What is under his cassock, Papouli, Papouli?
What is beneath his robe?

'Papouli, Papouli, oh answer me!
What is beneath your hat?
What is beneath your robe?
Where is the golden horn? Is it beneath the golden cross?
What is beneath your cassock?
Is that the passion of the lion?'

"The effect of this was electrifying. I was hypnotized myself, so that I fitted the tones of my singing to the very pantomime that she was acting. When she began that about what was beneath the hat, the robe, and so on, she began weaving her face back and forth, and then she began to touch her own clothes, flimsy as they were, lifting them up so that you could see her entire figure bouncing and melting in the moonlight. It was a combination, you see, of the strip-tease, deadly serious, and of something utterly ludicrous, at which you wanted to burst with laughter. The Bishop's face became pale with the terrifying effect. At the same time he wanted to laugh. I could see him in the moonlight not knowing what to do. The Athenian woman, who had doubtless seen this performance before, was also electrified, but not so much with the song and the dancing, not sharing any of the lust that was thick among us all, as with intensity of the effect that it produced on the Papouli.

"Papouli began to moan, like a dog in agony. It was half ecstasy and half fear.

" '*Noula mou, koúkla mou.* I can't bear it. Don't do this to me!' he began sobbing.

"At this point she quickened her pace of dancing and stepped with her bare legs right up to his face. He clutched at her, but she backed away from him.

"She began to take off her clothes. 'What is beneath his robe?' she asked, and she began very gently to undo her dress, very slowly, so that one went wild with desire. She quickened her pace. She clapped her hands above her head, swaying her bosoms to and fro.

The Papouli held his hand out to her. He tried to get hold of her dress, but now, removed, she wafted it in front of his face, catching his head in it, like a fly caught in a spider web. He began clutching madly, then, screaming with fury and with lust. Finally, she jerked it away and let him see her half naked in the moonlight. She snapped her pace up faster. She threw the dress over a rhododendron bush.

"The Bishop began laughing wildly, clutching at his own robes, his head jerking to and fro.

"Papouli got up. He started dashing wildly after her.

" 'Do like me. Do, do, do!' she sing-songed to him in a sharp, acrid voice, filled with sex. 'Take off your trousers there beneath your robe. Do. Do. Do!'

"Papouli did as she ordered. He let his trousers down, but they caught in his shoes and he almost tumbled over. Finally he had to sit on the ground to get them off. The Bishop was blinded by tears and laughing. Papouli began breathing rough and hot, and I was sure that the old man would have a heart attack and die, right there. The sweat began to light up from the moon. It streamed down his nose and eyes into his beard. No sooner had he his trousers off than he went after her once more, trying to catch her.

"The pace of the music was heavily frenetic. I lifted my head aloft to see her better and to push my tones beyond the hoydenish laughter of the Athenian woman and the guffaws of the Bishop. Under the moon the two heavy figures bounced, Papouli, his fat shivering under his heavy robe, and the other nude now except for her brassière and her almost transparent underclothes pressing against white buttocks. They ran to and fro against the rhododendron.

" 'Papouli, sit down!' ordered the belly dancer.

"He did as he was bid.

"She changed her stance. She changed the beat of the song. She clapped her hands, stood like a matador, and then began a parade to him. It was very slow and martial, with a jerk every two steps. Her breasts jounced wildly. Her flesh shivered. She loosened her brassière and dropped it to the ground.

"The effect was dazzling. Those two ripe, huge bosoms dangling, dancing greenish-white in the moon, with their nipples distended in desire. She marched, dancing like this, right up into his hands. He grasped the breasts in a trance, uttered a soft moan, and looked at them in his hands as if he did not know what he held. Then he lowered his head, his mouth opened like a hole, and he thrust the nipples in.

"She took his head, pulled his beard up, whispering to him violently: 'The horns. The horns. Give me the horns.'

"By this time he was breathing suffocatingly and supplicatingly. He pressed himself against her. He rolled her over and wallowed against her, pressing his flesh against her.

" 'Come in here. Come in my robes with me!' he whispered.

" 'Then will you do it?'

"You have to imagine the ludicrousness of it, as she ducked her head down to his feet and pushed herself in, wriggling, swathed until her head came out the neck hole and tore it. Papouli wallowed in ecstasy.

"Something strange happened. She uttered a scream and pushed away from him, ripping the gown in two. She pushed him away, half naked, in a moaning heap upon the ground sobbing:

" 'Yannoula, please forgive me. Forgive me, *koúkla mou.* You made me do it, but I can't!'

"There was even dignity in the way that he said this, so that one had to respect him for his efforts, even as he was crouched upon the ground with his bare buttocks stuck up and shining in the moonlight.

"The Bishop, half dead with laughter, now raised himself up. He went over to the angry Yannoula with a bray:

" ' 'Noula, greatest performance of my life. Better than even the Panagia. I have never enjoyed myself so much in all my born days. And for such a performance, you deserve a reward.'

" 'Reward me no rewards!' she shouted. She struck his face with her bare foot and plucked herself up, swearing and cursing like the sailors she was used to. 'Phony priests, all of you. One would and one wouldn't. That's what you get for nothing. Go get my clothes, you,' she said to the Bishop.

"He went to the rhododendron bush and fetched the dress. She put it on, drank one more glass of retsina, and shook herself as if to rid herself of all the past in one motion.

" 'Yannaki! Hey you, pure boy! Bring the donkey. How do we get out of here? You'll never get me in another church again for the rest of my life. Phoo! *Poh! Poh! Poh!* What a disgrace!' "

VIII Martha swallowed the flitting smile at the corners of her mouth. "*Panagía mou! Panagía mou!*" she uttered in a loud, sharp voice. She brushed imaginary crumbs off her dress. "*Den drépesai* to tell such a story, Ioannis *mou?* You should be ashamed! And in front of *to korítzi!* It is a crime!"

Ioannis grinned in appreciation of his material and himself.

"I tell it for Kyrios Athas' benefit. *To korítzi den katalavéni kathólou.* She understands nothing."

But Martha, not angry, having tuned up her anger chords, now began to sound more and more convincing.

"Get up from there! You are as bad as those women and those nasty popes!" She kicked his feet. She crossed herself.

"The Greeks have drunk the Christian sop and performed the Christian superstitions, not knowing they are good and pagan, until now they have betrayed the gods and philosophers both!"

Daddy arose, laughing, and led the way to the yard. We all sat down on the grass. Except for Martha. She stood by the parked motorcycle, clutching her fists to her dumpy figure.

"But we are Christians, Theo! We are Christians!"

"You do not understand me, niece. You are Jews. You are Jews."

I wanted to laugh like a hyena, but I could not face her proud, brown, benign protest.

"You are not right, Theo, in all things."

"With Jewish trappings," he continued. "Like your name. Martha. Martha, the Jew. Maria. Even Ioannis! But do not misunderstand me. These are as important as clothes. They only hide the Greek heart beating underneath."

"*Christós kai Panagía mou!*" murmured Martha, giving up.

The afternoon broke us up into separate dreamers. While Daddy delivered his conundrums in faultless Greek, all the more difficult and impossible for me to understand, Martha kept crossing herself.

Ioannis settled himself and listened eagerly, still with the smile under his mustache on the popes' behalf, and I felt the sun magnify my eyelashes and swarm my head with the hot images of history.

How did the Greeks ever get suckered by the Jews into Christianity? That is what I couldn't understand. But Jesus gets a lot more credit than He deserves. The Greeks don't really give a damn about Jesus, and they care less about His word. He is only good as a victim. Their goddess Mary has kept the idea of the goddess alive for three thousand years, and they still have a choice in saints. Greek Christianity like ancient Greek paganism is still ethic-less.

Since the Greeks would not listen to Paul when he first spoke on the Acropolis, Christianity made its headway at Corinth. But Mary always had the edge over Jesus. At Eleusis, you see, Mary is strictly from Demetra. Death as a marriage to Pluto is much more interesting than death as a moral martyrdom, and Persephone is not all the way a victim either, since she had a somewhat good time in Hell. (Only the people above suffered winter.) Persephone is Everybody and also a seed. Nobody has to strain his moral pretensions to identify with her. She was not dying for the world. This is the unpalatable thing about Christ. Through the Church Christianity has become a mealy-mouthed arrogance. Also Resurrection, Christ's way, is artificial since He died in fleshly pain. Pain was the Jews' forte. That also makes the appeal of Christianity. The result of Persephone's marriage is winter and spring, but Persephone didn't much know it. That makes her more attractive than Christ who died for a purpose too unrealistic to die for. The time came and went for a really anti-Christ movement. It is already post-Christ.

There is a connection between a multiplicity of gods and ethics. Textbooks have pointed out that the contribution of the Jews to the world was the idea of monotheism. Christianity still has that tradition of "Thou shalt have no other gods before Me." Northern Christianity through the Reformation re-Hebraized itself and cast out all evidence of paganism, such as the importance of Mary and the saints. It propounds, through teaching alone, a mutual opposition between the idea of one god and the idea of many.

The Germans, in the vanguard of the Reformation, have had the Jewish ideal so strongly, of one god, one father, and one state, that they applied it politically. Quixotically and with poetic justice it caused its very creators, in the Second World War, to play the part of the victim.

But the ancient Greeks did not recognize the quarrel between the conception of the plurality of gods and the conception of one. Socrates always spoke of God. But he mentioned other gods too. And this was because gods were as much poetic entities as religious ones. Socrates was such a natural philosopher that he could never pass up a poetic entity if it strengthened his point.

The original gods were forces. Forces do not contain "should be"s. They simply "are." The prime force was the beating, blinding, breathing sun, supercharging power at noon, merciless, pitiless and beautiful. His name then, as now, was *Ílios.* You can still hear the name as a prophet of Christianity. Elijah on the Jewish mountains. Elias on the Hellenic mountains. Worshipers put a moleculed, cupolaed church on every mountain to the Prophet Elias through the long Byzantine days. The Greek word for olives is "*eliés.*" They shine green in their childhood like miniature suns. They make the oil for the fire to burn, creating a mimic sun in fire. A slick, pathetic imitation of the sun. It is a pervasive god, un-Olympian, all-being, ethic-less, greedy, powerful, dangerous, a heat-giver and a drought-giver, but most of all, a life-giver. He is so physical as to have become metaphysical. Worshiped because of being the grandest effect known in life. Touch him and you burn. He killed Icarus. Live without him and you die. Charon will take you to the land of night. You are a shadow in the land of night even where there is no sun to make you shadow. Everything dim shapes.

Demetra, the earth, sorrows for any child trapped there. Deals, bargains, promises and broken promises have to be made with the sun. Finally a contract is made by the grace of Apollo. Demetra got Persephone out of the land of night. Spring came.

Crimes were committed for sun. For man's good, for the love of man, sun was stolen by Prometheus. He was punished, but then because he was a great hero (above men the way men are above apes) he was let go. He was resuscitated and resurrected and is still remembered.

Jesus, who had no word or message of the sun, has taken his

place. The sun as a god began to die when Jesus began to live. In the depths of misery, poverty, and ignorance, Christianity bloomed. In caves and holes, hiding out, persecuted, men worshiped Jesus like moles. Medieval Christianity deemed the sun and earthly life fruitless. Suns were to be seen only after death. Life was only after death. Elysium, once the land of shades, was promoted to be the land of granted dreams.

Paradoxically, it is in Reformed Christianity that Christ's resurrection has petered out. He has ossified, grown dusty, milky, meek, cowed, powerless, empty-eyed, and hollow-mouthed. He is as a symbol rotten on one hand and brittle on the other.

While in the realm of pagan god-dom, we must be careful to be capricious and heedful to be amoral. The ancients themselves in regard to their gods were never beleaguered or bedeviled or beguiled by any sense of morality. When the gods did them dirty they cried loudly. But all their crying and weeping and wailing was the result of real punishment that the gods dished out, mostly physical, and usually unjust.

There grew up in pagan society a great concern with Justice, one aspect of Morality. The spirit of inquiry and science was born. The spirit of inquiry extended into the matters of morals. So that morality was thought of in rational terms, not sat upon by their gods in their nests.

In *The Birth of Tragedy,* Nietzsche bemoans, bewails, and bespeaks the classical Greeks, and Socrates in particular, as the crucifiers of religion.

Our whole modern world is entangled in the net of Alexandrian culture. It proposes as its ideal the theoretical man equipped with the greatest forces of knowledge and laboring in the service of science, whose archetype and progenitor is Socrates. . . . Socrates is the prototype of the theoretical optimist who with his belief in the explicability of the nature of things, attributes to knowledge and perception the power of a universal panacea. . . . Now we must not hide from ourselves what is concealed at the heart of this Socratic culture; Optimism, with its delusion of limitless power. . . . But now that the Socratic culture can only hold the scepter of its infallibility with trembling hands; now that it has been shaken from two directions—once by the fear of its own conclusions which at length it begins to surmise, and again because it no longer has its former naïve confidence in the eternal validity of its foundation—it is a sad spectacle to see how the dance of its thought rushes longingly in on ever new forms, to embrace them, and then, shuddering, lets them go suddenly.

This picture, conjured up by Nietzsche in the nineteenth century, is conjured up every day today. People screech for the return to religion. They point to the tangible results of science: the mushroom cloud.

Yet each to his own century. A rationalism cannot be split from its century, and though you can make a correlation between the enlightened rationalism which gave birth to the American Revolution and the rationalism which Socrates birthed in the 5th classical century, it had different auras, different breaths, and different conditions. Though you can make a comparison between twentieth-century humanism and Socrates' humanism, the air that made it, breathed it, and released it had two different, rare climates.

In the 5th Century B.C., the One God had not been corralled as the Only. No single fence or altar had been created, for there were a million pillars, pedestals, altars, and fences for the different, split attributes of gods. If gods are one god, the one god must contain all. And for one man to contain all his own attributes to place upon his god, and then to endow that god with all causation and all power, is a fearsome and limited thing. It does not even allow that god to do the moral wrestling, and thus causes the man who worships him to have to do it for himself.

But smithereen your god, as any normal schizophrenic man would do, then you can play your gods against each other. You can relieve yourself of the necessity and vile results of carrying your mental wars on in your own heart. God cannot be great and God cannot be good, or else who will be bad? Yourself. He who admits to being bad under his god has given up utterly.

It makes sense that Paul could talk to the already defeated, the prostitutes at Corinth, the old ladies of death, the sick, the dying, the slaves, the imbeciles, and the underpaid common soldiers of the Roman legions. They had nothing to lose if this life was bad. They could gain in the other world after death. All the world was evil.

The evil-doers rank. The defeated and the meek and the sorely done by had the kingdom of God. But the kingdom of God could only be realized after death. This God, who had such a kingdom, so unrecognized in this earthly life, had the ultimate power, to retribute all in after-life. But the world always continues bad. In the eyes of monotheistic Christians, retribution and judgment must always be in the future. Mortal existence is a shadow. Death is the true life.

With a plurality of gods, the power of each is sure to be mitigated.

In ancient days, with the mitigation of the man-gods' power, man stood almost equal. Man did not have to make his god his enemy, as Job had to do. He stood, any time he climbed a mountain, right at the rendezvous point of his god. He sat down and ate with him, and he, man, kept the best piece of meat for himself. He was kissed all the time with the gods' kisses. And he grew into clarity. His life was pleasant, his discoveries great, and his possibilities infinite. The pulsebeat of life filled up his wrists and his heart. He teamed up his multitude of gods and played out his dilemmas in their wars. Thus he freed himself from despair. So freed, then he could pursue his natural life, exploration, observation, comparison, analysis, drinking, loving, and converse.

IX For a long time archeologists have known that Nestor's palace lay buried somewhere in the vicinity. Pieces of potsherds and other antiquities were always being dug up.

When Daddy was twelve years old he planted twelve cypress trees in a row on his land at Elaphrina. Elaphrina was a valley of olive groves lying just below the hill where Nestor's palace was discovered. While Daddy was digging the last hole for the last cypress, he uncovered an ancient terra cotta water pot with figures of warriors. The pot is gone now, but the cypress trees stand thirty feet tall, and you can see them from the diggings.

"Doesn't it make you feel like a speck on history to see those cypresses so tall, and to know that you were causation, and to know that they grew every day of your life when you had even forgotten them in America, and that here they are, taller than you could even imagine, and that when you planted them you did not even know that Nestor's palace was just above?" I asked him.

"It was my name day," said Daddy. "I was planting twelve trees for my twelve years. And just to show you how ignorant I was, not only did I not know Nestor's palace was above, I had not even heard of Nestor then. They did not teach the myths in school. The only thing I knew was Jewish criminal history of the Old Testament. And the pot I dug up, it seemed to me more like some relic of my grandfather's day than something they used three thousand years ago."

An old woman in Hora said: "To think that this palace was here all the time! *Ti oraía!* What a miracle. Who could have known! When I was a girl of sixteen, this place was covered with olive trees, ancient olive trees, ten feet wide of girth. What beautiful olives they gave! Here I ran, jumped, sang, and picked. This whole place was covered with them. And all the time, to think that this lay in the ground underneath. *Sképsou to!* To think that, having lived my life, I might have died and never known!"

There are stories about how the site was chosen to make the diggings. There was a family, living in the village of Koryphasion nearby, who said to Professor Blegen, the archeologist:

"There is a palace on that hill. It belonged to some king long ago."

"Why do you think that?" Blegen asked.

"Because my father said that his father's father had told him, and his father did not know where his father got it, even. Anyway, I've always heard . . . well, you see, who knows what is true, but if I were digging, I would surely dig there."

Now even the discovery of the palace has become legend. The Koryphasion family who knew it was there because their fathers had told them that their fathers told them, has become legend too. That the earth could cover the traces of former grandeur, and that truth could have become legend only to become truth again, makes one have wonderful suspicions about the nature of reality.

There are some who say that this palace is not really the palace of Nestor. The palace of Nestor, they say, is really in the sea somewhere in Pylos Bay.

Professor Blegen, reading the Odyssey, found that it took Telemachus, Odysseus' son, forty-eight days to walk from Menelaus' palace in Sparta to Nestor's palace at Pylos. Professor Blegen checked this. It is said that he walked from Nestor's palace one day, bound for Sparta. On the forty-eighth day he reached the palace of Menelaus.

In the first flush of the glory of the discovery, Nestor seemed an unbelievable grandfather. When seven-foot skeletons were unearthed in the common burial dump, Horaites knew their ancestors for having been giants, as much Titans as the Titans were to Nestor's people. At the appearance of each golden goblet, Horaites compared them to their own drinking vessels. What Horaite nowadays drinks his retsina from a golden goblet? Besides those goblets carried almost two pints of retsina. And the mosaic floor. What Horaite walks upon mosaic? Nestor had run a pipe from the cellar palace almost two miles down to the plain where we lived in the cottage. The slope of the pipe kept olive oil running in streams to giant *kouvélia* which stood in the yards of the slaves below. What brains! What an engineering feat! There was something self-deprecatory in having to admit that one's ancestors were so much smarter and richer than oneselves.

But Greeks are used to living miracles daily, inundating themselves with miracles as they inundate themselves with suspicions and evil-eyes. They got used to Nestor. And the more human he became, the less miraculous, unless they stuck themselves with pins daily.

They knew Nestor for the longest-living relative they had ever known. He was seventy years old when he went to Troy. He was the only one of all the kings who returned safe and happy to his home. He lived for three hundred years. He was an expert on cavalry and on ground tactics of the land army. He had a powerful navy. He and Agamemnon each sent more boats to Troy than anyone else in all the Greek cities. Nestor sent ninety-two ships. He was the greatest orator of all the archaic Greeks, and he was a great fighter, as were all kings in those days.

Nestor was the grandson of Poseidon. His father was Neleus, conqueror and founder of Pylos. Neleus was born of Tyro, the orphan daughter of Alcidice, a wife of Salmoneus.

Salmoneus was a king of Thessaly, hated by his subjects and ludicrous in his pretensions. He used to make altars to himself and proclaim himself Zeus. To back it up, he drove a bronze cart lined with bronze buckets through the streets of his capital so that the bronze buckets rattled on the cobblestones imitating thunder. He also carried big torches lit with rags soaked in olive oil and threw them burning into the crowd to make people think he was throwing lightning bolts. He scorched some of his people's faces. Finally, in disgust, the real Zeus threw a live thunderbolt at Salmoneus and his cart, killing him and destroying his city.

After Salmoneus was rubbed out, his daughter Tyro was brought up by a horrible stepmother named Sidero, whose name is derived from the word that means iron. Sidero made Tyro's life a torment. Lonely and weeping, she hung around a river bank, in love with easeful death in the form of the river god. He was amused, flattered by her attentions, but would not take her seriously.

One day Poseidon decided to take advantage of this unrequited love. He requited his own lust by palming himself off as the river god and seducing Tyro. When she came to her senses and found out what had happened, she was shocked. Poseidon told her to keep her trap shut, she would be rewarded by twin sons, better progeny than could have been created by a mere river god.

The result was Neleus and Pelias. But Tyro was ashamed and afraid of Sidero, so she took them to a mountain to let them die. A herd of horses found them and brought them up, although the brood mare kicked Pelias' face in once. When they grew up they found out the evil of Sidero and set out to avenge Tyro, their mother. They chased Sidero into a temple of Hera. There, while she clung to the horns of the altar, they killed her.

Later both boys were adopted by Cretheus, the grandfather of Jason, whom Tyro married. Even later, the two brothers fought with each other. Pelias put Neleus in a prison. He escaped, and led a band of Achaeans, Phthiotians and Aeolians to Pylos. He drove out the original people who were called Lelegans, and raised Pylos to fame as a city. He married and had twelve sons. All of them except Nestor were killed by Heracles in return for imagined dirty work that Neleus had done to him.

Nestor reigned for a long time. It was a serf kingdom in the style of Minos. The reign was stable. There were very few serious wars. Only occasional ambushes on hog, horse, or cow thieves. The days of the royalty was taken up with hunts, festivals, and duels. For the serfs it meant probably the same sort of existence that the Horaites live now. Rising early in the morning to cultivate the fields, singing during harvest time, two yearly plantings of wheat, flocks herded by shepherds, and living quarters in small stone houses with tiled roofs. The granary and oil stores were kept in the palace in Nestor's day. And his reign was prosperous because the land, though sandy, is some of the best in Greece. From Kyparisia to Kalamata is a loamy plain, perfect for vineyards, olive groves, and wheat and barley fields. Even today all the fruits you can think of grow there. Oranges, apples, lemons, grapefruit, pomegranates, peaches, pears, walnuts, pecans, blackberries, tomatoes, grapes, currants, figs, and olives.

One day during our two-week stay at the *chtíma,* Daddy and I visited the diggings, with Ioannis on the motorcycle. The archeologists had been long gone. We had the palace to ourselves.

The walls that were standing rose two feet, nowhere were they taller. They had a jumbled, crumbled appearance, sod-brown. A junky, dead, stone-pile effect that presented the character of bygone barbarism. We traced out the walls of the throne room and looked on the ground where the mosaiced floor had been covered with earth until the next spring. No beauty anywhere. The juicy finds at the palace were the trinkets, goblets, necklaces, and pots, the mosaiced floor, and a bathtub. But the palace itself was a more practical and ugly ruin.

The common burial mound was more impressive than these shattered walls, for it had been recently repaired and whitewashed. It was the only evidence to be seen from the road, for it reared like the huge head of a toadstool squatting on the earth. Inside was dank adobe, circular, a cool, moist cave that was murmurous and full of echoes. This was where they found all the bones and all the trinkets that decorated the dead.

These were the dawn people, the first of the civilized. They erected in squares, stone upon stone, for protection, not for aspiration. Their frivolities and their artistry centered on their bodies. They ate and drank from gold, and they adorned with gold. They lived their lights and shadows, and did not create them. They had not got hold of divine dreams or captured them in form. They were stuck with their morality, and now we have their bones and their trinkets. Nature was too great, and superstition provided their only answers.

They were the shadowed great upon whom all the legends of the world have focused. But they are dead, hideously, barbarically, and dustily dead. We unrolled the shadows and found this pile of junk that Nestor dominated. In big and bulky life when it was life. Imagine his whitened, goldened beard in the sun. Imagine the talking, the pouring, the listening, the laughing. Imagine the duels. Imagine the advice. Imagine boar hunts. Imagine the welcoming feasts upon the shore. Imagine the honey-tongued voice of Nestor, and the sweetness of the flowers attracting the ancient bees, so inalienably tied together in the literature. Inseparable from the conception of Nestor, resurrected in his resurrection today in Hora, the great grandfather. He was too early. He had not the conceit for immortality that the Egyptian pharaohs had. So he probably lived his life and cannot live his death. He lived by virtue of Homer, not in the still-standing stones of his palace. Dead. Dead. A hero. Now a dead hero upon whom Hora projects its visions.

"Brabius tells us," said Jane Harrison, "that in the courtyard of a pious man there was a precinct of a hero, and the pious man was wont to sacrifice and pour libations to the hero, and pray to him for a return of his hospitality. But the ghost of the dead hero knew better: Only the regular Olympians are the givers of good. His province as a hero was limited to evil only. He appeared in the middle of the night and expounded to the pious man this truly Olympian theology:

> 'Good sir, no hero may give aught of good;
> For *that*, pray to the gods. We are the givers
> Of all things evil that exist for men.' "

There was a rustle in a bush. The grass blows wildly and silver in the breeze.

Hora has Nestor's mortality in its pocket, but his immortality has escaped it, and lies where it always has, in the page of a book.

A lizard tucked himself under an ancient moldy stone of the palace.

Ioannis squinted in the sun.

"*Ti eíne zoí?*" he asked.

But he answered it himself, kicking the stone where the lizard had gone, "*I zoí den eíne típote.*"

Life, it is nothing.

x Since we had come to Hora, what had we come for? To visit the birthplace of Daddy, and to re-engage ourselves in the bloodstream of the family. The importance of lineage has dropped away in America. Not so in Greece. Family is all, beyond love and hate.

So far we had succeeded in insulating ourselves by living in the cottage in the vineyard. We had maintained a position of independence to be free to pick and choose those relatives we liked.

But I was growing curious. Having been protected from being swamped by them, I now felt a desire to know them. I imagined them unfolding like leaves before me and twining around my consciousness.

I wanted particularly to meet Barba Ioannis, as he was Daddy's *Doppelgänger.*

"A good old fellow," said Daddy. "Poor cuss, too good, and too much of a fool. Worked all his life away because he didn't have sense enough to do anything else. And progenited nine children on earth to boot. He never did have enough up here." Daddy pointed to his head.

One Sunday Martha invited us to an *arravóna* at Koryphasion. It was the engagement ceremonial feast for some niece of Barba Ioannis' wife. It seemed like a symbolic sonata to the theme of Martha's and Ioannis' foundering engagement plans. They had both applied to Daddy as if he were a Greek Dear Abby, to use his influence to make Maria cough up the dowry.

At this *arravóna* we met Thea Ioannou, Barba Ioannis' wife, mother of Martha, whom Daddy described as "the smart one in the family. She is half gypsy, half Turk, with a gigantic nose and a foul mouth. She is the biggest crook in Hora. She runs around the neighborhood all day begging and telling sob stories and lies. What she doesn't beg she steals. It is she who kept her children's mouths filled during the war while Barba Ioannis with all his noble emotions worked for nothing."

She was boiling macaroni in a huge pot in the cooking house. Martha led us in. The fire was burning in a corner of the chimneyless room. The walls were smoke-blackened. The room was dark and suffocating with smoke. Thea Ioannou was stirring the pot with a huge wooden spoon and wiping her weeping eyes with a huge rag.

She looked like a strong old weatherbeaten witch. She was wearing an old black wool dress, a black apron, and a black *mandíli,* so that she was ensconced in cloth. The only thing you could see of her was her crowlike face, out of which two beady eyes snapped through a pair of beat-up, pale-gold-rimmed spectacles. Her Turkish nose was so ugly that it gave her a noble air. Her complexion was weatherleathered, and her eyebrows were massive and prominent. She shook hands very strong, like a man. But she combined this rough, even noble countenance with a whining, pitiful and abject air. It was a very winning contradiction.

"She's your daughter?" she accused Daddy, squinting and glaring.

"*Vévea.*"

She stared at me. When I stared back, she turned witheringly blank.

"*Haírete,*" I said.

In spite of herself she smiled, though half denigratingly.

"Look at her," said Daddy in English. "She acts completely stupid, but she's one of the smartest women you'll ever see in your life. She tells the best stories of anyone in Hora. All lies. She makes her living at it. In the course of ten years she has probably begged, inveigled, and stolen at least two thousands dollars' worth of bread and money out of Maria. And she'll turn right around and tell you what a thief Maria is."

"What is that gypsy's tongue you're gobbling there!" she shouted, gesturing furiously at Daddy.

"I was telling how smart you are, and how you bring up a family of five children for our cousin Barba Ioannis."

She turned her head away, sniffing, refusing the flattery. She picked the wooden spoon out of the pot and pointed to the fat load of macaroni.

"This is the way we cook in Greece. No electric stoves. No refrigerators here," she said, half between cringing and accusation.

"And how are you getting along?" asked Daddy.

"How should I get along? We are poor. My husband works hard every day, tired unto death with old age and nine children. My feet grow older. There are creaks in my bones. Oooh-ha. How should I get along? *Ti na káno*?"

All at once her aggressiveness died down. She did not speak. She turned her full attention to the boiling macaroni and her attitude toward us became shy and almost embarrassed.

"*Manoúla mou,*" said Martha, "we are going upstairs. To see the things. *Páme. Páme,* Theo."

"*Echárika polí.*" I extended my hand to Thea Ioannou once more.

She took it, mumbling. She glanced at me for a wavering second through her golden-rimmed spectacles. Then she turned away, overcome with embarrassment. She wiped her nose with her hand, to hide her raw sensibilities under this crudeness and suspicion.

People were filtering through the portal door. Everyone stood milling around the yard. The bridegroom arrived in a truck which was piled high with presents for the bride, and decorated with red ribbons. A shout went up. People rushed forward to help carry the presents to the bedroom where the trousseau was being displayed.

We were presented with Mavrodaphne which we drank, and then we went in to look at the bride's trousseau. When we entered the room the loud chattering, whispering, and giggling stopped, as if in dismay. The girls were dolled up. White silks, gauzes, red flowers, white socks, patent leather shoes all quivered as they froze. The room was so silent you could hear a pin drop. The curiosity could actually be heard. All eyes were upon me. I felt as if I were taking on a massive texture, endowed by that multitude of focused eyes. And all the eyes were unashamedly curious. The concentration of the curiosity was accompanied by hard breathing. They waited, full of suspense. I felt that for this effort of concentration they should be rewarded by some outrageous manifestation. It occurred to me to do some shocking thing to prove that I was not a human being. But I could not think what. So instead I smiled. And such was their effort of concentration that they were utterly delighted by such a simple reaction as a smile. They felt as if they had been the cause of it. They smiled back in triumph, and there were tiny whispers: "She smiled! She actually smiled."

The bed looked like a dime-store counter. There were three pairs of cheap shoes, a silver-lined brush and comb set. There were piles of linen bordered by home-made lace. There were bought blankets and woven rugs. Gaudy trinkets were prominently displayed on top of the linen. Vulgar, pathetic. Patent testament that the execrable bought goods were considered far superior to those linens and stuffs which had been woven, embroidered, and hemmed in years of loving labor.

I was rescued by a man who stuck his head in the door.

"I been to Baltimore," he said. "I been in merchant marine. Baltimore is a hep town, man. You like some music? They got a record player here."

He was the brother of somebody's wife's second cousin. And that was the extent of his English.

Outside, there was a loud call.

A skinned lamb hung from a shiny hook set on a frame-post. Scalped and skinned, it was hideously naked. Its skeletal teeth poked out. Its forelegs flopped anguishedly, its hoofs still unskinned. Its haunches drooped languid and bloody toward the ground.

Everyone was swept up into a mood of exalted excitement at this spectacle. A man stabbed a knife into the heart of the animal and gutted it down with a vicious stroke. The insides at once spilled out flopping and jerking on intestine strings. Search began for the heart, the liver, and the kidneys. A stench of defecation arose. Men lugged useless parts of the animal to trash piles behind the cooking house. Other men pulled up their sleeves and plunged their hands inside the animal. A man with big boots found the heart. A shout went up. He raised it on high. It seemed too small for the extent of the guts. The liver and kidneys were also brought out. They were hurried to the well where they were washed by women.

Carefully and gently the man with the boots cleaned out the cavern between the ribs. He pulled out the intestines and placed them in a pail. With rags in his hands he wiped down the carcass inside and out. He hacked off the hoofs and placed them in a bowl. He washed the animal until it dripped and glittered in the sun. Then he began to quarter it. He hacked one haunch off. He hacked off the other haunch. Then he drew the knife down the back splitting it with the crunch of bones. At last all that hung upon the hook was that tiny, bony head with its insane, glaring eyes and ugly teeth.

The head was removed from the hook. The intestines were hung upon it. A man began to untangle the ribbon of intestines. Armed with a bucket, he began to pour water through them. The intestines were transparent and you could watch the water trickle through their jelly-like substance, as through macaroni. As each string of intestines was cleaned, it was put into a waiting bowl.

"*Dóxasi o Theós!*" was the cry of excited delight in the crowd. I wanted them to sacrifice, at least to the Panagia, but I did not suggest it. The *foúrnos* was lit. The coals were scraped out live and glistening to make way for the meat. The quartered cuts were dipped in oil, placed in a pan, and spiced with salt and herbs. The pan was poked into the *foúrnos* with long sticks, and a sheet of corrugated tin was placed over the mouth of the furno.

Everyone, at the smell of roasting meat, began to talk vivaciously. Spirits rose. Small glasses of ouzo with cheese were handed around. A space was cleared for the feast which was to take place in the cellar beneath the house. Benches were placed side to side for two long banquet tables. They were covered with long, large white tablecloths, unpressed. Shouts rang across the yard. The women in the cooking house said that the macaroni was almost ready. Men gathered in groups and talked politics loudly. Girls were sent scurrying with glasses of water and knives and forks.

In the background there was an argument between the lamb-skinners and the cooks about what was to be saved for a bigger feast in the evening. The men were loud and boisterous. But the women were tight-lipped and definite. It was they who made the final decisions.

At last the dinner was ready. Everybody was ordered to the table. It was one o'clock. The sun blazed hot from its throne in the sky.

The dark environs of the cellar gave the quality of an underground banquet hall. The floor was of packed earth. Overhead were large, cobwebby beams, lying upon gaunt, rough-hewn posts. Hung upon the hooks and nails in the further reaches of the cellar were stalks of camomile, picked for medicinal purposes. A small *kandíli* whispered madly in front of an icon. The windows of the cellar were opened wide. The sun printed patterns of brilliant light against the wall and table. Each window was a sudden, thrilling tableau of light. The sky was a delicate, yet vivacious blue. Outside one window an orange tree hung its scented bough. It whispered in the stiff breeze and rattled excitedly, spreading vibrating shadows on the floor. There was something familiar, personable, human about this tree, for the sun caught at it, and tugged its greens and browns and flung them joyously for every eye to see. It seemed miraculous that you only had to thrust your hand out the window to touch it.

In fact, there was a strange, rarefied, almost sanctified atmosphere about the place of this banquet, just because of its light. It brushed memories of an archaic Christian world of catacombs. The darkness was holy because the light existed all *outside*. The only light was that which streamed brilliant through the windows accompanied by that provocative, cold breeze. Already late September had come. Everyone was dressed in their summer best, and yet the crisp feeling of an impending winter was near. This was all the more profound for the streaming of the sunlight.

The bottles of wine tinkled as their necks touched the lips of the glasses. There was the sound of gurgling as the wine was poured.

Suddenly a man stood up and raised his glass. He made a toast to the bride. He spoke the toast with precision deep in the silence. Down the table everyone made a murmuring recitative. And then they drank. It broke the stubborn silence of expectation.

Plates were set before the guests. Loaves of bread were piled upon the table before the standing man. He took up one of the loaves and hugged it to him almost as an object of love.

Shouts began at table. Everyone urged him, egged him on to do the honor of cutting the bread. He picked up a knife. Then, brandishing a smile as sharp and joyful as the knife, he began the cutting. Holding the bread like a baby against his chest, he brought the knife in to himself, time after time, nimbly, swiftly, cutting the bread into slices.

All of a sudden plates of macaroni were set before each guest, rust-colored with tomato sauce, smelling of *orígani* and bay leaf. The roasted lamb sat like a king on top of each heap of macaroni. Each plate steamed. People breathed with sharp expectation.

Eating is peculiar in Greece. The head is bent low. Noises are not only acceptable, they are demanded. There are great moans of satisfaction, great mouth-smackings, and loud slurpings. The hand busy forking macaroni into the mouth may suddenly drop the fork with a bang and seize bread. The bread is torn casually to bits accompanied by flying crumbs, and then eaten in pelleted gobs. The mouth opens to receive the bread on the tongue rather than by the teeth. When the mounds of macaroni recede bread is used, like a rag, to wipe up sauce on the plate. It sops up the last drop of precious oil with its tomato and herb flavoring and puts it in the mouth where it belongs.

People ate this way at this banquet. They smacked their mouths. They talked with their mouths full. They left their wine, and did not drink again until the end of the meal. Then they wiped their greasy lips on napkins which were large and old, full of holes, but revered.

It was a gorging meal. It crescendoed. Spirits exploded into laughter. Toasts began again. The toasts changed from rhetorical to witty. Everything moved toward music.

"Song! Song!" demanded a man at the head of the table.

There was a bang of a fork.

"Martha!" called another man.

Martha was well famed for her singing. She had perfected her art while picking olives.

She dropped her eyes, and then raised them to look at everyone without expression. Now, with the *kandíli* flickering in the dimness and the sun making the highest catapult of its arc in the sky, about to descend in the waning afternoon, she began to sing. The muscles of her neck distended in the effort. I expected her to thrust her head back, and close her eyes, abandoning herself in the song. But she did not. She fastened her eyes upon everyone blankly, as if there were actual meaning behind the blankness. It was very strange. She sang in a very sharp voice, entirely without vibrato. She looked at everyone with those piercing, blank eyes. The music was in a wild 9/8 time incomprehensible to a western ear. In the falls of the cries, which are like trills or grace notes, her voice focused nasally on what seemed to be errors. Yet it was very definite. Her grave eyes and solemn expression inundated everyone with a terrible feeling of clarity and responsibility.

The song was of thaws, of melting snow upon the mountain, of springing shoots and just budded leaves. An evocation of spring.

I think this music descended from the European nightingale's song. A whole flush of notes explodes in a stream. If you are a devotee of the precise pitch of every note, it will drive you to distraction. You have to get off that train of thought. In western music you have a cluster. In eastern music you have a stream.

At the end of her singing there was no applause. Everyone was silent, as if deeply moved. And then Martha began "Barba Yanni," an ancient folk song. Everyone joined in, in unison, beating their hands against the table.

I thought of our Barba Ioannis whom I had not met yet, and of Martha and her predicament.

At four o'clock was the ceremony of rings. Martha pulled Daddy and me to the center of the great crowd encircling the bride and groom. We were packed against everyone tightly, like sardines.

The village *papá* was there. He intoned words. He placed rings on the bride's finger and the groom's finger. The bride and groom kissed his hand. They drank of wine and sweated with embarrassment. The bride looked down at the ground. The bridegroom was fat and zootsuitily dressed. His face was very red and he mopped it with a large handkerchief.

I looked at Martha to see if I could tell what she was thinking. But she was staring at them with that same blank expression she had maintained when she had been singing. She caught my eye, but she did not smile. She simply stared piercingly at me, and then bid me with those silent eyes to look. It was as if she had said:

"Look, look. This is the way we become engaged in Greece. Remember it well, for this may be the only time you will see it."

Afterwards I asked Daddy: "What will happen to Martha and Ioannis?"

"Mmmmm. I don't know. They are in a fix all right, because Maria is crazy. And Martha is too good a work horse. Why should Maria give her to be married when she cleans and cooks and scrubs and washes so well? What would Maria do without her? But Martha is smart, and she knows how to get around Maria all right. Who knows what will happen?"

"Is it all so full of doomed, ancient misery as it seems?"

"You know what the Greek word for misery is? You hear it every other sentence.

"*Stenohória.*"

"You know what that means?"

"What?"

"*Stenós* means narrow. Narrow mind. Very narrow mind. That is what Greek misery is."

I appreciated the conceit. I even had my suspicions. But the aura and aesthetic enactment of Greek misery was too powerful to dispense with a conceit.

XI Martha and Ioannis came almost every day now to visit us at the *chtíma.* They came late in the afternoon and stayed on into the hours of evening. There was a feeling of urgency and exaggerated excitement in these visits, for they knew that our time in the vineyard would soon be over, and it was as if they wanted to seize and gobble every moment of a magic born of the tension of colliding cultures. Perhaps too they saw in it the culmination of a crescendoing hope in regard to their marriage plans, for they discussed these with Daddy as if it were the final days of a conference on nuclear test bans. Night came down upon all of us. This gave these visits an additional suspense, and a febrile gaiety seized us.

Daddy appropriated the aluminum camp chair. He was in the middle of William James's *Psychology*. We removed to the inside of the cottage during the sunset. The three of us played a child's game, sitting around the oilclothed table. It was called "*Petâï, Petâï,*" It flies, It flies. In this game we put our forefingers next to each other's on the table top.

"It flies, it flies . . . the nightingale," Ioannis would say.

We would raise our forefingers.

"It flies, it flies . . . the eagle," Ioannis would say.

We would raise our forefingers.

"It flies, it flies . . . the donkey," Ioannis would say.

If anyone raised his forefinger, the penalty was to have his hand slapped. Ioannis slapped hard. We would laugh and look at each other in mock alarm. Daddy could not concentrate on William James, and we would remember, and clap our hands over our mouths.

In the dimness of the *chtíma* light, the magic of a language sparked. It gave off glitters. Every day new words flamed in the darkness, like a *kandíli* before an icon. These words were the leaks, the hints, the auguries of a paradise of knowledge full glazing. Each glimmer gave by its repetition a shock of recognition which lit the historical cavern of the English word. Each word, seen in its great-great-great-granddaddy, the Greek word, opened a millennium of historical meanings, implied an entirely new threshold of aesthetics. All knowledge changed, turned over and revealed a wealth never suspected before of poetry, philosophy, and history. Almost nothing remained untouched in my whole catalogue of knowledge. Homer had his stamp on common words. Hesiod had his fingerprint on Christianity. Plato had his thumb-scratch on science. The world was topsy-turvy. I, alienated from English, stuttered and groped to articulate the most common things in Greek. But I discovered that

Greek common talk is the most ancient poetry in all the world. Most elegant, most elegiac, most noble, it was taught to me by peasants who had no idea of the mammoth culture that it had spawned.

Everyday life became to me a giant guessing game in which there sparked and glimmered connections and derivations, not for the purpose of being a student or an academician, but for simply being able to understand what was going on. Yet, not only was there this procession from the ancient to the English to be explored by fingering the derivatives, there was also a reverse flow, that is, the imports of other languages into modern Greek. The result of these imports was something ridiculous. The imports are mostly French and Turkish and recently English from America.

The imports are neatly incorporated, given Greek pronunciation and spelled with Greek letters. Most people who used these words used them without any idea that they were not good Greek words. Because the Greek article is always used, these imported words always carried along with them their article. And because the imports were mostly things, they usually carried the neuter article *to* in front of them. To hear these words, familiarities, cropping out among the elegiacs of Hesiod and Homer, gave me the same feeling as if I were being served a magnificent charlotte russe pudding laced with horse turds. The phenomenon made me dizzy with laughter and schizophrenic by its absurdity. I wanted to challenge the universe. I wanted to proclaim my knowledge and enjoin Ioannis and Martha into my horselaugh. But if I had done it, my laughter would not have been understood at all. So it is an imported word! So what is *funny* about it? But Daddy laughed too. And Ioannis and Martha stared at us curiously, as if we were occult beings to laugh at the unlaughable.

There is another comic effect in the mixture of the sublime and ridiculous in Greek. This is the practice of ending nouns with *áki*, *-oúli*, and *-oúla*. These are diminutives. They are cute, childish, loving endings. They contain a charm, for they are used in the most unlikely words:

Mána. Mother. *Manoúla*. Little mother.

Griá. Old woman. *Grioúla*. Little old woman.

Papá. Pope, priest. *Papoúli*. Little pope, little priest.
Kaphé. Coffee. *Kaphedáki*. Little coffee.
Phasólia. Beans. *Phasolákia*. Little beans.
Potíri. Glass. *Potiráki*. Little glass.
Spíti. House. *Spitáki*. Little house.
Ioannis. John. *Yannaki*. Little John.
Louloúdia. Flowers. *Louloudákia*. Little flowers.
Kóta. Chicken. *Kotoúla*. Little chicken.

Ioannis and Martha, like all Greeks, played with words as with marbles, rolling them, tinkling them, caressing them, racing them, and clinking them. They literally bestowed love on their words.

There are numberless terms of affection, most of them containing these diminutive endings: *Chrisó mou*. My golden one. *Angeloudáki mou*. My little angel. *Koúkla mou*. My doll. *Paidáki mou*. My child.

For my repetitive efforts in learning Greek, Ioannis and Martha called me their "*papagaláki mou*," little parrot.

XII One late afternoon Marth and Ioannis brought all the Athanasopouloses. There was Thea Ioannou, Katina, her husband Elias, their two children Boulis and Yannoula, and all the stepbrothers' families. Only Barba Ioannis was missing. He had stayed home with a cold. We ate a large feast for supper in the vineyards, sitting on burlap sacks in a circle.

We could see the sea from the vineyard. The fire danced on the full September leaves of the fig tree, and the last violent rays of the sun shone orange and purple on Navarino as they sank languidly into the delicious sea. The air was calm. The flies went in. The world turned into purple silhouettes. The mountain of Navarino sat proud and peaked, rising out of the glassy, liquid calm of Pylos Bay. As the dark formed over the vineyards, and the mountains and the islands, it closed down the shade of the village of Petrahori. We could determine the village only from the flickering petrol-gas lamps being lighted in the houses. The sky was dark, breathless, perfect. The stairs came out shining endearingly over the whole of the Greek earth. Friendly *koukouváyes* played around the eaves of the cottage and cooed ghostily. We lingered over the glasses of light retsina, and our winy mood turned everyone into contemplation and wonder. The light of the fire shone in our eyes and drew us together.

Someone suggested a story.

"Praise God, think where Greece would be if it had not been for Navarino," said Ioannis. He began telling the story of how the fleet of Turks had stood high in the Venetian fort and how the Turkish navy had commanded the Bay of Pylos in 1821. How Kolokotronis, Mioaulis, and the wily ape-Odysseus fought by sea and by land in the nineteenth-century war against the Turks. And the day in 1827 when the great fight occurred between the Turkish fleet and segments of the British fleet augmented with French and Russian ships which ended in the destruction of the Turkish fleet right off Navarino. How Greece was liberated.

"Theo, some day we must go to Navarino," said Martha.

"It is far, Theo," said Elias, brother-in-law of Martha. "Nevertheless, you should go and see the great *kastro*."

"Isn't it funny how it seems at night," shivered Martha. "Sometimes it seems to me the very spirits would speak."

"Are you afraid?" asked Elias.

"No, but it seems to me that spirits are here."

"There are no spirits," said Ioannis. "That is bosh."

"*Paidí mou,* don't blaspheme," sniffed Thea Ioannou. "I have smelled spirits!"

"Perhaps the spirits '*stin archí*' are still here, in British admirals and of Turkish beasts who cut out the tongues of the Greeks. Other ones, no. It seems to me sometimes that those kinds of spirits speak from Navarino. That is what our freedom speaks with, the cut-out tongues of archaic Greeks." Ioannis sighed.

"I will tell you something," said Daddy. "Do you want to hear something?"

"Yes, Theo. Tell us."

" '*Stin archí vevea,* in the real beginning, that is, five thousand years ago, before Hellas was ever consummated or concentrated as a state, before she even had her freedom to lose, before the Turks had ever come out of the steppes, when they were still eating nuts and scratching themselves—they were monkeys then, not even barbarians —do you know who lived in the cave underneath the Venetian *kastro?*'

They were silent.

"You know the cave."

"Yes, Theo. Yes. I have been there," said Elias.

"Well, that belonged to Hermes," said Daddy.

"Hermes!"

"Hermes was a devilish fellow, a sly and tricky one. He had the aptitude to turn himself by tricks into anything he wanted to. He went up to Mount Olympus, up there by Saloniki and stole a herd of Apollo's cows. He made little wooden hoofs and put them on the cows back-side to. Then he brought the cows down here to Navarino and hid them in the cave. All the cows' tracks went the wrong way, so when Apollo tried to trace them over the mountainsides, he was always going the wrong way. He tried to find them for years, but he could not find them."

Everyone laughed. They liked Hermes already.

"Apollo knew Hermes had stolen the cows, and he went to Zeus and complained. 'What the devil,' he said. 'He took my cows and I can't find them anywhere.' At last Apollo found Hermes and he took him by the scruff of the neck and thrust him in Zeus's face, accusing him. But Hermes changed himself into a baby. 'What's the matter?' Hermes said to Zeus. 'Apollo is crazy. How could I have stolen his cows? Can a baby steal cows?' "

The whole group laughed.

"But you know that Hermes was so clever! He had killed one of those cows and taken out the guts and strung them over a turtle's back. Like the turtle that Yannoula found this afternoon. And you know what he did?"

"What?"

"He played them, he made music. He made the most beautiful music that you ever heard. He played it right over in that cave and you could hear it right where we are sitting."

Everyone listened. It was so silent that suddenly they believed that they could hear the music of Hermes. They were not bothered by classifications. They listened, never telling themselves that what they were hearing was a myth. They were the people to whom the bards sang the Homeric myths. Truth swelled them up and they were filled by the sounds of Hermes' music.

"Apollo heard it, you know," continued Daddy. "He was ravished. He went right over to Hermes' cave and tried to make a bargain with him. 'I know that you stole my cows,' he told him, 'but I will make a deal with you. I will give them to you free gratis if you will tell me the secret of how you make this music.' 'Why, to be sure, Apollo,' said Hermes, laughing to himself. Then he showed Apollo the lyre he had made and tried to teach Apollo to play as beautifully as he did. But Apollo could not play quite as well as Hermes. Then Hermes began to play a pipe that he had made out of a bamboo strip like we made the *kalíves*. Oh, you have never heard such beautiful music as he made! It was even more beautiful than the lyre. Where Apollo had been ravished by the lyre, he was now made mad by the beauty of the music of the pipe. 'What the dickens,' he said to himself. 'This is a mad crook. This is a scoundrel. But I would give my eye teeth to play this pipe as well as Hermes.' And he praised him and never asked him about the cows or ever mentioned them again."

All at once everybody began talking and interrupting.

"*Sópa! Sópa!*" cried Elias. "Let Theo talk."

"You can hear the music any night of the summer sitting in this vineyard just where Apollo sat then, if you listen hard," said Daddy.

"Oh yes, Theo." Elias began talking. "I am not superstitious. I don't believe in spirits. But I tell you something about this place." His voice descended to a whisper. "One night, a night something like this—it was two years ago—I was walking, right over there by that bush. All of a sudden I saw three women just as plain as day. They were dressed in white, two of them. And they were tall, just about the size of Maria. But the third one, she was short and fat and decrepit. I tell you I was scared. I knew that she was evil. She was evil. Suddenly she began to speak, the evil one. Her voice was very croaky. She said: 'A day is coming three years from now. A great wind will blow. Seven out of nine will fall. There will be a great ruination. A father will die.' That's all she said. But one of the tall ones added: 'But a sister will rise.' "

A silence fell on our company.

Then Ioannis began to laugh.

"Bosh! Bah!"

"I saw them!"

"How could you see spirits if there aren't any spirits?"

"I don't know. But I swear to you that they were there. I heard them say these things."

"He is a fool," said Ioannis, turning to Daddy.

Martha, Thea Ioannou, Katina and the other women crossed themselves.

"I was reading a scientific book," said Daddy pontifically. "It said that five thousand years ago all the people of Greece saw these very women. The description that you gave is the exact description that was in the book. They were the Fates. One of them was always short, fat and decrepit. And the other two were dressed in white."

"*Christós kai Panagía mou! Kakopópatha!* In three years! Oh saints! Saints, preserve us!"

The women echoed this and the fire crackled into embers.

XIII Our two weeks at the cottage were up. We were going back to Athens. The day before we left, we went once more to the Petrahori beach.

A great significance of beaches is whether they lie to the east or the west. Eastern beaches are morning beaches. The sun rises over them. When the first tint of the sun paints the sands and stones and seaweed, there is something inexpressibly familiar and comfortable about the eastern beach. The day lies before you, conceived as an entire universe, illimitable and never to end. Ships, sails, tankers, morning foghorns testify to the world's business. The sandpipers chirp and forage for food with the poetry of matter-of-factness. Morning birds. The sea gulls make long-morning shadows in the still-morning cool air, but already they are on the hunt for gill-netters and fishing boats, squalling coarsely like hucksters. As the sun rises higher, old tin cans shine and wink excitedly. Minnows come out, attracted by the brilliance, and nest in them. Crabs and lobsters in their green and murky dens begin to feel that far above is a busy, high octane, active, brawling day. In mid-morning the eastern beach is alive with sounds. The roar, whir, cries, breeze-dips, boat-creakings, shouts, rowing oars, scuttling crabs, and honking sea gulls testify to the high business of daily living.

Night comes early to the eastern beach. The sun moves over to drip its sunset upon the earth and leaves the beach in shadow. Then all the sea creatures close up at once, forsaking the long shadows without more ado. Crabs bury themselves. Minnows disappear. Lobsters forsake their hunt for food. Sea gulls stare blankly, and then fold their heads cozily under their wings. It is the business of sleep and of burial until day comes again.

Petrahori was a western beach. The western beach is the *Il Penseroso* to the eastern beach's *L'Allegro*. Morning comes to it late. The morning is spent in a half-guilty dark, afflicted with the long shadows of the earth.

Yet when the light of noon soars high into the heavens, the western beach is illumined in the most aerial radiance. It is fragile. The air is hot, pure, and whisperingly clear. The sand simmers, and the water has shocking clarity. No lumbering lobsters. No horny deep. Even the jellyfish are dainty.

On the Petrahori beach the rocks seemed like prehistoric monsters, wild, unformed, and strange in contrast with the tendrill-thin air, and the elegant blue waters foaming about them. Raw igneous lave, petrified. But they were razor-sharp. Delusive. They were betrayers and would cut you bloodlessly. They would snag the tiniest thread of a piece of cloth and hold it fluttering helplessly.

The Petrahori beach reached its prime about three in the afternoon. Its life seemed then to stretch out, not for labors or business, but for philosophy and for the music of a waning afternoon, promising the crescendo of sunset. This might seem nostalgic. But it has to do with immortality. The thought of immortality is strong. It takes more guts than memory or impending death's acceptance. It seems strange that such a delicate, radiant beach could be the scene of the greatest pageant of death and of immortality that you can see anywhere in the world. But this is the essence of the western beach.

In each heart-strung beating of the sun's blood mirrored soundly on the flat, clipping sea, there is something perpetuative. One knows that it will give place, not to threatening Absence, but to definite Night, to the moon and the stars, the imitation in the heavens of human, bobbing fishing lights. The sun will die in the water every night. Let us concentrate on its last hours. This is the secret of the sunset on the western shore of Greece.

The ceremony is transparent and clear-cut, as is everything concerned with nature in Greece. It presents itself to you not only as poetry, but as an X-ray of itself. The sun travels in the threads of the clouds and makes blood vessels of them. You can point to it and say: "That is the vein of Life itself." At the same time, you know that this day is dying. The sun is throbbing in the body of the sky and this is a fact, a medical vision. But think of the poetic effect of it. The pink sheen against the green of left-over yellow rays. The yellow lemon color of flowers against the mountain. The plum blue as the sun sinks lower. The vein in the cloud begins to throb more violently. The sea near-to changes. It is a complete reflection. It is nothing without the sun. It changes to silver and green, contrasting peculiarly with the purple shed of the mountains. It conveys a sense of beautiful futility. To reflect and to reflect, and then to dare to be the vessel of poetry. It gives back importance multifold to the sun's agony.

XIV

Daddy went on to Tripolis a day before I left Hora. We arranged to meet in a few days in Athens.

I said good-by to all my relatives except Barba Ioannis whom I did not meet.

I stayed my last night in the one guest room at Maria's. In the morning at four o'clock Martha came into my room with a candle to wake me up. I arose and washed from the pitcher and bowl. Martha boiled a cup of coffee over the kerosene burner. We drank it sweet, with gobbets of white bread. She had packed a lunch for me and wrapped it in a newspaper. It contained three pieces of bread, two hard-boiled eggs, a sardine, a packet of goat cheese which leaked waterily through the paper, and five vinegared black olives.

When we descended the creaking stairway in the darkness, Maria heard the commotion. She appeared at the top of the stairs dressed in an old dressing gown with her eyes popping.

"I wish to thank you very very much," I said in Greek.

She cut a rose from one of the vines and gave it to me. At the same time she shouted to Martha:

"Have you given her a lunch! Good. Good. But shame on you for not having awoken me to say good-by to such a treasured guest." She turned back to me. "Promise that you will not stay away long. You must come back. In two weeks. Yes? In two weeks. Promise me that. And you will not forget me, eh? How we rode down to the *chtíma* in a motorcycle? Eh? Ha ha ha. Well, now, good luck and *kaló taxídi.*"

Below we could hear the creak of her footsteps and the crunch of her bed as she got back into it.

Martha knew her way through the *kípo* perfectly in the darkness. Her cigarette lighter flashed. I heard the rustle of a branch. She put into my hand an orange still wet with night dampness.

"Don't make a noise," she breathed. "We don't want her to know. She doesn't like it if we pick the oranges in the garden."

This furtiveness was a delight. A rose and an orange!

The gate clicked and groaned on its hinges. In the darkness there was the pale glow of a cigarette. It was Ioannis come to see me off.

The streets were empty in the darkness and we could see the stars. Our footsteps echoed. By the church of Agios Ioannis a donkey clopped by us, walking very slowly. A flashlight turned upon us and blinded us.

"Eh-eh!" growled Ioannis.

The peasant knocked his knees against the wooden saddle and turned off the light.

"*Vláhos!*" spat Ioannis.

It was strange, the feeling of this departure so early in the morning. I felt as if I had lived in the cottage for a year, and that Martha and Ioannis were the only people in the world who were real. I could imagine no other existence than the one in the vineyards. I could not even imagine that the sun would rise this day, or that there was such a thing as the future. The atmosphere was cold and greasy with dampness from the sea. We all held on to these moments with no idea why we were hanging on. We were like three strangers and three members of the same family. But the one conception could not contain the other.

Yet we acted very formal. Martha did not ask me if I would ever return. I think she believed that I never would.

"Remember I am your cousin. You are my cousin," she said.

"*Na érthis pálin.* Come again, and we will all go to Navarino with a little donkey," said Ioannis.

We all shook hands, and I climbed into the bus.

V Barbara

1

I WAS AWAKENED from a doze when the bus jerked to a screeching halt. Everything was pitch black. There was not yet the faintest appearance of dawn. In the darkness sounded the noise of shricking, wailing, and weeping. It was as if I had waked up in the World of the Dead with bodiless voices screaming in eternal torment.

"What is it?" shouted people around me.

A man jumped up and rushed down the aisle to look out the front window.

An entire village of people was grouped on the road in front of the bus. It looked like an El Greco tragedy scene. Women tore their hair and beat their breasts. Men stood blank-eyed with a hollow expression of tragedy. Girls held their faces in large white handkerchiefs and raised them with streaming eyes and large wails. Young men with mustaches held bouquets of flowers and wiped the tears from their eyes with their coat sleeves. A pope stood in the middle of the scene with a befuddled expression, holding up a cross.

It turned out that two young couples from this village of Little Pyrgos were emigrating to Australia. This was their farewell scene. The whole village, cousins, aunts, uncles, brothers, and mothers had risen to see them off. Presumably, this was the last time they would see them in this life.

"*Afstralía, Afstralía!*" went in whispers and exclamations through the bus.

Some people in the bus laughed. Others turned to look at me, slyly smiling.

"*Englézika, Englézika!*" shouted one man, excitedly, pointing to me and to the two couples out on the road to imply that I would be able to speak that language to the emigrants.

"Come on! Break it up!" another hollered to the bus driver. "These people will lose their boat in Piraeus if we don't get this *aftokínito* moving."

"Be quiet! *Sópa!*" shouted others. "Let them have a little more time."

I thought: 'Emigration is inconceivable to Americans. America is the place where people come. The Home of Homeless Millions, Haven of the Outcasts and Refugees, Home of Freedom.' The Statue of Liberty dangled before my eyes.

But not any more.

Now the two places are Australia and Canada. After these the two places are South Africa and South America.

How history changes! But it has not changed for Little Pyrgos. They are still emigrating. They have been emigrating since the days of the first Greek colonies of the ancient world in Italy and Asia Minor.

"How long are we going to stay here!" shouted a man.

The bus driver threw his hands in the air. Then he got up and said out the door in a tender voice:

"Come along, *paidákia*. Let them go, people. We can't stay here forever. Come on. Kiss and say good-by now. We have got to get along the road."

As one the crowd acknowledged the final wrench. The weeping and wailing increased to a higher pitch. Flowers and gifts were hoisted over the crowd's heads and pressed into the hands of the couples. The pope lifted his cross and uttered some words. A young man planted a passionate kiss upon the mouth of his best friend. Mothers and aunts clasped the couples in their arms and dragged along like leeches as if they would not let them enter the bus doors. Other women tried to pull them away. One woman uttered a screeching yelp: "Yip. Yip. Yip." Last gifts and kisses were thrust through the door, as the two couples climbed in.

Flowers, packages, coats, luggage, baskets brushed people's shoulders as they made their way to two empty seats. It seemed as if they were occupying twenty places instead of four, they brought so much stuff with them.

No sooner had they selected their seats than they thrust open the window. The bus throttled, and last hand-wavings, screechings, and kisses were exchanged as the tires left the weeping crowd in a trail of night-dust.

The girls continued to sob. But the young men lifted their red eyes, looked around them, and put on a proud, overbearing air as they witnessed their new surroundings. They even began to talk with their neighbors. They talked in a large, self-important way as if they were above the people in the bus.

"Who knows when we will ever see them again," one young man sighed. "But it is better to go to Australia. We will have a chance in Australia."

II Near Tripolis in the blaze of noon we passed a mountain on which was gouged in stupendous white letters the word "O X I." It was like the earth itself saying "NO."

At the beginning of the war the Italians occupied Albania. At 3 A.M., October 28, 1940, they issued an ultimatum to the Greeks demanding "protective" occupation of unspecified zones of Greek territory. Metaxas, the Greek Prime Minister, answered: "*Óhi.*"

Italian troops, spearheaded by the Centaur Division, thrust down from Albania 30 miles into Epirus. The Greek army was partially mobilized. Immediately a great wheeling movement started. Companies were stripped from the Bulgarian and Yugoslavian borders. Reservists streamed to call-up centers. Equipment was short. The Greeks had little except infantry weapons. Tanks, ammunition, and food were seriously lacking. But in a remarkable, transcendent show of morale, the Greeks united. Thus far and no farther. Men too old to fight served as muleteers making their way over the Pindus Mountains. Supplies were brought over the few roads by car or wagon. Peasants of near-by villages cleared the snow from the roads. Cavalcades of donkeys, carts, and trucks crawled like worms over the mountains. It was a human chain of artillery. Supplies were even carried on human backs, often by local peasant women.

In mid-November at Zygos Mountain the Greeks defeated the Italian Centaur Division. The Italians were unprepared for the attack. They retreated. Their retreat turned into a rout. The morale of their soldiers cracked. Precipitously they fell back into Albania.

The word "*Óhi*" became an emblem all over Greece. It appeared scrawled in large letters on walls of buildings. It appeared painted on roofs. It appeared on the sides of careening trucks. It appeared in giant letters upon the faces of mountains.

Every year Óhi Day is celebrated as a Greek national holiday.

I thought how in all crucial human conflicts there are two clear-cut answers: The Everlasting No, and the Everlasting Yes. The Everlasting No is the cornerstone of Western Method. The Greeks who put up the O X I were founders and descendants of the West.

Compare this to the Japanese story upon which Kurt Weill and Bertolt Brecht based their opera *He Says Yes*. It is the tale of a sensitive and sickly boy whose greatest desire is to join the yearly pilgrimage of his school across the mountains to the Great Land Beyond. It is the rule of the pilgrimage that any boy who lacks the physical stamina to keep up with the rigorous pace of the journey must abide by the vote of the majority to throw him off the mountain to his death so as not to keep the party back. Just before the pilgrimage begins the boy's mother falls sick and is dying. Although warned by the schoolmaster, and the other boys who love him, that he is too frail to keep up with them, the boy makes the final decision to go. Medicine is in the Great Land Beyond, and he must get it to save his mother.

The first day of the pilgrimage he keeps up with the others. The second day his footsteps lag. The third day he slips. The fourth day the boys warn him. The fifth day he admits his error, but begs them to give him a chance. Their hearts are softened, and although they have little faith in his stamina they allow him to continue with them. The sixth day they reach the top of the mountains. The cold is extreme. He pauses by the wayside to breathe. On the seventh day he falls down in a fever.

The boys demand a vote. He begs them in his fever to pull him up, he will continue. The teacher bends down to his ear and reminds him of his promise to obey the rules. He tells him that the boys must now vote and that he must die.

In a final aria of his brilliant, stunning, doomed life, in delirium he sings: "Yea. Yea. Yea." The boys vote. Still singing "Yea," he is heaved over the precipice to his death.

By the Everlasting No the mortal faced with the ravages of inevitable doom turns an imperturbable face against it and fights for the last pulse of life.

By the Everlasting Yea the human agrees actively to go into the doom itself, embracing the tragedy as if it were the core of life.

III

The minute I hit Athens I had to change the gears of my universe. Civilization! Dazzling lights, big buildings, movies, trolley cars, and catapulting automobiles. But it was not only these. It was the visit of my friend, Barbara, and the speaking of English.

Barbara was an English girl. She was slightly Americanized from having worked for some years at American Air Force bases in England. She had been a ballet dancer, a seller of perfume in Mayfair, a Service Club director, and was now a librarian with the U. S. Air Force near London. She was on her three-week vacation.

The important thing about Barbara was her beauty. The reason it was important was that her personality did not fit it. She had a graven, marmoreal face with a prominent, elegant nose. It was enigmatic and grave. Her eyes were liquid and dark and obsessive. People always turned to look and gasp as at a quick clutch in a moment at a perfect image not really to be believed. In point of fact she was a delusive person. She was outrageous and shocking, much given to lying, cheating, swearing, and stealing, with a passion for Tennessee Williams and other decadences, all for the purpose of making fun of the absurdities of the universe. She had a neat, witty, and enticing tongue, and was very merciless. And she was loyal, conscientious, and very hard-working, with a terrible sensibility and fatal compassion. She was also very penny-pinching. She always bought her clothes at bargain-basement sales or at C & A, the Grant's of England, where the Russian athlete, Nina Ponomareva, stole those hats. The clothes on her looked like Dior originals, and she always varied her story about those purchases according to whom she was talking to.

"Let us go to a cheap hotel, bag," she said when she had gotten out of the train. "Not only does the stinking Motherland not allow more than a hundred pounds out of the country, but you know the Queen's salaries for British civilians employed by the U. S. Air Force."

"How bad do you want it to be?" I asked, thinking of the Rodos.

It was the Rodos that we went to. The minute I had told her what Daddy had done to the manager, she wanted to go there.

"Let us vow," I told her conspiratorially, "that we will not pay over one dollar for any hotel in all of Greece. We can get decent rooms at that price, and there is no reason why we should get gypped just because we look good."

At the Rodos the fat, greasy manager came dripping out to greet us. Instead of being a deterrent, the past history with Daddy seemed to be the cement to a long and overpowering friendship with me. The maid, Aphrodite, greeted me like a long-lost friend. But the sight of Barbara galvanized her. She stared her up and down as if she were some golden jewel just dropped out of the sky. She put out her hand and felt the cloth of her suit, clucking and breathing with praise.

"We have no room vacant just now," simpered the manager, rubbing his oily hands. "But there is a little back house that you could sleep in tonight. . . . All the hotels in Athens are filled up right now, you know. . . . Tomorrow, we can move you into another room. . . ."

We went out to see it. It was a little cement room in a back courtyard where clothes were hung to dry. There were four broken windows. A greasy curtain hung flapping at the doorway. There were four cobwebs and three known spiders sitting malevolently in the middle of them. There were two dirty cigars lying in a stinking ashtray, and the two beds were hard. Also, the door had a key that did not work.

"See? Not too bad," winked Aphrodite wickedly. "I clean those cobwebs. Nobody come in here, even if key don't work. The only thing is, few *kounoúpia.*"

"What are gnoopies?" demanded Barbara.

"*Polí kakó,*" I said loudly and sternly to Aphrodite.

"Cobwebs are nothing," said Aphrodite. "I clean them all off. I put good sheets on bed. I wash floor. I spray with *to* Fleet." She was becoming very familiar. She pounded her hands on the beds to show how soft they were. She winked and clucked with her teeth.

"What are gnoopies, Greek thing," asked Barbara again.

"They are mosquitoes."

That decided it. Barbara liked the name gnoopies so much that she wanted to stay. She began to plan the entire rearrangement of the room, and had it figured out that this was Aphrodite's own room. "This is where she sleeps, and those cigars are her lover's remains. It is an absolute sty, but after all, what is sleeping? We'll probably never get a place so cheap."

"How much?" I asked Aphrodite.

She hemmed and hawed. Finally she said: "Forty drachs."

"For this dump?" I said indignantly. "Impossible."

"Thirty-five."

"It is not worth twenty."

And so on. I got her down to twenty-five, to which everyone agreed. But then she did not want to leave. She was so entranced by the glamour of Barbara that she hung around shivering, scraping, bowing, and drooling.

"Lock. Key." Barbara made motions to her in the air. "Also Flit. Gun. Squeeze. Squeeze. Hiss. Hiss." Barbara made imaginary Flit guns shoot into the air.

Aphrodite laughed and clapped.

"And now you may go," I said, pointing to the door.

"Bag," said Barbara when the door closed, "you have brought me to the worst place in Greece. We may die of malaria, but thank God we have nothing worthwhile to steal."

IV

"Listen, bag, I have a horrible thing to tell you."

"What is that?"

"Robert is coming."

Robert was a tall, blond, and handsome athlete, a first lieutenant who had just been separated from the Air Force and was now kicking around Europe. Before his Air Force career he had been a football star at some West Virginia college until he had been kicked out either for bad marks or cheating.

"He is trying to con his way into some Swiss medical school because no decent wholesome American medical school would accept the likes of him. But he had a week's vacation, and he thinks it is cheap here. I don't know when he is arriving and I don't care. All I want to tell you is I don't want you to let him bum off you or Greek Daddy."

"He couldn't bum off Daddy as Daddy is a far better con artist than he is."

"I don't know why I ever bothered with Robert in the first place. You know how every time he opens his mouth he tells lies. Stupid me, I was just on my Lady Christianity kick."

For two days Barbara and I lived in the gnoopie shack. Then we were transferred into the hotel. Every day we kept expecting Robert, but he did not show. Then it turned out that he did not even have Barbara's address in Athens.

Every day we had breakfast with Daddy in the Piccadilly. We wandered the shops with Daddy comparing the prices of goods. We wandered all the city streets and the ruins. Every afternoon we went to the movies. We always went to big, American, cheap, gaudy, technicolored movies.

"My mother says what is the use of my taking vacations in foreign countries. All I ever do is go to the movies. 'You can just as well go to the movies in Wimbledon,' she says. But the point is I would never see any moves at all if I did not go abroad."

In Athens the movie theaters smell of perfume. After each reel there is an intermission, because there is only one movie projector, so everything stops. The lights come up. The perfume-sprayers come down the aisles with suction squirters. They squirt in the air, in your face and every conceivable place. The reason for these squirtings is to keep the smell down, and also, I imagined, to discourage fleas, lice, and other varieties of bugs. Along with the perfume-squirters come peanut-vendors. They sell pistachio nuts, *stragália*, and stale chocolate bars with coconut. Barbara was a chocolate connoisseur, so she always bought a chocolate bar.

"GI's always warn you never to eat anything but American chocolate bars as all the others, they say, are filled with worms. But I only struck one worm in all the chocolate bars that I have ever eaten, and that was a French worm in a chocolate bar in Nice."

It was I who unearthed Robert. I was in the American Library on Panepistimiou, reading Sherwood Anderson. In he walked. He was wearing filthy khaki pants and an old pilot's jacket which he had stolen from the Air Force. (He had never been a pilot.) His hair was bleached yellow from the sun and he had a two days' growth of beard.

"Robert!"

"Hey! How are little old you?"

"When did you arrive?"

"Why I just walked in, honey chile." He was carrying a khaki pack and a small dirty TWA bag which he deposited by the door. "Where's Barb?"

"She's supposed to arrive any minute. You sure do look beat."

"Well, see, I hitched through Italy. I got in with this Italian wino, he brought a car over from Brindisi. We sat in it all day on board the *Angelika* while the peons were on deck, and we drank wine. He must have been some sort of crook or something, because they unloaded the car at Corfu and took him in custody. Anyway, he was a nice fellow. . . . Anyway I liked him, you know?"

"Sit down," I told him, as if I owned the American Library.

Every Greek eye was upon us. We hid behind the newspaper rack.

"I thought they blew up this joint with some bombs," said Robert.

"They did, but it only blew up the second floor. They moved all the magazines down here."

"Where's Greek Daddy?"

"He's here, waiting to meet you. He's heard so much about you from Barb."

"Aaaach so?" He had picked up "Aaaach so" from Germany and used it at every opportunity when he wanted to be polite.

Suddenly Barbara came in. All eyes turned up to inspect her elegance as she entered. She walked to Robert.

"You look like a flea-picker," she said.

"What the hell do you expect?"

"I expected at least Sir Edmund Hillary," she said. "But here I have a big unkempt load of healthy football flesh dropping its way right into my lap."

"I hope you have a pair of scissors," he said.

"What for?"

"You know. To cut my hair."

Barbara was famed for her hair cutting. She cut everybody's hair she knew, her mother's, her father's, Robert's, and her boss's. Once people discovered her hair-cutting ability, they were always after her to cut their hair. But for her, hair-cutting was an act of honor and admiration that she bestowed on people, and she was in no mood to confer that honor on Robert.

"You may go to a Greek barber," she said. "I would not contaminate my lily-white hands with the filth of seven countries."

It was thus that Barbara and Robert got off to a very bad start. Robert put up in the gnoopie shack that we had abandoned, as his financial resources were at bottom. They bickered all the time.

"I know I'm vile," said Barbara. "But he's such a moldy creature. . . ."

At last an incident happened which brought them together in roses and moonlight.

Daddy took them to an establishment in the Syntagma which sold Rhodes pottery, all kinds of china and *objets d'art.* This shop was run by five Greek sisters and their husbands. The shop was very modern and sported a large plate-glass window which looked right out on to the sidewalk where the American Express and CIT tours came in with their busloads of tourists.

The sister Anna was sitting behind the cash register knitting while Robert, Barbara, and Daddy were browsing. I was outside sitting in a café chair. The sister Maria entered with a fatal step. In Greek she asked her sister Anna to return some money which she and her husband had previously borrowed.

"*Óhi,*" said Sister Anna, and went back to her knitting.

A quarrel arose. Maria grew angry. She shook her fist. She began to cry.

"*Óhi,*" said Sister Anna, knitting calmly.

Maria stamped her feet. She picked up a glass ashtray and began to bang it against the glass counter.

"Quiet down. Quiet down!" warned an assistant.

The warning had the opposite effect. With Hellenic abandon, ravaging and tearing her hair, Maria launched into a five-minute peroration, crying, weeping, and screaming. Sister Anna arose and shouted back at her.

"Call the police! Call the police!" someone shouted.

A bus tour had just arrived from Delphi. Fascinated by the furor, all the unloading people gathered around the store front to stare. Greek shopworkers and housewives gathered at the window clapping and laughing and cheering. A policeman stopped by to watch.

"Greek Daddy!" whispered Barbara. "What will we do? We are in a goldfish bowl."

"They're going to kill each other," whispered Robert gleefully, yet electrified.

The two women were staring at each other in hatred. The one swore and muttered threats, omens and oaths. The other flapped her hands across the air in utter derision. The noise grew louder.

"Greek Daddy!" begged Barbara. "It's humiliating."

"It would be even better if you could understand the language," said Daddy. With a very dignified attitude, he went to the door and locked it.

"Greek Daddy, you have trapped us in here!"

Daddy picked up his newspaper. He sat down on a stool directly in front of the window. He opened his newspaper and pretended to read boredly, yawning, as the ruckus in back of him grew louder.

"Greek Daddy, that's marvelous," breathed Barbara. "How did you think of anything so marvelous."

Suddenly she went to Sister Anna in the middle of the fray.

"Scissors," she demanded, snipping the air with her hand.

Sister Anna pulled a pair of shears out of the cabinet below the cash register, waved them in the air at Sister Maria until Barbara extracted them from her hand.

"Sit down, bum," she said to Robert. And she pulled a chair out from the center of the room to the key place in front of the window. She tied a dustcloth around his neck like a bib.

The first plate smashed as she made the first cut, but her hand was impeccable.

"Yawn, bum. Yawn like Greek Daddy."

Outside the crowd clapped in ecstasy. Robert yawned. Daddy yawned. Barbara cut. And the Rhodian plates smashed as threats rent the air.

From that moment until he went back to Germany, Robert and Barbara did not have another fight.

V After Robert left, Barbara and I decided to visit Rhodes and Crete. Our plan was to leave Piraeus for Rhodes, find another boat from Rhodes to Crete, and return to Piraeus from Crete.

We embarked one early morning from Piraeus on the *Semiramis*. The sun was singing high in the sky, and rays of it funneled joyously in the portholes and lay streaming across the white linen tablecloths in the dining room. A group of stewards stood wiping the water glasses at the bar. They were handsome and mischievous, and their thoughts were on us. They glanced at us as we finished off our chicken and rice *piláfi*. They smiled dazzlingly. They laughed. We ignored them. But being the focus of their admiring glances we could not help but feel glad and joyous ourselves. Therefore we made remarks about what silly fools those stewards were, and as they got a boot out of our not understanding a word they said, we got a boot out of their not understanding a word we said, and thus we talked about them even worse.

"Don't look at those stupid boys," said Barbara.

"If they come over here I will speak to them in Greek. Then they will think we have understood everything they said."

At that moment, a pope, a *papá* came into view. He sauntered past us on the way to the bar. He smiled a radiant smile upon us. He was a thin, aescetic-looking *papá*. His robe was black and silky, but a little frayed with age. It was like one of those cheap Halloween costumes which, once they become old, turn moldy-grayish color. He had a noble, yellow face with a long nose, Castro eyebrows, and a full, silky beard. His face was really mournful because of his eyebrows and his delicate mouth, but it changed in the smile and became almost gay.

"I want me a *papá*," whispered Barbara. "They are so dignified."

"Daddy says they have lice in their beards and wash twice a year."

"Greek Daddy is jealous."

"When they come to America the American College of the Orthodox Church makes them shave off their beards because they know how dirty they are. Also, Daddy says, they are very ignorant."

"After this I won't believe a word Greek Daddy says. Don't tell me things like that."

"What do you want a *papá* for?"

"I want to know what's behind its beautiful beard. I want its noble eyes to drop jewels of wisdom to me. I want to put it in an ivory box and keep it beautiful and glittering and wake up every morning and comb out its beard and have it make litanies. If it has lice, I will make it get rid of its lice, and I will keep it all shining and noble and pure. . . ."

"Will you have it squirt perfume and incense and tinkle little bells?"

"Oh yes!"

By this time the *papá* had stationed himself at the bar next to the group of stewards. He knew we were talking of him. He smiled again.

"*Papádes* shouldn't wear trousers under their robes," said Barbara. "Look, the cuffs of his trousers are spattered with mud."

"You are a perfectionist," I said. "Look, he's flirting with you."

He was vastly amused. One could see his pupils enlarging until they became so large that they almost spoke. He looked at us almost wickedly. There was something so human in this glance that we were embarrassed. But the offense was his rather than ours. This gave him a new dimension.

"*Papádes* can't be naughty," said Barbara. "I don't believe it."

"We'd better not talk so loud."

"Do you think he understands English?"

Because of Ioannis' story I felt that I was an initiate into the terrible, orthodox mysteries of all *papádes*. But I did not want to wreck Barbara's illusions. She was engaged in creating a work of art and imagination out of this *papá*. How to destroy a work of art? To create another one; art cannot exist upon lies. After all, it is spice to introduce naughtiness to nobility, and if anyone was wicked, it was certainly Barbara. If anyone could appreciate incongruity, it was Barbara.

As I told her the story of the errant *papádes* a mysterious aura of hepped-up wickedness surrounded us. The sun, magnified by the Mediterranean, danced like mischievous sprites on the tables, making infinite possibility and insistent suspicion. Barbara's black eyes were wide open, drinking up the story. She was galvanized in a spell.

The *papá* himself stood by the bar, drumming his hands and staring at us. He was aware of the spell and aware that he was the focus of it. His sallow nobility, his imposing beard hid the twinkle of something goatlike, mysterious, and impalpably clear. He was nimble, darting, and guilefully imposing. Crotchets of breathless possibilities were etched in the crows feet leading from the corners of his eyes.

The stewards, seeing that the focus of attention had centered on the *papá*, decided on a plan. They moved toward him. They were respectful, but their respect showed edges of laughter. Testimony to the democratic spirit in Greece, to ridicule the hierarchy in which they are caught. The *papá* was the butt of their ridicule, but he was also the object of their respect. They began to whisper. Someone began counting as if bets were being placed.

The *papá* received their attention with insouciance, but he loomed larger. Even while they were talking to him, he did not take his eyes off us. His expression became more calculated, but at the same time more ingenuous.

"He is going to do something. They are putting him up to something," I whispered.

The *papá* walked toward us very slowly and regally. He looked very piercingly into our faces, but he did not smile. He sat down at once beside us. His gold cross swung out and settled glittering on his bosom. It was electrifying, but so simple that it seemed entirely natural.

The stewards watched breathlessly.

The *papá* did not speak. He looked at us quizzically, but in a friendly way that was irresistible.

"*Kali iméra,*" I said.

An expression of joy and amusement appeared on his face.

"*Omileíte Ellinikà!*" He had the air of a proud parent, quixotic and druidical, pouring out his blessing.

"*Nai, allá omiláo kakó Elliniká.*"

"*Óhi! Óhi!*" he said with joy, insistent on paying those few words of Greek more praise than they deserved.

"*Ti oraía iméra!*" I said.

"Yes, it is a beautiful day," he agreed in Greek.

But he had become pensive, even absent-minded. He changed the subject. He leaned toward Barbara, fastening his rapt gaze on her.

"*Vous êtes anglaise?*" he asked her.

"*Oui,*" she said. But she did not believe in speaking any language but English, even in France where she understood French well. She wanted all the talk to go through me.

"You speak to him," she ordered.

"I only know droppings in Greek, and obviously this thing doesn't know a word of English, thank God," I said.

"Me no speak English," he said. To hear such English drop from his sallow nobility was strange. It diminished his malevolence, his bad intentions, and his nobility, and gave him a ludicrous air. But also an insinuating one since he had said it as if to corroborate what I had said in English.

"*Américaine,*" said Barbara, pointing to me.

"*Anglaise, américaine,*" he repeated, looking from one to another of us.

"*Apó pou eísthe?*" I asked.

"*Asía.*"

"Asia." I repeated the English way of saying it. Both Barbara and I fancied that this added additional glamour to the *papá.*

"I speak Araby," he said. "I have passport Araby. *Kaphé?*"

"*Óhi,*" I said.

"No thank you," said Barbara.

He snapped his fingers. One of the stewards came, as if in collusion.

"Ask him why he has an Arab passport. Do they have *papádes* in Arabia?" said Barbara devilishly.

The steward left.

"You go . . . where?" asked the *papá*.

"*Ródos.*"

"*Ródos?*"

"*Ródos.*"

"*Polí oraía, Ródos.*"

He had a peculiar habit. Once you had satisfied his curiosity about a subject he no longer had any interest in it. He fumbled with his gold cross apathetically. His mind seemed far away. Suddenly he came up with a piece of oracular news.

"I go to *Beirúti,*" he said. He had to pronounce the word several times before we understood it.

"Beirootie!"

"Beirootie!"

In Greek he began broken sentences about how beautiful Beirootie was. He was going to stay in the Ritz Hotel in Beirootie. He asked us what hotel we were going to stay in in Rhodes.

"*Den gnorízome,*" I said. "*Den gnorízome Ródos kathólou.*"

"Beirootie is better," he said. All at once he began a long peroration with urgings and wheedlings.

"Do I hear aright?" I exclaimed loudly. "I think he is telling us that we ought to come to Beirootie!"

It was true. He was urging us to come to Beirootie. He would show us the town, he said.

The conversation grew and enlarged like a mushroom in the woods. It grew horns, bumps, and toads of mismanaged meanings. It was half in pantomime and half in Mother Goose language, pink, white, and green in turns. Was he propositioning us or not? And on what terms?

"Stay Ritz Carleton Beirootie."

"Rootie tootie, Beirootie," said Barbara.

"Tootie fruitie?" I suggested.

"Tootie fruitie. Yes!" said the *papá*. "You stay at Ritz too. We sleep." He put his face on his hands sideways and pretended to snore, opening one eye to look at us innocently.

"I don't believe he means it. Ignore it," said Barbara. "Get this conversation onto another track. Ask him what he is doing on this boat."

I asked him.

"I return from international meeting of World Council of Church. I Asian member. I return from Alexandria."

"How could he be returning from Alexandria to Beirut by way of Piraeus?"

"Maybe he's an Armenian!" I said enthusiastically.

"Ask him."

"I don't want to ask him if he is really Greek. If he isn't, I figure he will hate to admit it."

To frame the question I asked it this way: "How can you be Greek Orthodox and have an Arabian passport?"

This rudeness was simple encouragement to him. He grew. He floated with eagerness when the word passport was mentioned. He brought out his dusty green one with a hard cover and opened it. Inside were many Arabian letters and a handsome picture. He pointed to the picture and then to himself.

"We have barked up the wrong tree," I said. "Either he is dull or the language makes him dull. Besides, I would not trust him as far as I could throw a piano."

"I make the motion that we ditch," proposed Barbara.

"How? I don't mind being rude in English, but in Greek it is another thing."

"I will do it," said Barbara.

She stood up. She held out her hand. "We are very pleased to have met you. But I have to go now."

The *papá* stood up. "Go? Go?" he repeated staring at her intently.

"I must go to read a book." She made a gesture of reading a book.

"Read book! Very very wonderful!" he exclaimed enthusiastically.

"Good-by," she said.

"Good-by," I said.

It was to unhearing ears. We moved away three paces. He followed on our heels.

"He knows very well what good-by means," I complained, looking at him crossly.

His robe swished as we stopped abruptly.

"Well, tootie fruitie," said Barbara in a loud, significant voice. To cement it she put out her hand and waved good-by. This was an irretrievable error. It was too late to tell her that the American good-by sign means "Come here" in the Middle East. For good-by they turn their palms upward and flap their fingers inward, the "Come here" sign of Americans.

She moved away again. He followed eagerly.

"Greek thing, save me."

"Go out the door to the deck. I will meet you at the stairs."

The stewards began to laugh gleefully and bang the water glasses on the bar.

Barbara disappeared. The *papá* followed her, black, hungry, bearded like a flowing cat. Out the porthole windows their two heads passed like a series of punctuation marks.

I sneaked out to the deck through another doorway and met her hurrying to the head of the stairway with the *papá* following ravenously.

"What shall I do?" she wailed.

"Halt! Stop! *Arrêtez-vous!*" I commanded.

The *papá* hung over us beady-eyed, breathless.

"I am sorry. I have a headache. I am seasick. Excuse me. I must go!" she moaned, draping with agonized gestures.

"Good-by. *Auf Wiedersehen, Adieu. A rivederci. Sto kaló. Hairete!*" we both screamed out in every language we could think of.

We fled down the stairs like escapees, leaving him standing there with a glazed and indefinable expression. Below we dashed through the corridors, panting. We found our cabin and knocked the door open with a loud bang. We smashed it closed, locked it, and dissolved on the bunks with laughter.

"Saved!"

"And he was such a beautiful-looking thing!"

"What do you want for nothing?"

"We should have known better, since those stewards sicked him onto us."

When our laughter subsided we looked vacantly out our one port-hole.

"How long have we got on this boat?" asked Barbara.

"Five and one-half hours of daylight, and then night, and in the morning we arrive at Rhodes."

"We are trapped," said Barbara significantly. "We will never be able to leave this room."

"We have to! We have to eat!" I insisted.

"Then we will be followed. From morn to night. And who knows what will happen?"

"You will have to make yourself look ugly. That's all there is to it."

"I don't believe he is a representative *papá*," said Barbara, yawning Chekhovianly. And then she turned over on the bunk and went to sleep.

VI The shadows of afternoon had grown long when she awoke. Due to sleep and to dreams, the approaching night seemed phantasmal. We no longer thought of the *papá* in a definite way. He had grown larger in our minds and accrued the quality of a dream, a lurking dream, part and parcel of the shadows the falling sun made on the deck. Immense, long-robed, and malevolent.

We opened the door a crack and looked out. No sign of him.

"The coast is clear," I announced breathlessly.

We crept through the corridor on tiptoe. We sneaked up the stair-way toward the dining room. There was yet no sign of him.

Instead of relief we had a feeling of disappointment.

In the dining room we avoided the eyes of the stewards. We ordered dinner.

"I believe he is hovering about some place waiting for us," said Barbara.

"Isn't it strange that a mere costume lends a person this mystery and prestige. There is nothing identifiable in his actions that makes him more dignified, more noble, more outstanding, more extraordinary than any other mortal man with suit and coat. . . ."

"Yet I want my illusions," sighed Barbara. "Greek thing, you know we are in some sort of spell."

"He has become sinister!" said I. "We are trying to avoid him, but here we are looking for him."

"I have an idea," said Barbara. "After dinner let us sneak up into first class. There we shall be sure to escape from him."

All through dinner the rocking and gentle tipping of the lamps, the glow, the murmuring hum of people conversing, the light laughing at the bar, instead of being reassurances as to his absence, seemed a façade to cover in community and geniality his lurking presence.

We rose to go. On deck the night was cold. The sea was dead calm under the stars, and the boat, of which we were members, seemed a lonely entity, stealing its way across a vortex of silence. The sea neither buoyed, bounced, nor cradled it. It seemed a voyage across space, rather than across sea.

A flap of canvas rustled in a sudden gust of wind.

"It is he!" whispered Barbara.

"No. No. Come on."

At the entrance to the first class a steward stood on guard.

We threw up our heads. We pulled at imaginary mink stoles. We took on a haughty and disdainful nonchalance. The steward bowed slightly and made way for us to enter. We climbed over the threshold.

A sea of conductive heads rose to watch our entrance. The lights shone from tinkling lamps, orange and velvety. The floor was thick with oriental carpets.

The *papá* was standing against a post in the center of the lounge. His expression did not change one iota as his eyes followed us to the seats we chose in a corner. He did not move a muscle. He did not greet us. He did not even acknowledge us.

"We have created him," whispered Barbara.

At once his eyes turned away from us, and became moodily engaged in space. His back was half turned on us, arched delicately against the post.

We ordered coffee. It was Italian coffee and it tasted bitter. We wanted to revive our old gaiety in regard to him, to reinstate the lice and tootie-fruitie aspect of him, but it was impossible. He had become another thing.

"It is enough to make one blindly join the Orthodox Church," I said.

"And have wreaths upon your heads when you get married," murmured Barbara.

"Isn't it strange? No one ever 'goes over' to the Byzantines the way you 'go over' to Catholicism."

"To me 'going over' means like from the Dodgers to the Red Sox," said Barbara.

"To me," I whispered, "it seems more like crossing the River Styx and going into the shady world of the dead. Not so literal, but of far more significance."

The air had grown thick and close with smoke. Everything seemed muffled and illusive. The throbbing motor of the ship was not even honest. It was stifled into mere purrs of vibration, giving the sensation of hidden power striving to explode. All was artifice, constricted and confined, the dim lights, the upholstered material, the thick oriental rugs, strapping us, swaddling us in a first-class couch of goose down.

In the center of all this stood the figure of the *papá* in his crow-like robes. His cross glittered. His stovepipe hat seemed hung motionless, suspended. His liquid eyes perused the room morosely.

I can only describe those black robes as vessels of ancientness. Here and now, in this Oriental boat making its way to Rhodes, this ancientness had risen insidious and foul. It contained all lawlessness, all power, and all superstition of the smoky Pythia, all the turgid titillation of archaic mystery cults, from paganism through priest-ridden Christianity.

This is the mystery of him, I thought. You have to separate the man from the garb. But no one wants to. It seems like an offense against morals. And yet we are not fools! Here we are, up against a conception of ages. To think that an idea gains mass and potency simply because of its existence in recognizable physical form through a thousand centuries. Well, it seemed inconsistent and foolish of me to think that, since an idea does not exist except in a human head.

Yet there was this priest, this creation, in a ship crossing the Mediterranean, and the man engarbed in the idea was small and unfathomable. If only he could throw off his robes, that would be a new idea. Was it the confinement of the ship that made it impossible to conceive of any idea of any goal, of any past or future without the priest? What was the priest without his robes?

Suddenly he moved forward to us. We sat there, almost indifferent.

He inclined slightly forward over the table.

He pointed to his head and to Barbara.

"Sick now?" he asked in Greek. But his voice contained no hint of sarcasm or irony. He was kindliness and consternation itself.

"No, I am much better now, thank you."

"*Kalá. Kalá.*" There was a pause. He nodded up and down, ruminating. Then through his beard he formed the barest smile. "Well, good-by," he said in English. His robes rustled as he moved away to the door and disappeared on deck.

VII The American Navy was in port at Rhodes, the *Forrestal*, and two of her destroyers. There was a spanking breeze. The sun was dazzling bright. But the air was not the light, delicate wine of Greece. It was heavier and omnivorous as it wattled the ropes, the sails of small boats, and the tentlike frames of the object sellers on the stone wharf. It made the cheap, glittering jewelry tinkle on its cheesecloth.

When we got off the boat we were seized by hotel touts. We ditched our bags in a restaurant on the quai and escaped them.

Rhodes was a green island of luxuriant vegetation, palm trees, and grass. It wore a dusty halo of sparkling mist. It was tame, mild in comparison with Greece, and we could see the English influence at once: oleander hedges, private gardens in the hotels, private beaches, careful beach huts, greenhouses, leather armchairs, cultivated gardens, and luxurious, silent golf courses. The Hôtel des Roses sat on the beach, a squat, ugly, bile-colored embattlement with a quiet asphalt entrance bordered by clipped hedges. Greeks in the town wore Bermuda shorts and carried umbrellas.

The U. S. sailors were a rash of unbelonging pimples on the face of the town. The Navy had poured three thousand men in because the Turks were moving against the Syrian border, creating a mild international scare. The main shore of Turkey was an invisible eighteen miles away. The *Forrestal* sat out on the calm blue water, very gray, squat, naked, yet not fierce. It did not look as large as it pretended, being eaten up in size by the sheer horizon of sea. Its silence was imposing. It had an impersonal essence, very strange. One expected it to be blown up in sheer size, as in its technicolored portraits. But in these things you can always count on the thud of their reality. To be small and to be there. A human artifact on the waters, a mere weapon of war, that was all.

The Greek islanders were out full force. They spread their goods. They took bicycles off the rack to rent. They jumped up and down hawking in front of their shops. Everything was activity. All the restaurants were preparing to double, triple their business in one day. New foods were being prepared. Bottles of booze, retsina, whiskey, wine of all types were being unloaded from European automobiles into the bars. Tables were being set. Buses were lined up, commandeered for exclusive use by the Navy. Records were set on ancient phonographs and piped out into the street. All jumping eastern music. Blare contacted with blare and set off competition in the street. Lights were strung up over the street for the night's expectations. Drink, women, and song. The Greeks were making hay. Electric wires were strewn everywhere. There was a big search for light bulbs. The Walled City was Out of Bounds. Prices had doubled already.

All these incongruities smashed in on one another, the Greek town, the British superimposition of elegance, the Greeks, themselves, tilted for exploitation, and the American sailors floating, running, jumping around in their bellbottom trousers.

But incongruities are the fertilizer of shoddiness, cheapness, and crime. And we were in the situation of making choices. We were back in the home language, American. A particular, jazzy, swinging note of it too, what with these artificialities. Of the Greeks we were presented with only one side, the shell of the turtle. I already knew the underbelly, so I knew the secret of them. I was damned if I was going to bite on their tourist face, brilliant, gold-tooth-lit, oozing with charm, convinced of the ignorance of all tourists and sailors, ready to suck them in and sting them with the smile and charm of a snake's bite. Time is the answer to all things, but there was no time.

"If we get a room under forty drachs apiece we will be lucky," I said.

"Let us refuse to pay over forty apiece," said Barbara.

"Shall we stay in a dump?"

"No."

"How then? Look at the rules of supply and demand. The Navy will pay anything for one night of boozing, and there are hundreds of them to two of us."

"We will sell them the Air Force and the future."

"Half-truths! Goody!"

"We will show them our credentials."

"What credentials?"

"You'll see. I'll do the con work. And don't let them know you speak a word of Greek. Everything must be in English."

Sailors were eying us—in pairs, in threes, in gangs, elbowing, shoving, wistful and greedy. We picked the first sailor who paid no attention to us. He was walking alone. We stopped him.

"Please, could you help us? We would like to know the name of a good hotel."

His eyes lit up. He took off his cap.

"Yes, ma'am."

He was the *crème de la crème* of our American youth.

"We want a Grade-A, but not an A-plus like the Roses. Understand?"

He told us the Astor, the Cairo, the Grand, and the Rhodes Palace at the top of the hill.

"We sure do thank you," we said.

"Do you mind if I ask you something?"

"What?"

"You wouldn't mind if I went with you, would you? I mean, I don't like for any American woman to walk alone in a townful of sailors like this. You know what I mean? I mean it isn't like an ordinary town at home. Some of these guys are already drunk. You know. I mean, if they see you with me, they won't bother you."

At the Cairo Palace Hotel we shucked him off. The manager of the Cairo Palace was a tall, plump man with a fat, milky complexion and manicured hands. He spoke English with plenty of saliva. He considered himself big stuff, on a par with English and Americans. He looked down on other Greeks.

"How much is the price of a double room?" asked Barbara.

"We could give you one at a hundred and ninety-two drachmas."

"That is too expensive."

He shrugged, but he believed in American courtesy.

"We can't even find enough accommodation for the Navy. All our rooms are taken—"

"All?" said Barbara with a coy glint in her eye.

"There are a few, of course. But I suggest that you try the Astor or the Nicomachean. A hundred and ninety is the cheapest for a double room here and all those are gone. I am terribly sorry. . . ."

"So am I," said Barbara, "because there is a rhyme in our reason."

There was no sense to this witticism, but it took him aback because he was a sucker for idiomatic English.

"When we inquired at the Hellenic Tourist Bureau in Athens," she began, "we picked the Cairo Palace because it looked like the biggest and the most moderate at the same time. Since we were here on vacation it seemed sensible to give it a look-over and see if we could work out some kind of a deal. We're civilians employed by the U. S. Air Force in London in the Special Service Branch. We arrange tours for Air Force personnel. Not only the men, but their wives. Of course we would expect some reasonable arrangement for party booking . . ."

He was beginning to drip saliva like a Pavlovian dog. On cue Barbara and I pulled out our credentials. Mine was my old I. D. card. Hers was a library certificate.

"Low prices are what sell our tours. We can package our tours at a low price if we schedule them in off seasons. What we had in mind were two parties, of sixty people apiece. Chartered plane. Couple to Paris last winter. One to Copenhagen. Go to Garmisch every week. Etcetera. Etcetera."

The manager kicked the toadlike clerk out of the way. We were ushered into a private room. Papers were brought to us. Conditions, services, accommodations, and propaganda were presented on silver trays. Telephones were stopped from ringing. We were offered a beer which we refused.

"And of course, it goes without saying, the room for two days for a hundred and ninety-two drachmas."

"A hundred and ninety," bargained Barbara. "Including service. We have never paid more than that in any of the hotels we . . ."

"What hotels? What hotels?"

"Georges Cinq in Paris, the Savoy, the Petit Palais in Athens . . ."

He bowed low. "Never let it be said that the Cairo Palace did not consider itself the equal of the Petit Palais. . . ."

". . . nor said that the Air Force did not consider itself the equal of the Navy."

"Touché."

"To you, sir."

We all laughed, greasy and winking and conspiratorial.

VIII The afternoon sun was pulsing in the molten sky. Liquid afternoon. We stood gazing at the breakwaters where the Colossus was said to have stood. All was calm. To sail beneath the knees of a giant into port. Strange idea of haven. Try to imagine the grand figure pirouetting out of such flatness as the flat blue of the sea and the tawny stones. But it did not pirouette. It stood, feet planted on a finality. The finality of shore. Each incoming sailor, reproduced from the ocean and born from the knees of a man-giant, looking homeward from fishes to hearthfires. Vermin under the crotch of such a creature. Nice to twist the subject of progeneration from woman to man. But man was the protector of all shore cities.

The languidness of the sea affected the sailors as they strung around us, beginning their beer guzzling. There was an orange glow from the sea, characteristic of the Mediterranean from Corfu to Asia

Minor. This was the island for sailors from ancient times. For soldiers too. The Crusaders stopped here, Knights Templar. They holed up in the Old City. Venetian traders, pirates, criminals, and monks. This was their nesting place.

The whole island wore the air of an intermediate hostel, transient. Think of the tales of far-off places told by German and English religious knights who thought only of home. Nostalgia. These houses of Rhodes still have listening walls. They are full of memories, these stones. Think of the tales they have heard, of Christs, dragons, pernicious Jews, Saracen raiders, Holy Grails, Venetian splendor and ancient oracles, stories of killings, of tongues cut out and hands cut off, of unseeing eyes which remembered that their grandfathers' stories told of grandfathers who had lived once in days of light. If stories had meaning and stones had tongues, think what one could learn! Miserably ancient, it smells of medievalism. The light was lost at Rhodes, the temples ruined, and the Colossus sunk. Only stones and stories remain. The wanderers who rested here spoke, the sea wayfarers, the traveling knights on their way to restore Jerusalem in the name of Christianity.

Rhodes is the place of crimes and schemes. Religion is rank. It smells in the mustiness of the old city. It drips in the dank walls, and whispers like sneaking cats in garbage. Christianity was one crime among the many, but had a demonic eloquence and febrile, sun-seared fanaticism which screamed its holiness. I think that the war-weary Crusaders lost their religion here. Dusty and tattered, full of holes, Christianity shed its skin like a snake, reared its new head, looked about the earth bewildered from this one green island in the sea, and sought with its tongue for new holiness to replace, and uttered old prophets' words in the new militant rhetoric of Crimes for Purpose.

Rhodes is the place for resting, for reflection, and for misdirection. Christianity was reborn as crime and justification. It got its new eloquent tongue. God was demeaned. The only thing left were bobbing, weary heads, and the remembrance of some long-ago childhood land of mild skies, English dews, the gentle rain down-falling, all lost, lost in the hotbed of feverish enemies and sun-scorched

Christianity. What was there to do but plan new campaigns, to whip the already whipped, to drink to satiate all-consuming thirst, to imagine more blood for the sea of lost blood, to dream and dream again for the satiation of a greed greater than God's greed, juster than righteousness, brighter than gold or blood or jewels. Out from the Colossus stood the infidels, the Arabs, lost Jerusalem, and the oriental East, the cradle of the Christ they thought they knew.

Not feverish Christ, but his malignant, warped shadow stands today in the stones of Rhodes. The shadow is as dead as the stones it falls upon. But it is unburied. I wished that a Geiger counter could issue sounds like a microphone of history. But the only sounds of history's record would be the sharp noise of crime. If anything is left here it is blood upon the unsheathed blade.

IX Barbara and I discussed pick-ups, since we could not move without having to shuck off sailors.

"I only just got rid of Robert."

"Let's not dither," I said.

A lieutenant commander and a captain leaned out of the lobby window. The lieutenant commander was very drunk, flushed of face and smiling with bravado.

"Say girls, I hope you don't mind. We saw you here this afternoon. Would you join the Captain and me for a drink?"

"Why, Greek bag," whispered Barbara, "you want an officer!"

"It is you who are complaining about getting stuck with the stinking swabbies. Besides, with officers we don't have to have any conscience about how much money they spend, whereas with swabbies . . ."

"Why do we have consciences?" moaned Barbara. "If that lieutenant commander would take us to a movie on the *Forrestal,* I would go in a minute. But we'll have to drink."

"Who wants to go to Rhodes and drink?"

"What do you say, girls?" shouted the lieutenant commander.

"We say thank you an awful lot, Lieutenant, but we're going to see the Old City right now."

"Maybe afterwards . . ."

"Be delighted."

"Yip ha-ha-hooray!" They made loud noises out of the window and threw their arms around each other.

"They won't remember, thank God," said Barbara with relief.

"You know what you called that lieutenant commander?"

"What?"

"Lieutenant! Ha ha ha ha." I doubled over with laughter.

"That's because I am a noble and democratic thing," said Barbara.

X The Walled City was made of steps rising upon steps and small filthy alleyways. Buildings rose crookedly upon buildings. At a stony crest in the narrow road stood a gilded, whitened church. People passed it, crossing themselves. Donkeys' hoofs echoed against the buildings as they ambled through the labyrinthine ways.

The glow and glitter of evening was beginning. Women leaned on their brooms and peered out at the church in the pink-gilded, green sky, giving their thoughts to the last of the day. Men stood in white aprons outside their shops calling us to come and look at their wares. Small boys with white coats rushed through the streets carrying trays of *kataïfi* and copenhagens. The lights came on. The bootblacks got busy with their customers.

The Walled City was such a tangle of streets that, having walked for five minutes, we found ourselves back in the same square where the church stood. Rising from the jumble of houses was the huge, medieval wall which bordered the old town. We headed for it, intending to make a circuit of the town. It led us, along a cobbled path, out of the area of the town to an abandoned precinct of grasses and small bush. It was a large park quite separated from the town, in fact, a little higher, so that when we looked down we could see the winking lights, as if they were far away. This park was the site of an ancient fort. It was deserted. The hush was very strange after the ancient town noises. We were directly under the wall. It dominated everything and made our voices sound unnaturally loud in the silence as they rebounded against it. The night emboldened around us. The sky showed like a purple rind filled with cold stars. But there was an edge of raw and glittering pink at the horizon which, reflecting against the medieval wall, gave our faces a burnished pink cast, changing us into haunting, shimmering, gilded images.

Suddenly in the silence was the sound of a cry. It was a suppurating and mournful sound, but not human. It was a cat, a yellow brindle cat with stiff fur ears of starched gold, and two piercingly vacant blue eyes. It was in a strange predicament. It was caught in a niche in the great wall, the type of niche in which Madonnas stand. At the place where the niche was carved out of the wall there was a three-hundred foot drop to the Outer City of Rhodes below. We stood on a cobbled bridge three feet from the niche where the cat sat. To escape from the niche the only possible route for the cat to take was to jump the three-foot aperture over the three-hundred-foot drop.

"It will starve to death."

"How did it get there? If it jumped, it certainly ought to be able to jump back."

"Maybe some boy lured it over with a piece of meat and then left it there as a joke."

The cat looked at us with pale, imploring eyes. It opened its mouth and cried again. Its golden whiskers vibrated delicately with the sound.

"I can't stand it, Greek thing. We'll have to get it out."

We stood ruminating at the edge of the bridge, looking into its eyes. It stalked at the edge of its niche. It was hypnotic. The cat did not take its eyes off us, and its expression was inhuman, half malevolence, half pleading.

As we stood there, a man leading a donkey passed by. He stopped. He looked at the cat. He looked at us. Then he gave a short laugh and continued on his way. The clopping of the donkey faded in the distance.

Must we be made responsible for Rhodean cats caught in Madonna's niches? There was something profound, though, about its plight. The situation smelled of mystery and hidden implications. Even of some outside force mischievous and tricky in intelligence. The laws of nature were thwarted somewhere. A cat perched in a Madonna's seat, so near the road of life, and yet impossibly far.

I began to weave a tale.

"In another thousand years this cat will be one more skeleton in one more catacomb. It will sit in the Land of the Shadowy Dead and there count on its claws the number of people who passed by in its lifetime and did not heed its cry. One hundred and ninety-three people, the total number, who passed by and heeded not. Its flesh will shrink to bones only three feet away from where countless people walked. Do you see how simple it is, and what a crime? The greatest crimes are not those of commission, but those of omission.

"Every one of the hundred and ninety-three people who passed and heeded not," I continued, "will be paid out in Damnation. They are walking their inevitable path to hell right this minute. Yet this cat will not rejoice. Perhaps even now it is bewailing their fates even as they create them."

"Help me look for a plank," said Barbara. "It's getting dark."

"No. That is too pat. This cat is an instrument in a completely different lesson. But what is that lesson? I know! Never aspire to the pedestal. He Who demands his own Sainthood, even his own Immortality, Who places himself in the niche by the wayside, will discover that the niche is a barren and fruitless place. Never aspire to be the image of superhuman values. People will pass by you and heed not."

"I can't find anything!" Barbara hissed furiously, searching on the other side of the bridge. "Greek bag, get over here and help me!"

"No, I reject my own theory," I muttered. "It cannot be right that men cannot aspire. They shouldn't stick to the little road of their lives. That is Paddy Chayevsky, the pernicious poison of the Little Man. It is a Psychological Fable."

I got up to go. The cat was transfixed. It looked startled. As I turned away it opened its mouth and cried again. The pink edge of the sunken sun flared in its eyes. I ran away hurriedly. While we were searching, the cat cried intermittently. It imagined that we had really abandoned it. There was despair in its voice.

We found a rotten plank by a tree. A feeling of spooky elation caught us. We brought it to the niche. The cat was sitting in the same position as when we had left. Mute and transfixed it stared upon us. We pushed the board over, like a gangplank, from niche to bridge. We waited.

The cat ignored it. It was as if it did not see it, though it was only one inch from its paws.

"It won't come out!" breathed Barbara.

"It is stupid."

We prodded the plank. The cat hunched and drew back. It fastened us with its eyes. The yellow of its whiskers had turned to gold. Its ears were pricked. Its haunches were majestic. It opened its mouth and breathed out a long, wild cry.

"I wondered why that man did not recognize her!" whispered Barbara in a tone of occult discovery. "It is an Original Cat!"

"What do you mean, Original Cat?"

Barbara's eyes were very black. Set off by the pink shimmer from the wall, they seemed spectreish, but with no sign of mischief.

"Original Rhodean goddess," she intoned. "The Original Asiatic Cattess, the one on which the Sphinxes were modeled!"

"What Cattess?"

"This cat has sprung out of the walls full-fledged. Look at it. It is sitting in judgment on one hand, yet not fully aware of its human condition on the other, calling with a voice which it does not even recognize as its own! It has immense power! It's a matter of form, that's all. It could be a reincarnation, a goddess incarnate, anything! It supersedes both morality and metaphysics. Don't ask questions. Just look. This is just the time of evening when goddesses begin to play. It has stopped us on the road and called us out . . . all for nothing! See what power it has!"

"It's stupid, that's all."

"Don't say nasty things in front of it, Greek thing. It hears."

The cat looked out at us. It had grown dark now, and its blue eyes had turned into wild bubbles of yellow. Enigmatic.

"Let's go," I said.

As we turned away, Barbara whispered warningly in my ear: "Don't look back."

XI The drunken captain and the lieutenant commander looked beefy-faced and hangovered and ridden with financial burdens in the morning sun. The lieutenant commander's gold tooth winked unpleasantly, and he did not recognize us.

Privacy was not possible. Sailors, jingling their bicycles idly on the road above, caught sight of us. They changed their course and cautiously began to cavalier us on the sand of the beach, not approaching directly, but driving their bikes sideways onto the sand. They gazed at us from afar. They were trying to decide to speak. One rode the packed sand at the water's edge and, confronted with our moody indifference, kept right on going, whistling, as if he were not interested in us at all.

We could not get out of the cynosure. We could not get out of the center of the stage. Even the *Forrestal* itself, a gravy-colored monster sitting in the morning sea, had its eyes upon us. Little white specks of sailors ran her decks. It looked so close I could have reached out my hand and touched her. I thought of swimming around the *Forrestal* and then proclaiming to the world that I was the first woman to swim rings around the *Forrestal*. I heard tiny whittling bells, whistles, shouts and laughter. I could smell distinctly a New England boiled dinner being cooked in one of the messes.

Barbara kept towels spread over her legs because she was ashamed that they did not look like Marlene Dietrich's.

"Now I know how movie stars feel," she said. "And it isn't good."

"Let's ditch," I said. "We will never get to see the butterflies at Lindus, because the Navy has commandeered all the buses. Besides this is a medieval town. It tells nothing about Greece. It is too green. It is too lush. It is polluted with medieval Christianity which is ingrained in the complexion of the whole island. It cannot be washed away."

"The Original Cattess has spoken," said Barbara. "But do you think we can get off this crumby island, bag? There is only one boat a week to Crete."

XII It left that very afternoon. It was a caïque of the type manufactured by the British in the middle of the nineteenth century, and now used for inter-island runs. It carried a few people. But mostly it carried livestock. Cattle, sheep, horses and donkeys sat and stood around on the deck like families. Sheep baaed loudly and stamped their hoofs. Flocks of geese and turkeys cackled vociferously and beat their wings like women beating rugs.

We were taking potluck as to transportation. We were counting on the probability that a bus would leave for Herakleion from Sitia the morning we arrived. This would take us along the northern coast of Crete for Knossos.

The motor of the boat kept up a grinding sound, puffing and wheezing. It weaved and rolled insolently on the waters like a puffy porpoise. Our cabin was immediately under the deck. It was large, but there were no portholes and no vents. It was stifling. Directly at my ear, outside the walled curvature, I could hear the water sloshing. Above, through the thin boards of the deck an animal breathed.

Night fell early. We slept fitfully. Some time in early morning we were awakened by shouts. Heavy, clanking footsteps above. The boat seemed stationary, but the motor still played. There was the grinding sound of an iron chain being pulled. It was the early morning stop at Karpathos, a small island onto which donkeys were being unloaded. The wait seemed interminable. The duration was of perhaps two hours. But the strangest sensation assailed us. Of being in the dark, with strange animal life all around us, suffocated and blindfolded, at once, in a passage most unreal from some place that had been Rhodes, to a figment of our imagination, Crete. We could have dressed and gone above to witness a starry sky and actually to see the action of the noise that grappled around us, the dock, the donkeys, the chains, the men unloading, the skiffs. But we were too lazy, and so these remained mere figments, mere evidences, fragmentary. And so it was as if what we heard was not really true at all.

"This is impossible," I muttered. "I can't sleep."

"We are coming to Crete. To Crete," murmured Barbara.

About four, as the motors took on a larger rumble, and the waters began sloshing at our ears again, we knew that the caïque had left Karpathos, and was at sea again. We settled into a determined sleep.

Awakened by ferocious knocking at our cabin door and a hoarse voice shouting: "Awake! Awake! Hurry! You have five minutes to get off the boat or the dory will leave!"

"Is it Sitia? Is it Sitia?" I screamed.

"Sitia. Five minutes! Five minutes!" The knocking continued hysterically.

"All right. Drop dead!" I hurled out in English because I could not think of anything bad enough to say in Greek.

I got dressed in two of the five minutes, but Barbara took longer. She pretended to be poky and nonchalant, but I saw her eyes glitter and she packed her bag with sneaky efficiency.

"This is an uncultural and lousy method of transport," she said, fastening her fake pearls. "I do not even have time to put on lipstick."

"Do you want to be marooned alone on this boat somewhere in Egypt for ninety days?" I fumed.

"Egypt! Maybe Doll-baby Durrell will be there to lay on some delicate Alexandrian decadencies. I have half a mind to stay and finish my beauty sleep."

We opened the door and jimmied up the passageway to the deck to be confronted with two faces. One was the Greek who had knocked at our door. Grinning and smiling out of his bristle beard, pointing to his watch: "*Éxi óra. Éxi óra!*" (six o'clock!). The second face was the visage of a mad-horned black bull staring at us wildly, his ears dripping with salt water, and his huge nostrils white with fury.

This bull was slung in mid-air, hanging by a rope from a crane which had lifted him (sitting in a four-holed leather sling, like a ski lift) from the harbor water and was about to deposit him on deck. Slowly he rose above us, his four feet waving uselessly in the air. Five cows grunted and sloshed and mooed, swimming in the water at the ship's bow. They had been shepherded from the shore on to the beach, then driven with sticks into the water, and beat like a flock of dolphins to a depth over their heads, forced to swim, piloted by three or four skiffs full of boys with sticks shouting and laughing in tune to their grunts. Now they were awaiting their turn to be lifted aboard the boat. They looked up at the snorting bull with eyes full of wild alarm.

"Stand back. Attention!" said the grinning Greek, motioning us toward the stern. A boat full of peasants lay against the ship, bobbing, extending their arms for us to be lowered for our transit to shore. We dropped our bags. They were suddenly in the small boat. We put out our hands. We let ourselves go. I had the sensation of a cheap movie's depiction of Christ in physical ascension, only this was a descension. My eyes were on the bull ascending as I was lowered down, down to the cows.

"They have captured the Minotaur," breathed Barbara.

"And he has gone to Heaven," breathed I.

At that moment something happened which made it all seem worth while. The Minotaur, scrabbling in his lift, looked down upon his captors with the sticks in the small boats, looked down upon the cows to follow, lifted his head, screamed riotously, lashed his tail, and let to fall from himself, and to heap upon the heads of the Cretan boys seven large bomblike turds. Five were direct hits on the boys' heads. Two others landed in the sea and spurted the waters in the cows' nostrils and the boys' eyes.

The peasants in our boat broke into loud claps and laughed until they could not see for their tears.

XIII The village of Sitia was a string of white-boxed houses and corrugated store-fronts. The shades were not pulled up. Brick-colored roofs sang, orange and splendid in the infant rays of sun along the gravel road. Eucalyptus trees made a beaded lacework on the quai. The *kaphenía* were not yet open. Tables and chairs stood in front of them still damp from the dew of night. Grass bubbled in tufty foams under the trees. We bobbed along in our dory. The water was clear. Directly beneath us we could see a fathom down where starfish lay.

The morning was incredibly cold and very gentle, with sparkling sun. The Cretan October morning had the nip of glory. There was a smell of salt. The sun had just come up from behind fierce mountains and had left them scattered with blue and purple dew among the dusty, golden rocks.

We sat in the *kaphenion* chairs on the quai until ten o'clock when, wonder of wonders, our bus was due to depart for Herakleion. We looked out at the morning sea and dozed.

XIV The Cretans say the letter *chi* with an *sh* sound. They say "*Oshi*" for "*Óhi.*" This elegance makes even the truck drivers sound effete. It is the sound of swishing, wishing, washing, fashion, and fishing. Thus do they encapsule the tradition of their Minoan heritage.

The onomatopoeia is the more devastating because Crete's coastline, along which we traveled for hours that morning, is a series of slashing, stabbing attempts by the gray-glinted mountains to murder the sky. It is a formidable journey. We were trounced in the orange bus, and it spit stones over precipices like sword hilts, the loose rocks dropping dizzily down behind us over the gorse-edged road into the sea below. Lonely, gaze-gray rocks stared bland and huge at us. It was the end of the world. The mists drove around us like ghosty sheep. We rode out of wraiths into the exploring sun. Everything was quick once more, dew-pearled, purple, radiant. The sun drove up to the noon sky, threw his showered blaze on us and then disappeared into a sullen cloud. He left the world lonely, giant and empty, like a moon waste. What were we to do with this? The only thing we could do was to imagine the end of it. The mountains inspired a monumental and inhuman strength in us. Yet it was irrelevant. We were human and the mountains were not. We were confronted with these meaningless, scabbered heaps of rock upon rock, dead and cold when sunless. Everything unworkable, inapplicable and deserted. Yet when irradiate with sun, a Gargantuan blessing of purple and sapphired wonders revealed themselves risen up from the sea.

What does the great *sh* sound mean? Why does it sound? How was it born? What is its connection with the Minoan civilization with its fancy dresses, its bared and painted bosoms, its painted lady-faces, its bull dancers, its stunning water drains, its gentility, its comforts, its luxuries and frivolities and indolences? *Sh* is a gentle sound, very lyrical and very poetic, antagonistic to the sight of the mountains. It belongs in one's imagination of Knossos, in the refined patter of nobles and in the sighing of ladies. It is irresistible as an enigma and paradoxical when you find it. It makes Epimenides have sense. "All Cretans are liars," he said. Epimenides was a Cretan.

Sh means more than a secret. It is a conspiracy covering in its façade of high civilization a basic barbarity. This is the secret of Crete.

Even today Cretans are considered by Peloponnesians to be untrustworthy liars, to be dour, sullen, thieflike and miserly.

Why?

The sea sneakily licks at the lip of the rock which rises out of fathoms into height. It, the sea, says "*sh*" when you stop and listen. Above, one tiny mountain stream trickles, sluices down the highway of the mountains, making the sound *sh*. Aeolus' air never stops. "*Sh*," it sighs, sliding, sneaking, slippering around mountain peaks and down vales, brushing gorse tops and grass blades, ruffling poppy necks and soughing around solidly profane granite heads. This sound is the only thing that lives in these upper regions of Crete. A gentle, perpetual sigh. A sigh which will not allow silence. It is the sigh of the Cretan mountain. It will not allow even death. It is a fatal prohibition of solid death. It knows that the mountains are death incarnate. It chooses this graveyard to play in. Snickering, slyly cavorting, never ceasing.

In the Greek mountains the breezes play a little and then stop, as if to rest in the heat. Then they begin again, dashing off a little puff and twittering at the heads of poppies and ruffling goats' beards. But in Crete the winds never stop. They are perpetual motion.

In the midst of this archaic and barbaric spectacle of death, I myself wanted to scream "sh!" to stop its sound. For it contained horror.

XV

Being with Barbara in Rhodes and Crete was in a sense like floating over the landscape, compared with sitting down in the midst of it, being dug in, as I had been at Hora. There was a sensation of the dream about it, in which particular figments, almost occult, became symbols. The *papá* on the boat, the Rhodean cat, and now the *sh* of Crete. We floated like wraiths making contact, as tourists will, meaningless wanderers, with those aspects of the outward face of the country out of which they create meaning. We knew no one. Yet everyone knew us for the tourists we were.

It was useless for me to tell them: "I know you. You are my relatives. You are Greeks too. I even understand your jokes." For they would not have believed me. And so I settled easily into my dissembling role, and was prevented from discovering in any but the most superficial way the difference between the Cretan people and the Peloponnesians.

And yet it was this very freedom that allowed us to meet Knossos face to face, not on the ground, but in an outer dimension somewhere between space and time, captured in that conspiratorial *sh,* not discovering, but simply recognizing the secret.

Of all the sites in Greece, Knossos is one of the most sensational. This is because there is so much there, and it is so early. You have seen the Acropolis and Delphi, both religious and late. It is better to work back through time.

Knossos is in technicolor. Knossos is a matter of geometry. It is Braquely placed, painted, put, cubed, and worked up. From the base of the valley floor it rises and descends in many different levels with innumerable staircases. The classical Greek ruins are fluted, using the circle as well as the square (in the columns), and simple. Crete, being midway between Egypt and Greece, affects the look of Egyptian dwellings, makes use of the square column to get a squat effect, very solid. The palace was a veritable city. Ruins in Greece are mostly religious temples. But the Olympian religion, with its sacrifices having evolved from the human to the token level, it appears, had reached a less gutsy, less barbaric, more enlightened level. Religion had come in Olympian days to be more associated with art than fears. Knossos is at once more modern and more barbaric. Everywhere, in large and small, the horns of the bull raise themselves out of banisters, in wall paintings, out of roofs, and out of the courtyards to remind one that God *is.*

God is threat. God is gore, both blood, and the stabbing of the bull. The horns are of a yellowish white stone. They are bleached and nakedly sharp. Bereft of the body of the God or the Bull, they become a terrifying symbol. They are great and they are dangerous.

Their other attributes are to be put there. They have an aspirational quality as they are always set stabbing into the sky. But they did not seem heroic. This is because they are still inalienably connected with the bull. The bull does not naturally point his horns at the sky. If they toss and spurt in the air, it is at the moment of indecision or madness. There is never any deliberation. The moment of deliberation is the moment of attack. At the moment of attack, a bull's horns are always thrust forward parallel to the ground. This is the profound thing about the might of the double horn. It is at its greatest moment being rushed headlong at parallel action with the surface of the earth. It never points sky-bound. Thus the emblem has a basic artificiality. These horns, so magnificently poised in stone, so incarnate, so motionless, possess a quality of grisly deadness. There is nothing so dead as a dead civilization. But this deadness of the horns is something more. It is the deadness of a symbol. In effect, during the age of the might of the Minoans this symbol was scalped right off the living edge of the mind. It is the ultimate perfection of a schizophrenic ideal. Just as the Cheshire cat's grin is when the cat disappears from the tree.

But we know something. That the ladies had perfume and smiles, that there was dancing for the bulls. So Knossos seems now in this undeniable condition of death because the Minoans' living was done so totally with their bodies. I would have given a lot, standing in that glistening square-cut complex of geometrical piazzas, to lift a hand and command the Minoans back to life. It is consequent on any truth of Knossos to hear the sounds of the music, of the voices, of the sluicing water baths, and most of all, to witness the dancing sacrifices to the bull, whose only life now is the abstract pattern of the horns.

Despite this deadness, perhaps because of it, you have at Knossos the best indication of an ancient life that is to be seen in Europe, barring only Pompeii. You follow the drains down the sides of the stairways to their end, marveling how they turn the corners, exactly according to the engineers' calculations, and how they drop off at the very edge of the city palace. There are all sorts of treasures to discover.

The king's throne room is cool. The floor is smooth stone. It held the courtiers, the king, the queen, the people of the court. The stone throne, rather tiny, sits almost human by the wall. Above hangs a shield in blue and earth brown. The walls are brilliant with color. The famous dolphins play in blue-green water to dazzle.

You pass out of the throne room. You walk down a passageway, down a flight of stairs. It promises nothing but an expedition to some underground granaries or storage vaults. There is a small courtyard. The sun plays about the square columns. You come to a room. This is the queen's room. It is pleasantly domestic. There is no bed, but there is a bathtub. The queen takes baths! She has women to help her. Babies. Children play about these halls. The bathtub is a domestic marvel. You revel in it. You clap your hands for glee. You think of the water that was poured into it. It is an elegant bathtub too, not of porcelain, but of the same pinkish white color, in an elegant, Victorian-shaped oval with its arm rests. It is ludicrous. It is delightful.

You run back into another passageway. You walk, and your footsteps echo. You pass through darkened passages and suddenly come out on the queen's courtyard again. Ah! So you are here! Is it this that was Minos' labyrinth? Everything is silent under here. No lizards scuttle. It is precisely, you think, as the queen left it, cleaned, brushed, polished, sluiced with handmaidens' water. You look for one growing thing that the queen loved, one grapevine, one geranium, perhaps. You know that she grew geraniums in this courtyard. But there is no trace.

The labyrinth is enticing rather than fearsome. You believe that you will meet someone down there. Some left-over Cretan workman perhaps. No one! The palace is yours alone. It is chilly. You run pell-mell through the passageways. What a licentious freedom!

At last I climbed out of the labyrinth into the courtyard. The granary. Giant jars stood empty. Smoky marks etched the walls. Was it an earthquake that caused them? Was it an invasion? Was it a deliberate fire set by conquerors?

I found Barbara. She was sitting on a stone in a grove of pine trees by the edge of the courtyard.

"About the bull," I said . . . "About the bull—"

"Yes, what?"

"There is a theory. And this is the one that I believe. The bull, you see, was really Minos. Minos the king. It was him that Theseus slew. Have you seen down where the queen lived? There was the labyrinth. Theseus slew the bull, Minos the king, and took the queen. He overturned the bull. Knossos was overturned. The slaves then revolted. It was an invasion and a revolution all at once. Three thousand years ago . . . And they found Linear B here. . . . But all it said was the price of eggs and wine. Tabulations."

She held up her hand.

"Listen," she said.

The breeze was sifting elegantly, yet sneakily, through the pine boughs above. "Sh-sh!" it said.

"The same breeze," I murmured.

"Sh-sh!" it said.

Knowing that we would die, we ran out of the courtyard across the road and bought some grapes at a store. They were very juicy, very sour, and very quick.

XVI At noon we embarked for Piraeus. We slept aboard and arrived in the morning early. We found Daddy in the Piccadilly. He bought us two cups of American coffee.

Before Barbara left for England we saw three movies: *Peyton Place, Boy on a Dolphin,* and a rotten musical with June Allyson.

At the train station Barbara informed us that she was going to sneak into first class. "I just can't stand Yugoslavia from second class." She carried an umbrella and switched it to her left hand to shake hands with Daddy. "Good-by, Greek Daddy," she said. "Don't get any more women in compromising situations."

"*Kaló taxídi,* Varvara. It is you who better watch out. Be careful in what barber shops you practice your talents. Also, practice the study of Greek and when you come back we will erect some fake ruins, put candles in them, establish our own temples in competition with the Greek *papádes,* and mop up the moola."

"No, we will create our own organization and hire the Greek *papádes* to run them with candles and incense! We will give them a small cut of the gross take from the tourists!"

"You are a smart girl, but you can't fool them that easy. Greek *papádes* are good thieves and cheats, the best in the world. They will have you out on your ear before you can say Her Majesty Queen Elizabeth the Second."

"You are right, Greek Daddy. I know."

The train began to move off from the platform. Barbara stepped elegantly aboard. Her umbrella swung daintily.

"Good-by, Greek bag."

"Good-by."

She waved, and the minutes made her a shimmering, waving speck on the edge of the snake-train against the silver-gray mountain.

"Listen, Daddy," I said, as we began walking from the station to Omonia. It was the same route that I had walked that first moment that I had stepped foot from the train onto the limestone of Athens. "I am going back to Hora."

"There might be mud there," he said. "They say in the season of rains it gets knee high. Besides, where will you stay? Maria is in Athens right this minute. . . ." But the more he heard his protests the more he liked the idea of my going to Hora. "Well, you can always sleep in that room under her house. Besides, what have you to worry about? Martha will find you a place. Yes . . . Yes. I'll tell you what. Maybe I will come down myself after a week or so. I want to egg on standardization in the provinces. I want to show them these bottles I have found which are perfect for the preserving of meats in olive oil. It doesn't do any good just to tell them. You have to show them."

"All right. I will go tomorrow. As soon as I get there, I will write to you."

Daddy did not come. For something happened when I reached Hora that changed the face of the town.

VI Typhoon

1

On November 7 at five o'clock I arrived in Hora. The sun was pale yellow. The heat of the day was spent. The sky was blue and the air was so clear and so transparently thin that the night boded cold.

I got out of the bus and ran up through the alley way once more to the house of Miss Maria Ekonomopoulou. Frail lemon-yellow etched the whitewashed walls. The town rose row upon row above me. The tile roofs slanted in all directions. And it fell below me toward the direction of Kato Rouga. The bell tower of Agios Georgios was stunning white against the blue sky.

I entered the portal gate once more. It creaked shut behind me. I was in the *kípo*. There were still some pomegranates hanging on the tree and some oranges. The horse was knocking in its stall in the inner courtyard. But I heard the noise of footsteps and some cackling among the hens.

I called.

It was Martha. She wore her black *mandíli* like a shawl.

"Eh! *Ti* Daphne! Ei-li-li-li-lu!" Such was the sound of the clamor of her surprise. Then everything was silent. She clasped me in her arms. After our embrace she looked me over. I was embarrassed; she was concerned.

Her mind had the thought: 'Where will she sleep for the night? What shall I do? She is my cousin. But she is not used to a place like my father's house.' For they slept like animals, Katina, her sister, and her husband Elias below with their little girl, and little Boulis the four-year-old boy with his grandfather, Barba Ioannis.

"I want you to stay here," she said with passionate eagerness, "but . . . *kyrá mou eíne s'tin Athéna*." She always called Maria "my lady," or "my mistress." "Kyrios Nikos, *to Paidí*, is here but he—" She put her forefinger to her temple and screwed it, implying we must dismiss Kyrios Nikos as not competent to deal with practical affairs.

"Of course I cannot stay here," I said, "since Maria is away. I will go to the hotel."

"Are you a *xéni?*" she asked angrily. "Are you a stranger? You should be ashamed!"

I had this attitude: I have arrived, dear cousin. Take me as I am. I am a mendicant charmer. I have arrived. My occupation is quester. My method is to look and laugh. All I need is one blanket without lice, one slice of bread, one cup of coffee, and I will sleep on the ground. I have great expectations, but very little expectation of anyone. I do not need anything. See how light I travel? See how delightful it is to be here? I want to gobble up every lyrical color in the sky, to breathe every atom of air in the whole of Greece. See how marvelous to be in Hora, seat of Nestor, ground of my forefathers, birthplace of my father! So no complications, please.

"You go with me to the hotel," I told her, "so you can tell them what I want in good Greek."

She did not bother to answer this. What a crime if she were to allow her own cousin to sleep in a hotel! It brought her impotence to a head. She wanted to share it with me.

"I would ask you to stay here. But this is a stranger house. Are you the stranger? No. Am I the stranger? No. Maria is stranger to us. Nikos is stranger to us. Am I the daughter of the house? No. I am a servant. Maria says lock the house up. I lock it up. I have nothing. I can offer nothing. I cannot even offer you this house. What have I to do with this house where I cannot even ask you to stay, eh? Better that you should stay in my father's house though you have to sleep with eight goats and the donkey. You understand?"

Yes, I understood. "But I will stay in the hotel," I said.

She led me upstairs.

"Sit down."

I sat in the tiny dining room. She set the table. She served me a secret dinner. *Fagitó kryphó*. It was *dolmádes*, with wine and bread and olives.

Understand whose food this was. Understand the enemy. We were stealing from the enemy.

The clock ticked loudly. It grew dusky out. She lit the *kandíli* and then the kerosene lamp. The house had electricity, but the town generator was broken. The room sagged. The floor was of rough board and sank under her footsteps. The house tipped out toward the window, so that the foot of the iron cot was lower than the head, and the table was lopsided.

Martha pulled the day's date out of the calendar. Each date had a motto. This read:

> If you lose a mother, you may gain a brother:
> If you lose a father, you may gain a sister.
> Hail to all arrivals, and bemoan not departures.

She gave me the paper to keep as a souvenir.

From this dining-room window which opened out with shutters, we looked at the whole town below, and over the bell tower of Agios Ioannis all the way to the sea. From the cockatoo courtyards with the busy sounds of hens and night suppers, over the sloping tiled roofs, perched as they were below us on the mountain, and past the sounds of town life, the smell of the *foúrnos* baking, the gabbling as the women took the last pails of water from the *vrísi*, the trickling of the water from the town faucets, away from all the reviving life of the town as the men came out from supper to spend the evening in the coffee shop, to the last plateau of the mountain, grayish green in the night, where Nestor's palace stood. It seemed to hold its sea in its arms, though the sea was in reality at least two miles away. The sea was a dusky green with a kind of golden glow. It seemed quite impartial, very distant and very calm. It would soon be obscured with utter darkness, unless the moon, which shone frail and golden in the sky, became glittering and hard and threw a harder light on it.

Having finished my meal, I arose and, excitedly beating my wings, I talked Martha into doing that which she so disapproved of, accompanying me to the hotel. She acquiesced very quickly. She was tight-lipped and stern. It was not a place for *korítzia,* she muttered. Commercial salesmen went there. It was still filled up with sleazy artists, players and *tragoudístres* (women singers), prima donnas, theater women, no better than prostitutes, left over from the *panegýri.*

This prospect was very appealing. What better than to get acquainted with fourth-rate traveling music and theater troupes who made tours to the hinterland. But I did not want to disgrace Martha.

The electric lights now came on in the town. They had fixed the generator. The moment we stepped out of the alley in which Maria's house stood, into the main street, there were crowds of men. They had finished their home meals and were now out for their evening outing, bound for the *kaphenía.* They walked in pairs and in groups. They parted to let us through. They stared. Among themselves there was much laughter, shouting and greetings.

We raveled our way through them quickly, almost furtively. They whispered remarks about us among themselves. This was not only because I was a foreign woman, but also because I was with Martha, one of the most humble, and more respectable, girls of the town. Women do not parade the streets at night. Had I been alone, I would have stared them in the face freely. I would have enjoyed it. But I was caught between two cultures. Such is the penalty of playing two roles at once. I felt like a cloistered woman on the loose.

The hotel was a shambly, decrepit building on an alleyway leading from the main piazza of the town. We went up a flight of board stairs, into a wooden corridor. The hotel was no larger than a large house, possessing only twelve rooms. The rooms were separated from each other by thin cardboard partitions.

The proprietor was a fat old cougher who lay in his bed most all the night and day sleeping, and eating vile delicacies cooked by his wife in rancid olive oil. At intervals he rocked the hotel with his moist, phlegmy, and luxuriant coughs. When he did this his efforts made the springs of his bed creak, and the straw rustled in his mattress. This made a perfect symphony, since it was in rhythm to the coughs. To hear him you would think he was dying, but he had lived this way for twenty years.

The wife of this proprietor came out, grunting and calling at our presence. She wore a dirty polka-dotted dress. Her hair was greasy, and she looked out with black eyes from under the frames of her glasses. Two bobby pins stabbed up from her hair like broken devil's horns.

"What do you want?" she honked. She stared at me with voracious, consuming curiosity.

From the first moment it was obvious that the hotel was full. Beds lined the dim corridor, like an overcrowded hospital. In some of them people were sleeping. Other people strayed out of the rooms and came down the hall aimlessly, bumping up against each other at the head of a bed in which there was a sleeping man. The object of their pilgrimage was a sink which stood in the corridor. Underneath the sink a man lay sleeping. The sink was very dirty. Unwashed dishes lined it. There was one cold water faucet. It dripped. Next to the sink, separated from the hallway by an oilcloth curtain of greasy poinsettia design, was a kangaroo toilet. People flipped their way in and out of it, twitching the curtain. Every time someone left it there was a roar of waters which drowned out the sound of Martha talking.

During the conversation the proprietor lunged up from his bed and appeared in the doorway, wanting to know what was going on. I could hear every motion. His face was fat, peppered with sweat. He grunted like an unwashed hog for his wife.

"It is all due to the *panegýri*," apologized the proprietor's wife, interpolating this politeness through a grunt for him to go back to his bed. "*Den échome domátia . . . kathólou!*"

It was hopeless. We thanked her and left.

It was the height of the evening. Back in the crowded street the coffee shops had put on their records and were broadcasting from horn-shaped loudspeakers tacked to the tops of their doors. Heady excited music, wild singing, one song against another.

"We will go to my father's house," said Martha.

We descended the way we had gone my first evening in Hora. The crowds diminished. The light of the main street twinkled in the distance. We passed the schoolhouse where Daddy had gone to elementary school.

Suddenly Martha stopped, possessed of an idea.

"Ioannis' house! There is room there! You will have a room to yourself. Now! If only he is home!"

We turned down an alleyway.

She ruminated: "It is a much better house. There is no question. And then, Ioannis said before that if you came back it would be best for you to stay there. It is so. It is surely so. But he has been fishing at Methoni for a week now. What if he is not at home yet? No matter. Let us go. Let us see if the lights are burning. If Ioannis is not there, then we will go to my father's house."

The alleyway was stony. It was pitch-dark. A few houses showed feeble kerosene glimmers. Our footsteps echoed loudly against each building.

Martha flashed on her flashlight. We proceeded, led by the small jellied blob of light bobbing before us.

The dark seemed like my ignorance of the language. Made manifest. It was an uncertainty of my next role in my next moment. So total that I had no heart for regretting or even for eliciting my known past. I was cut off decisively from what I had ever been before. I was bent with bated breath on what would happen to me this night. And yet I surveyed it with complete equanimity.

At last we came to Ioannis' house. It was separated from the alleyway by a huge porticoed wooden fence.

"Ioannis!" called Martha.

No reply.

"Ioannis! Oo-oo! Ioannis!"

There was not one sound.

She scooped up some pebbles from the street and threw them at his windowpane.

There came a yelp like a wolf's protestation.

"Ioannis!" Her eyes glittered.

"*Oríste*. Who is it?"

There was the sound of a window opening. He stuck his head out.

"Who is it?"

"*Egó eíme, kai i* Daphne!"

"*I* Daphne!"

"*Kimáse?* Are you sleeping?"

It reminded me of "Frère Jacques." But it was Brother John for real.

"*Érhome. Érhome,*" he said, and closed the window.

After a long time we heard his footsteps descending the stairway, With the sound of panting, Ioannis removed a giant forked stick which kept the gate closed. He swung it open. It creaked on its hinges.

"*Ti* Daphne!" he whispered. "You have come back."

We entered the courtyard on tiptoes. He led us up the stairway onto a rickety porch.

His mother and father were asleep, he said. He himself had arrived from Methoni only one hour ago. By all means I must sleep in his house tonight.

He led us into what appeared to be a huge room. All was dark, but the flashlights darted beams into the darkness until he lit the kerosene lamp. Then everything came into focus.

It was a large room. It was the parlor. It had board floors and whitewashed walls. Upon the walls hung six or eight pictures, old family photographs. There was one of Kyria Katerina's grandfather dressed in an Afghanistani cap and a uniform of khaki. The grandfather's mustaches drooped very long and importantly, and in his weather-beaten eyes was a voraciousness and twinkling mixed. The room held very little furniture. There was a wardrobe dresser in which hung all the best clothes of the family. There was a chest of drawers, topped by a hand-embroidered linen bureau scarf. There was a long table. There was one bed with an iron headstead and footstead, and a mattress of straw. Beside it on the floor lay a little rug called a *tápeto,* made of flapping bits of cloth sewed neatly together. The bedstead was covered with a white linen coverlet, much darned and much patched. I saw at once that this was the best room in the house, and that it was barely used.

Martha and Ioannis talked in whispers. She told him how we had gone to the hotel. But there were great innuendoes in their conversation. Maria's name was mentioned sixteen times, accompanied by hisses and other denigrating sounds, and epithets like *gaïdoúra* and *gouroúna,* she-ass and sow. She was being made the character of evil in this story.

All of a sudden we heard footsteps. In the doorway, carrying a lighted *kandíli,* appeared an old man. This was Kyrios Elias, Ioannis' father. He was dressed in baggy trousers and wore a suit coat over his thin shoulders. The light of the *kandíli* illumined his face. He was white-haired and walked feebly. His face was smooth-skinned and filled with innumerable fragile wrinkles. He was striking in appearance. A glow seemed to shine on his forehead because of the *kandíli.* His nose was long, and his white mustache shone purely over his lip. He had the appearance of one of those old saints, or one of Dickens' old fathers in travail. He was truly a gentle man, and his appearance was an exact transfiguration of his aspirations, for he was self-taught, and was forever reading the history of the Greeks and Turks at war or the *Lives of the Saints,* his favorite book.

He came up to me with his hands stretched out.

"Welcome to our house," he said. "Our house is your house. You are to stay here as long as you want to. You are to consider yourself like to a daughter. Have you had anything to eat or drink, *paidí mou?*" He talked with great dignity.

Everything had become quiet and gained importance. Martha made the bed. Everything was deliberate, almost fateful, as if there had been some great and huge reason that this house of all Hora houses should be visited and chosen by me, as if there were some design, not just a sudden thought in Martha's mind as we were passing the alleyway to her father, Barba Ioannis', house.

These events stick in our minds because of what happened later, to be gone over, to be wondered at, as if there truly were some great significance in its having happened in just this particular way. And every minute action, every word of greeting, even to the very coincidence that Ioannis happened to have returned from a week's fishing in Methoni to be here this night, just at the moment when Martha first conceived the idea of leading me down the alleyway to this very house, . . . even to the fact that he was almost asleep, but not quite, even at this early hour (it was now ten-thirty), and that he had heard the pebbles at the window . . . that Kyrios Elias had also awakened and greeted us . . . All of these mundane, household acts of welcome and of hospitality magnified themselves later and became the hinge upon which that later event hung so miraculously, and yet so unbelievably.

Before Martha left for the night she turned to me and said:

"My father could not wait until you returned to Hora. 'Dino's daughter!' he has kept saying for these last four weeks while you have been in Athens. He wants to meet his cousin-niece. Yet you came so suddenly that now he does not know that you are here. Tomorrow we are all going to Megambelia for the olives. Will you come? Perhaps you will not want to, for we start early, at sun-up, about seven-thirty. . . ."

"Oh yes, I want to. . . ."

"Not tomorrow," said Ioannis, making a face. "Make it the next day. She can sleep late tomorrow."

"No, not that," I said eagerly. "But the day after tomorrow will be better. I will take out my typewriter tomorrow and do some work. And then the next day I will come. For then I will feel that I have accomplished something."

"Good. Good," said Martha. "On Friday, then. Now I will leave you. I am going down to tell my father that you are here. Good. Better on Friday, the day after tomorrow. Oh, how happy he will be!" She turned to take her leave. "*Kali níchta,* then. Have good dreams. I will see you tomorrow night. *Kali níchta.*"

The flashlights, the voices, the footsteps disappeared into the hall and I was left alone in that parlor now become my bedroom.

The lamplight glowed extremely. And Kyria Katerina's grandfather stared down at me from the walls very frowningly.

II Dawn was at seven. I woke at nine-thirty. Everyone had been up for hours. I got dressed hurriedly and emerged into the hallway which led out on to the porch with my toothbrush in hand.

The morning had that quality of pure and powerful energy that all Greek mornings have. It was cold and the sun was shining clear and potent in the perfectly speckless, huge blue sky. The sun unnerves you on first awaking.

At first glance the house was both larger and much more primitive than I had imagined the night before. My own room, the parlor, was bigger and much more bare than it had seemed in the light of the kerosene lamp. In the hallways some onions and corn were hanging on a nail upon the whitewashed wall. A bag of meal sat in a corner. A straight chair faced it. The walls of the house were very thick, about three feet in depth. The doorway to the porch was two rickety, worm-eaten portals of wood. The key was a huge, rusted iron implement. The door was opened by an old-fashioned latch of the thumb-pressing variety, and it creaked on its hinges.

The hall led directly to a room with a closed door, which was a bedroom, I assumed. It was Ioannis' room. To the right of the hall was another room. It looked like a kitchen but was not. It had a table with an oilcloth cover upon which sat a small kerosene lamp, three balls of string, two empty boxes of Aroma cigarettes which were filled with nails, screws and *amígdala* (almonds), various white, chipped dishes covered over with clean but patched dish towels. There was also a pile of books and papers at the end of a long settee. On the floor stood a small wicker-seated stool. On a home-made shelf stood cups, boxes of garlic, *orígani* and other herbs. The shelf also held the little kerosene stove, its base painted red. This room was a dining room. The kerosene stove was for making coffee. Meals were cooked outside in a separate kitchen building.

I went out onto the porch. It was very rickety, with two board railings, and lines to hang washing. Over the porch railings, against the wall of the house was a small slanted cement sink with a little pipe at its lower end. A large metal canister hung over the sink-trough with a faucet in its bottom. Inside the canister was the day's supply of water for washing hands, drinking, and brushing teeth. The canister was filled daily by hauling five-gallon cans (army surplus) of water from the well in the street.

Below the porch, the courtyard, half stones, half mud. It was smaller than I had thought it to be last night. Across the courtyard was the kitchen house. Smoke emerged from the door. Underneath the house the horse knocked in its stall. The courtyard was running and clucking with hens and small chicks. A goat was tied to one of the posts which held up the porch. In the yard was a huge wooden trough filled with black olives swimming in oily water. An old woman sat on the ground before the trough, washing the olives in the water, picking out the bad ones and throwing them onto a separate pile by her side. The court was surrounded on all sides by stone walls. On one side lay the neighboring house, but vines crept over the wall obscuring the view into its yard. On the other side of the court through a portal gate in the wall a path led to a garden filled with orange trees, apples, laurels, mandarin oranges, lemons, and myrtle bushes. There was a garden full of celery, tomatoes, carrots, lettuce, beets, and radishes. Also in the garden were two or three peeling white hives which sang with clusters of bees.

Where I was standing on the porch I could see for miles. A field scattered with cypress trees backed the garden and a small white Byzantine church. Suddenly I looked far away to the sea, calm, blue, and sunlit, lying between the purple mountains and the peak of Navarino, the island in Pylos Bay.

Voices came out of the cellar beneath the porch. Ioannis and Kyrios Elias emerged. The old woman, aroused by the voices, looked up and saw me.

They greeted me. The old woman got up from her crouching position by the olives. She was fat, creased, bent and old. She could scarcely make her way to the stairs. When she arrived at the bottom, she put her hand on the post. She panted voluminously, mounting one step after another. She was about five feet tall, but she could not stand upright. Her mouth was toothless and her eyes were very blue, twinkling in their sockets of crow's-feet and fat. One eyelid would not stay open, so she had taped it open with adhesive. This gave her a look of continuous, bloodshot surprise. She was arrantly curious and had her eyes focused on me quite suspiciously. She looked both prophetic and ignorant.

Kyrios Elias was feeble and nimble at the same time. He staggered anciently up the stairs, so thin that he seemed skeletal inside his baggy khaki pants. Over his shoulders he wore a worn-out, magnificent sheepskin coat which gave him the air of a magnificent old shepherd with a cape.

I put out my hand to shake hands with Kyria Katerina. But she made a loud, grunting noise. She wiped her hands hurriedly on her apron before she would touch my hand. She was coarsely polite, but I could not understand her toothless Greek.

Kyrios Elias spoke a gentle and excellent Greek. He repeated his formal greetings and salutations to me. Then he showed me the sink where I could brush my teeth, and he expressed regrets that this was not the type of accommodation that I had been used to, but this, he said, this humble and poor way of life, was what they were used to and what they could offer.

He then ordered Kyria Katerina to prepare breakfast for me. I saw at once that though she was the prop and dominant force of the household, she was a mere woman, and had to mind the orders both of Kyrios Elias and of her son. She was at a loss with me. I was a strange animal. She did not know what to prepare. Did I want milk or coffee? What did Americans eat?

Ioannis was a steaming bull of energy beside his old and gremilitic parents. He knew that the French drink *café au lait,* so he decided on that as a good bet. He filled the pan with water, lit the kerosene stove. It smoked and the entire house stank of kerosene. He extracted a huge loaf of black bread out of a large tin can. He brought out a dish of olives and goat cheese. He offered me many choices, explaining that he did not know what I wanted. Would I have an orange? What fruit did I want? All he had to do was go to the garden and pick it. In Hora they grew all the fruits imaginable in the whole world.

They watched me while I ate. My Greek was so impossible to them that they began to talk *to* me in signs and *about* me in Greek which they believed that I did not understand. Kyria Katerina decided that, not knowing Greek, I was not more capable of anything than a baby. So she did not talk to me at all. But Kyrios Elias looked upon me as an educated challenge. He began using French words. Whenever I recognized them, his ancient face lighted up with rhapsodic ecstasy. We began to talk simply in Greek words. Spoon. Fork. Olives. Plate. Coffee . . . The vocabulary of eating. I said the words after them. They went into raptures of enthusiasm.

I filled my plate with bread and cheese and olives. This was the strange breakfast that I ate this first day, and every day afterwards in this house. Everyone ate olives. We put the pits in the ashtrays and at the end of the meal each ashtray was filled high with olive pits.

Kyrios Elias showed me his book of saints. He was so pleased, so anxious, so concerned with his prize treasures, that he thought he had found another soul with whom he could share them, that he believed fortune had sent me to his house. He told Kyria Katerina that I was to be treated more preciously even than he had at first instructed, for I was a well-learned, *polí morphoméni* person, a treasure in their nest. He prized and relished every motion I made, every olive that I ate. I was become a magnificent mystery about whom they were privileged to make speculations and of whom they were the protectors.

At last Ioannis got up. He and Kyrios Elias had to go to work in the field.

I was left alone with Kyria Katerina.

We stared at each other. We were silent. She was perplexed, and out of her perplexity she became afraid.

Suddenly I got an idea.

I went and fetched my typewriter. I took it out, and I began to write.

III

"*Michaní!*" She looked at the typewriter with amazement.

I zipped off a few words fast.

She pressed her hands together. "Ma ma ma! *Dóxasi o Theós!* God be praised!" she intoned. She stood up. She came closer. She breathed heavily on my ear.

I showed her the words that had come out on the paper. At the sight she plucked her hands together once more and breathed the sound of something miraculous.

"*Grámmata! Grámmata!*" she muttered.

It was an old clacking Underwood. Because it clacked so much the effect was more miraculous than if it had been a silent machine. I invited her to touch a key. She refused and backed away. She confessed that she did not know how to read and write. She did not know all the letters. But she knew an omicron. I pointed to an *o* and she said "Omicron." She also knew alpha. I pointed to an *a* and she said "Alpha."

She went to get a chair. She brought the chair around and set it two feet from the table. She sat down on it and folded her hands.

"*Káne to! Káne to!*" (Do it! Do it!) she ordered me.

Being bidden so, I did. I began to write her name: "Kyria Katerina. Kyria Katerina. Kyria Katerina.

"Kyria Katerina sits two feet away from me watching the hand of God peck at the vitals of a machine. A word comes out. This room is whitewashed. The sun is in the sky. I am at the house of Ioannis Ekonomopoulos in the town of Hora, Messenia, Peloponnesus, Greece. Oh, I too am amazed. Kyria Katerina is confronted with the miracle of the machine. I am confronted with the miracle of another human being in whom the machine can make such light."

I looked at her. She looked at me.

She put up her hand. She giggled, and then she rose with great dignity to leave me. She tiptoed, her creaking, ponderous body waddling conspiratorially over the board floor. At the doorway she turned and closed the door with great ceremony. It was with reverence, as if she had been in church.

IV It was five-thirty. All day had been transparently magnificent. The sun so clear and shining that all the cool pores of the earth seemed to have opened to take the light. In the middle of the day it had been hot, but the air had been cold. Fire and ice. It was invigorating. Toward the end of the afternoon purple and azure shadows set in. The ropes of the mountains lay indomitable over Hora, and each stone was clearly outlined. Every sound rang clear, the footsteps of people sounding on the half-cobbled alleyway, the hoofs of donkeys returning from the olive groves passing the little church above the house. There was the sound of whirring as November birds flew from the cypress trees.

The sun had warmed the house. Ioannis returned from his work excited from the day's sunning. Martha appeared. The house rang with shouts of greeting.

Preparations began for the evening meal. Martha took dishes from the eating room down to the *kouzína* outside. Kyrios Elias unsaddled the horse and gave it hay. Underneath the house there was the sound of swishing and crunching as the horse ate his meal. A fire was lit of sticks and twigs in the *kouzína*. Windows were still open in the house.

Martha had been picking olives. Her father, Barba Ioannis, had climbed the tree. He had beat the olive tree with a stick. The olives had fallen onto the canvas below. They had sung at work.

"Barba Ioannis says, 'Greetings and good night to Daphne.' He will see you in the morning."

"I say: 'Greetings to Barba Ioannis.' I will see him in the morning!"

In relays the meal was brought up the stairs to the *trapezaría*. Ioannis brought the silver and the eating plates. Martha brought the dish of *chórta* dressed in olive oil. Kyrios Elias filled the wine bottle from the barrel in the cellar. Kyria Katerina groaned her way upstairs carrying a dish filled with *psária*, small fish rolled in flour and fried in olive oil.

The last shots of pink were glowing in the sky when we sat down to eat. A scapegrace black cloud hovered over the sea giving an additional glimmer to the pink. Martha ladled out portions of *chórta* and fish onto the plates.

Kyria Katerina looked particularly lined and dirty tonight, like a prune. She had a fierce, everlasting air. She was like the mound-shaped burial blobs that housed the dead of Nestor's city. Her one tooth shone and she uttered many jokes. Her mouth was like a prodigious flap. Each time she uttered a joke she shut her eyes, her mouth, and all orifices and laughed in a gigantic grunt, her eyes pointed upward. She was like a smoking mountain. She had her own stool upon which she sat. She did not favor chairs, she said. She was too bent over and her feet could not reach the ground.

It grew dark. We lit the kerosene lamp.

Kyrios Elias' fine brown eyes gleamed over the snow-stubble of his chin. He ate very slowly and methodically and gently. At the end of the meal, when we were all drinking wine, he lit a cigarette. He smoked it in a holder. The kerosene lamp flared. He was beautiful. The flare made a sudden vision of him, his benevolent, white, saintly face studded with dark eyes jumped and glistened before us.

Outside the night grew exciting. It began throwing sheet-lightning capers. Through the window the landscape of olive-strewn acres with sudden orange trees and cypress sentinels flashed momentarily in an eerie prophecy of that kind of solemn, silent storm which in southeastern American summer evenings come to nothing. Just an hour or so of suppressed flashings of gigantic lightning. A storm somewhere else, perhaps miles away. Silence between the growls of thunder and a stillness in the air. Not a sign of breath. Perhaps, we thought, a few drops of rain.

But we were inside and the kitchen was full of laughter. We were closeted in by a pool of light, the kerosene lamp, in which we saw each other's brows cast. Our silhouettes beat like hearts on the whitewashed walls. Someone closed the window because it was a bit cold.

We were getting high on the retsina. We paid no attention to the atmosphere of the world. We were our own world. I knew what was being talked about: the price of olives. Dances. It was nine o'clock in the evening now. There was a flickering on the wall. The kerosene lamp danced on its own flames. The wine. Our state of gaiety induced additional glow-lights. There was a gypsy eloquence and intimacy.

Kyria Katerina said she was going to come to America with me and dance.

Will you take me to Paris?

Oh yes!

Dóxasi o Theós! What would I do there? You can talk. You can go around. But I won't even be able to walk down the street . . . I won't know a word people are saying!

That's all right. You can sing Greek songs, Mother!

What! And have pennies thrown in my bosom?

Out of the laughter it began.

It began with a strange sound, far away, as if the gods were moaning, or a train in the distance were struggling up some unknown hill. We heard it, but we did not stop to listen, as if it were an explainable thing and thus had no need to be explained. Ioannis was talking now. The Van Gogh chairs knit us all close together in the threaded flare of the lamp.

I shall never forget the smile on the old man's face. I did not understand. But the sound was persistent.

An anguish, insistent, beginning to be pervasive as if something had taken entire control of all the land outside, as if it were coming close to us, threatening the kitchen and the food and the mainstream of life flowing out of the lamp. Yet it was outside, not with us. And now the portals to the window were closed.

All of the outside, all the land outside was caught up in that onrushing purr-roll of anguish while we were still eclectic and uncaught.

We stopped talking though. We cocked ourselves to listen like rabbits. It moved, a thousand trailing, writhing gods, the sound like a tape recording of the tormented in Hades. The important thing was that it could not be seen. There was nothing one could identify.

All the time it was forcing nearer, we knew this ball of hell, but what the ball was, since it was composed only of that electronic music out of a land ignorant of electronics, we did not have any idea. Nothing we could pin onto. Everything was the same except for the sound. The land was the same. The kitchen. The atmosphere was still.

And then it began to be identifiable. A puff knocked the window gently. It was the wind. It was wind not here, but coming. The first faint knowledge in the wriggle of the olive trees outside. They sent signals. Ioannis uttered a warning, a guttural warning. Someone started to speak and then stopped. I heard another warning. I did not know the word. I could not concentrate to understand the word. It was only there like a backdrop to the screaming anguish outside. Ioannis rushed to the door. Too frantic, I thought, his black eyes staring wild. Martha rushed after him. I was rigidly nonchalant, my Anglo-Saxon half thinking: "A phenomenon is coming, but I who am ignorant of this Peloponnesian country, I who do not know of its weathers, its nuances, its rains, its storms in which I am not ancient, I will leave it up to them for knowledge. Perhaps they are experienced in Poseidon's winds."

But I could not remain nonchalant. I rushed after Martha. The three of us suddenly were out there on that second-story porch. It was a flimsy thing of rotten boards and wood, rickety, a balcony from which to survey the land as far as Nestor's palace. Below the horse whinnied. A few neighboring roosters crowed.

Outside the scream was bloody. It was like a pulse-wild termagant, wringing the hair of the olive trees, shooting along the bamboo fences and the orange orchards. A huge and ancient VOOOO-OOOM! continuous, inarticulate, chasing itself across the mountain from the sea, coming our way, churning the grasses, the bamboo, the cypress trees far away, its angry head wind already upon us, thrashing the plants on the porch and the neighboring olive tree, throwing hay, sticks, mud, filling our mouths with sand. The lamp in the kitchen flickered with terror. The old mother and father piled tumbling upon us.

But the thing had not arrived yet.

The next few seconds were filled with shouts, contemplations, warnings. We had those seconds . . . or I had those seconds to contemplate the scientific thing to do, and I chose the wrong thing, I think. I was in terror, yet thought of the movie with Jean Marais, a hideous French technicolored ape of American earthquake-type movies, about a typhoon in Japan. I knew Ioannis' house was unsubstantial. I knew that this was no ordinary wind, but a concentrated ball of wind sent to us thick, terrible, pinpointed, with us as its pivot point, calculated to take us into its middle where the others, the ancients, the cosmos, the damned were its screaming entrails. Yet I did not know its name.

Think of a typhoon coming. Or a cyclone. Or a hurricane. Or a tornado. But I did not know what this was. Neither did they.

"What is it? What is it?" shouted Martha.

The advantage of being able to identify a catastrophe, at least to the literate, is that you can begin to concentrate on saving your life. There is a tiny corridor in your mind which fills you up completely. You can take action, which is a comfort. My mind was very clear in these seconds before it struck. It did not look like any hurricane that I had ever seen. The hurricane is a steady and powerful mass of wind spread over a large area. But this was concentrated like a tornado or twister, more tricky, more capricious, and far more lethal.

"The house is going to go! The house is going to fall down on top of us! We are all going to die!" shouted Martha.

In that second I knew there wasn't much time left. I knew that there was something scientific that we should do to save ourselves. Close the doors, I thought. I grasped hold of the door and tried to slam it shut. Ioannis suddenly threw himself against me and pushed it wide open again. He was shouting to me but I could not understand a word he said.

I whirled around where he had thrown me. I had landed in a corner. I wanted to say "We must do something," but I could not think of the Greek words for it. The thing was so loud by now that one had to shout to make oneself heard. I could not think, conjure up the Greek words in my mind, let alone say them. There was no time. Also, I thought that Ioannis must know what it was, or he would not insist upon the door's being open. I perceived his idea. It was: wind: suction: vacuum; keep the doors and windows open so you will not create a vacuum in the house. Then it will not explode from great force on the outside and great force on the inside meeting. Maybe he's right, I thought. My heart felt: No, it is wrong.

These Mediterranean things. Damn them for their fatalism, for their shouts, for their emotionalism, for their lack of quiet thought and scientific procedure. If it were English or Americans we would know what it was. Someone would know what to do. They would not stand here in the force of this blast saying, "*Ti na kánome? Ti na kánome?* Let it come, because it is coming and there is nothing we can do anyhow." If it were English or Americans there would not be this blatant admission that death is possible. All attention would be focused on what can be done to prevent death.

I knew what we should do. There was still time. We should run down to the cellar and crouch under a table. If the house fell at least we would be on solid earth.

I tried to think up the Greek words. It was impossible. I could not think of the words. If I could have, the others would not have listened. The same reason that I conceived myself to be an authority would be proof that I was not one to them. In the final analysis I was the *xéni,* stranger, which Martha would not admit that I was.

I am a stranger. I am a stranger. What do I know of their country or their village. To stay up here and die is to be a fool. To run down in the cellar and save myself, that is the only sensible thing to do.

At the moment of this dilemma I knew that my concentration of terror was a vast excitement and glory. I wanted to laugh. I knew that the whole thing was monstrously important and vastly ironic. I had always wished to be in a cyclone or in a war. Now my wish had come true. I had become as primitive as I had always wanted. I had nothing to lose but my life. To lose it in such a way was more magnificent than by disease. This puerility beat out my terror. I did not think of losing my life, only of keeping it.

My resentment at their ignorance was terrible. And yet I could not make the decision to go down. It was not nobility. It was a choice of one ignominy against another. To go away and leave them simply because I could not communicate to them how to save themselves! Besides, the animals were down there. Imagine after the holocaust finding yourself with the animals, alive, and all the humans dead! And I must die because these humans do not know enough, and because I do not know enough to tell them! Oh God, God, they made it so easy! They made the possibility, the inevitability, the powerlessness of the human will against the fact of death so easy! They made the risk of death so easy because they could not imagine anything but that!

I could not leave them. They were human. They were human. I would rather die or get buried with people than live alone without. I would rather die with their ignorance than live alone with my knowledge. This is how it was ignominious.

Ioannis rushed into my room to close the blinds. The old lady rushed into the kitchen. There was the sound of splintering glass.

"What is she doing? What is she doing?" screamed Martha.

"Close the blinds!" shouted Ioannis.

Before he could get the blinds closed, the window glass burst. The kitchen lamp went out in a paroxysm of terror.

All was dark. Dark broke contact with will. Light is the language of reason and control. The dark issued in the reign of chaos.

"*Mitéra! Mitéra!*" shouted Ioannis.

In the darkness the old woman heaved out of the kitchen toward us. She dragged her stool under one arm. She placed it in a corner. She sat down upon it. Her air was of one hypnotized. In complete silence, all alone, in stone faith, she began crossing herself.

I huddled in the corner by the doorway protected from a direct onslaught. Martha and Ioannis stood silhouetted in the doorway. They were outlined against the impending blast like two stripling trees. Kyrios Elias stood trembling in the corner by them.

The outside came inside. All was a lashing dark. We were in a quivering structure of darkness. Boards flapped around us. Tiles catapulted a hundred miles an hour into the stream. The VOOOOO-OOM grew louder.

It hit. Mud, bricks, straw fell upon us. Our mouths filled with dust. Our eyes, wide open and staring, filled with dust. One side of the house fell to the ground. Tiles blew off the roof one by one, whooshing like giant swallows' wings. Then half the roof flew off. In the scream of the center came a sharp CRACK CRACK CRACK as if the cyclone's jack-in-the-box were having a jest of joy jumping mechanically through those liquid screams of the tormented. In the tail of the wind were giant sparks. Boulders smacked up against houses and tiles smashed to pieces. The house buckled once clockwise. It was a tipping sensation, accompanied by shuddering creaks in the structure.

At this moment Ioannis stretched out his hand against Martha and took mine. Martha grabbed hold of my arm with one hand and Ioannis' arm with the other. Ioannis held out his left hand to his father.

We did nothing but hold. We endured. We waited that minute, holding each other tight. Not a word was spoken. We were tiny things there. We were mortal in outrageous force.

The house buckled again, counterclockwise. I closed my eyes and held my breath. The roar was deafening. The shattering force of the wind strangled the lungs with an excess of air and made each human body feel as if it were about to explode. I hid my nose and mouth against my knees and felt the human hands holding my hand.

The wind abated. It gave way to a cloudburst of rain.

We received the rain in joy, like tears at the culmination of shock. We loosed our hands. We looked at each other. We were silent. We did not know what to do. We raised our hands up and put them down. Then we surrendered to joy. We screamed. We were like ecstatic monkeys.

"*Dóxasi o Theós!*" grunted the old woman.

We pretended that the rain was a catastrophe.

"God! God! There is no roof! It is raining in!" We laughed.

We fled to the roofless rooms. Spinning rivers made great oblong mud cakes of the beds. The table became a sink. Water filled empty dishes left over from our supper. The roof ribs drooled. The house became a gigantic mire. Clothes hanging over chairs became a wet paste of dough. My typewriter was muddy.

"Oh my God! How terrible! What a catastrophe!" we shouted in triumph.

In an excess of superabundant graciousness, with the triumph of God in them, and the generosity of gods, Martha and Ioannis rushed for my papers. They collected them. They put them under the table to keep them from being soaked. The old woman snatched at the picture of her grandfather. She clasped her hands, half crying, half laughing. She talked to him as she clasped him to her bosom.

"Don't be a fool, *Mána!*"

"What should I do? Allow him to drown in the rain? Oh my previous one, my ancestor! Oh, all holy saints. God has seen to it that you are not ruined by the wind. Now should you be ruined by the rain?"

"They are all right. They are dead already! It's only a picture!" And so forth. Ioannis and his mother flapped their hands at each other angrily.

All of a sudden there was a great silence. The rain stopped.

Weak and triumphant we looked out upon the ravaged night, the broken houses, the battered olive trees, the oranges scattered like pale dots upon the ground. The night seemed silent as if ashamed. The moon sneaked up in the sky. It began to smile with that same weak triumphant hardness that we recognized in ourselves. The moon too had not been killed. It shone, atrociously bright. We looked out filled with joy. There lay the rumpled, ravaged beauty of utter destruction.

V From a nearby house on the street came the sound of a woman crying. In the beginning it was a moan of amazement. Then it rose to high, agonized yelps. The voice was joined with other women's voices. A man's voice broke in angry and fierce, bidding them to shut up. There was a silence. Then the women's voices took on a sound of steady and uncontrollable lamentation.

This brought on, like a rising tide, our first consciousness of others. Our triumph passed into a different phase.

"Barba Ioannis, *o patéras, i mitéra, mitéra, kai ta paidiá,*" breathed Martha amazed. "What has happened to them? And *to Paidí* Kyrios Nikos? Where is the flashlight?"

"No, I will go," said Ioannis.

"The flashlight is in the kitchen," said Kyria Katerina. She roused herself. She shuffled like a slow train picking up speed.

In the light of the moon the house was unrecognizable. Tiles were broken on the floor. A bag of flour had been ripped open and was spilled in the doorway.

"Give me the flashlight, Ioannis *mou.*"

"You don't know what it's like out there. Trees in the road. Houses. Maybe some wires. You will be electrocuted. You stay here."

"Are they your family? Do they belong to you? Did you leave Kyrios Nikos alone in the big house? What do you think? Eh?" Martha shook, half between paralytic fright and terrible anger.

"*Proséhete, proséhete,*" warned Kyria Katerina.

Ioannis lit the kerosene lamp. We looked at each other for the first time. We had the flary, wild, hop-lighted expression of animals who do not recognize each other.

"I go," said Martha.

"All right. Go then," yelped Ioannis.

But he snatched the flashlight out of her hand.

"Hurry up."

"*Sópa.* I am coming."

"Oh God, *Panagía mou,* I am afraid," groaned Martha.

"You go, *paidáki mou.* You see that they are all right, pray God," whispered Kyria Katerina.

"The house was new, but only made of mud. *Dóxasi o Theós. Dóxasi o Theós.*" Martha crossed herself.

Ioannis led the way. As if forgetting something he turned back. "You, *mitéra kai patéra.* You stay here. Don't go out. You stay and wait. We will not be too long. Not more than an hour."

He went down the stairway. Martha followed. Their footsteps sounded loud and strange. Kyria Katerina hung over the rail. She uttered blessings on their departure. She implored them to be careful on the way, to watch for loose wires and falling balconies. At the portal door Ioannis shouted:

"Go inside."

Their footsteps died away. The house seemed strange and solitary. It was a house no longer. It was a strange, disarrayed shelter. Tiles were strewn upon the floor. The rugs were matted with water. A clock, unstopped by the catastrophe, ticked loudly.

"Sit down, *paidí mou,*" said Kyrios Elias.

He lit a lamp in Ioannis' room. He brought a chair from the *trapezaría.* We sat down, the three of us, facing each other. The cry from the next house ceased. All was silence.

It was strange to be alone in this house with these two old people. I had wanted to go with Martha and Ioannis, but I could not. I was a stranger, in limbo.

From her seat Kyria Katerina suddenly gasped.

"What ails you, woman?" asked Kyrios Elias.

"My *kandíli!* My *kandíli!*" she muttered.

She hoisted herself from her chair. She pushed in front of the old man, rushing rudely to the kitchen. We heard the sound of bottles in the *trapezaría.* In a moment she was back. She carried a tray of burning frankincense. She wafted it before our noses. She set it smoking before an icon of the Panagia. She lit the wick floating in oil in front of the Panagia. Then she crossed herself and began to pray. The air was filled with a holy, churchlike perfume. The old man crossed himself.

For a long time we did not speak.

Then, from her crossings, Kyria Katerina winked out with an evil, childlike smile.

"Did you feel the way the house buckled?" She moved her hands together in a circular motion. "Crack. *Dóxasi o Theós!*" She giggled slyly.

The old man began to laugh. He rubbed his nose.

I snickered.

"*Panagía mou. Panagía mou!*" muttered the old woman.

We looked at each other again.

"Did you see the sparks!" she demanded. "Did you think you were going to die? Oh my back hurts. *Ponáo!* I feel stiff all over. Terrible. Terrible."

She looked at the old man and laughed sneakily, full of delight.

"Maybe we should try to fix up the house. Clean up!" I cried.

But we did not make a move.

"*Kakó pou páthame.* O misery where we live and suffer!"

The old man jounced hilariously. Kyria Katerina exploded in laughter.

'O feast, O indulgent banquet. O malevolent triumph. Old age has foiled the gods. We have cheated the fates. We have triumphed. For Martha, for Ioannis, for any of the young to cheat the fates is good, but for Kyrios Elias and Kyria Katerina! A supreme triumph!' they seemed to say.

We laughed. We trembled with ancient and lonesome joy.

VI

There was a shout from outside. It was Ioannis. Kyria Katerina shot up from her stool.

Ioannis held Martha under one arm. Her feet were walking, but she hung on to him fainting.

Kyrios Elias knocked over a stool to clear the way to the bed. Ioannis dragged Martha into the room and laid her on the bed.

"Get the alcohol."

"Bring lights."

"What happened?"

"What is the matter?"

"She fainted."

"Barba Ioannis *péthane.*"

VII "*Péthane*" was uttered, whispered, repeated. Shock, disbelief, doom, reverence. Kyria Katerina crossed herself.

"What is *péthane?*" I shouted.

No one paid any attention.

"What is *péthane?*" I insisted to Ioannis.

He stopped. Amid the great altercation of cries, orders, and counter-orders he shouted back:

"*Péthane*—kaput. Barba Ioannis kaput." He clicked his forefinger across his throat. Then he smiled evilly, and I broke into laughter.

VIII Ioannis unscrewed the top of the bottle of alcohol. He lifted Martha's head and put the bottle under her nostrils. She jumped as if she had been burned. Her eyes were staring and rolling wildly. She sat straight up on the bed and then leaned forward to vomit. Kyrios Elias went to the kitchen to get a basin.

"Blankets, blankets," ordered Ioannis. The old woman went to the back room and brought two large, heavy quilts.

"She has a bad heart," said Ioannis. It sounded very professional and cultured, because the Greek word for heart is "*kardiá.*" It amounted to saying she was a cardiac case. "It is necessary to rub wrists and breast with alcohol." He began rubbing her hands in his own. He plopped the alcohol out of the bottle and rubbed her wrists. Then he handed the job over to me. He unbuttoned her clothes. The room became permeated with the smell of rubbing alcohol.

Kyrios Elias and Kyria Katerina sat down on their chairs and stool. The *kandíli* flickered at the icon and Jesus' face jumped out. Ioannis was in the momentum of necessity. He could not stop moving. His face was in a sweat. His eyes were narrowed, brilliant, even vicious with the necessity of action and the burden of responsibility. He waltzed up and down the room, rubbing his hands which were dry with the evaporation of alcohol. Through his strides he made ejaculations:

"*Ptohós.* Barba Ioannis was a poor man. He was a good man,

but poor!" He addressed these remarks to me, and when he said "poor" his face broke up into a grizzly grimace which was eloquent. It was ugly, it was fierce, it was helpless, and it was furiously compassionate. It held the outrage of thousands of years of poverty and injustice.

"During the war, he did not have enough bread to eat. And no oil. He starved. But he lived. Oh, he was thin, thin. Like this his belly swelled out. She—" he pointed to Martha—"she stole oil from Maria's cellar. She kept him alive. . . . He lived. All during the war he starved, but he lived. Now. A wind. And Oooooop! He is a carcass."

He looked at me. I looked at him. He uttered a short, sharp, intense crack of laughter. It was ironic, godly laughter. I was swallowed up in it. I wanted to laugh too. It was schizophrenic and therefore godlike. It had the ability to see all mortals as pitiful and triumphant at the same time. It had the ability to appreciate the freakishness of a wind playing havoc with feckless tribes of mortals, willing them netherward and forward like wisps of straw. 'What stupid creatures we are to be beaten by a wind. And we call ourselves greater than the donkey. Also, we cry, we tear our hair out, we suffer wars, we live and we die.'

"Tell me," I said. "Tell me."

"When we got there, there was no house. Only a pile of mud. The wind took the house . . . like this—" he gestured—"and blew it up the hill in a pile. All there was left was the cellar. Katina was in the yard with the baby in her arms crying for joy. 'We are alive! We are alive!' she was shouting. Elias was at her side with the little boy, Boulis. 'We are safe!' they shouted as soon as they saw us. 'We ran out of the house with 'Noula. It was only Boulis. He was buried in his bed. But we found him, under the mud, praise God.'

" 'But where is *o patéras?*' Martha asked it right away.

" 'Around here somewhere.'

"They went right on talking. Nobody was worried at all. He was sleeping with Boulis. Thea Ioannou had gone to visit Thea Stavroula in Metamorphosis. They were talking about how glad they were she was not here, that she had missed the whole thing. Elias was strange, as if he were hypnotized. He sat on a stone. As I say, nobody was worried about Barba Ioannis except Martha.

" 'Where is Barba Ioannis?' I asked Elias.

"He began to cry.

" 'Why are you crying, fool? Has something happened to him? I ask.

" 'Nothing happened to him,' grunted Katina. She was embarrassed at her husband crying, you see. 'He was sleeping with Boulis. He is here somewhere.'

"But Martha, now she couldn't find him, began running around like a chicken with its head cut off calling for him. '*Patéra! Patéra!*' I tried to shut her up. I made her go sit with Katina while I began to look.

"How are you going to look? There was no house. There were no trees where there used to be. There was only rubble. How could you recognize anything? I looked at the pile of mud. I tried to estimate where it had been, where was the bed where Boulis and Barba Ioannis had slept, which wall was which. There was a chair sticking out of the muck. It was dark.

" 'You, Elias!' I get hold of Elias' arm. 'You are a man. Act like a man. You've got to help me look. If he's dead . . .' That was the first time I even thought of it, and I said it . . . but I had to whisper, so Katina and Martha couldn't hear. Otherwise, *den phantázese . . . Klámata! Klámata! Phasaría!* Besides, who could say? He could have been hiding behind a bush!

"Now, how was I going to look? I started picking up stones and bricks, clawing in the mud. I figured out where it was likely the bed had been. Nothing there. I began picking up stones on the other side of the mound of rubble. Then I touched something clammy and lukewarm. I got the flashlight. I pulled another stone away. Some hair. Some flesh. It was Barba Ioannis' head. I got away all the bricks around his head, and I saw his face. His eyes were wide open.

"I called Elias. 'The old man, he's dead. Over there. The old man is dead. You understand? But don't say anything yet.' He acted like he understood nothing. I wanted to get Martha away from there, you see, before . . .

" 'I can't find him,' I tell Martha. 'It will take hours. We've got to go up and find Kyrios Nikos. Leave Elias to look.'

"But she guessed anyhow. I pulled her away before she could see him buried up to his neck. She didn't know what she was doing. I just pulled her out of there, and we went up the hill to Maria's. Now, can you imagine. In the *kípo* half the fruit trees were down. Oranges were rolling among the bushes. All the chickens were loose, because the hen house had flown away, but Maria's house was perfect. And when we entered the house, imagine where Nikos was, *to Paidí!* He was sitting on top of a ladder in the kitchen, examining a loose tile that had flown away and let the rain in.

" 'I was sleeping,' he says. 'What's the matter? What are you doing here with the flashlight? I heard a noise. What happened? Was there a storm?' "

Martha came to. She began to groan.

"I am cold."

She recognized that her father was dead now and she began to fight with nothing.

"O, *pateráki mou! Pou eíse tóra?* Where are you now, *pateráki mou?* Where are you?" She flung her eyes from the blankets toward Ioannis. "Ioannis *mou, chrisé mou.* Ioannis, my darling, my golden one! Tell me. Where is my father now?"

Like a spiritual, a piece of art, no less. Affected. I wondered, can a person under the stress of this kind of death produce such a description of it? But the Greeks are always eloquent. Hep to the appearance of things, cynical, they don't even have to have a belief in language. They simply use it, reflex, and it comes out in this poetic way, the most primary of things. It is likely that this is the way they distinguish themselves from animals.

Anglo-Saxons, who are obsessed by the discrepancy between language and things, who are upset by the symbolic and semantic, will in the final analysis throw a language out as useless because fifth-rate. Then, trapped in silence, the difference between their rational capability and their emotional experience unbridge and grow chasms apart; they will in stress feel themselves no more than animals.

Martha was an animal now, crying, shearing, shuddering, groaning and fighting the demon of loss. How could she have the courage to speak? Or was it blindness reflex?

"Why? Why? *Diatí? Diatí, patéra mou?*"

"Quiet," growled Ioannis. "*Sópa, morí!*"

"*O patéras mou péthane!*"

"He was an old man!" shouted Ioannis. "Every man has to die!"

She turned over, hopeless.

"All right, he is dead! Would you rather it would be Boulis? A four-year-old boy with all his life to lead? He was an old man. Every old man has to die. My father has to die. Even Kyrios Elias has to die!"

"*Dóxasi o Theós,*" murmured Kyrios Elias with a bent head. "It is true."

"*Patéra. Patéra mou. Pateráki mou.* Beloved *patéra mou,* where are you now? Where are you? Do you see me now, you my father who spoke to me only three hours ago? Who told me to say 'Greetings and good night to Daphne'? Who told me how he would meet the daughter of Dino in the morning? Do you see me now, *patéra mou?* Do you see me?"

IX There was the beam of a flashlight in the hall.

"Who is it? What is it?" growled Kyria Katerina. She lit out from her stool groaning. She shuffled herself to her feet and went rolling like a stone. "Ach, what is it now? Who is it?" she called.

"Mitso," said a voice. "Are you all right? Is Daphne here?"

It was my cousin, thirteen-year-old Mitso, son of Thea Panayota's son. His dark eyes lit up like a frightened cat's. I left Martha and went to him. I held his shaved head (shaved because the school did not want lice and bugs in the pupils' hair) in my arms.

"I am all right," I said.

"My father sent me to see if everything was all right."

"Yes. Yes," I said rudely.

But around the room were the words *péthane, péthane.*

"*Patéra! Patéra! Patéra!*" called Martha from the other room.

"They hid under the bed when it came," said Mitso. "But I was in the store. I was behind the desk. The wind blew all the windows in. I hid behind the desk." He laughed.

"*Péthane. Péthane. Péthane,*" sighed in whispers around the house.

Kyria Katerina crossed herself.

"The main street is filled up," said Mitso. "The *estiatório*, Gramboulis', and the *bakáli* fell down in the street."

His wide eyes shone in the darkness.

"Who is dead?" he finally asked.

"Barba Ioannis, *paidí mou*," said Kyrios Elias. "The house fell on top of poor Barba Ioannis."

"Barba Ioannis?" breathed the child in an unbelieving whisper. He looked at me as if he did not understand, or as if it were too dramatic to be appreciated. Then he turned and left the house, having fulfilled his duty.

X For an hour the house was filled with Martha's cries. Then she lapsed, as if from fatigue, into another gear of grief. Practicalities took hold of her.

"I have to go. I have to go. But I cannot wear this. Red! O, *patéra mou. Patéra mou.* Would anyone have believed three hours ago I would have to wear black. I have to go! I have to go!" She sat up in disarray, disheveled.

"You go nowhere," said Ioannis. "You are sick."

"Sick. Yes, sick. I am sick. My father is dead. Ioannis *mou, chrisó.* Will you do a favor for me? Ioannis *mou, chrisó,* my father is dead. Now I must go to sit by him. Will you go up to the house . . . to Maria's and get my black suit. It is in the wardrobe in Maria's room."

"Go to sit up with a dead man? Are you crazy? You are sick. Now you listen, Martha. You stay here. Try to sleep. Then in the morning . . ."

"Night? Is it night? No, it is morning, Ioannis *mou.* There is no time. My father is dead."

Ákouse, Martha. Listen."

"I am getting up, Ioannis. That is the proper thing to do. I want to show my respect. *Patéra mou,* beloved *patéra,* my father where are you? He will not get my black suit, *patéra mou.* But I am coming. I am coming to sit with you if I have to get it myself."

"*Sópa.* All right. Ridiculous! Crazy!" Ioannis took the flashlight again. "All right. I will get the black dress. Then I will go down there with you."

Ioannis walked down the rickety steps. The air was chilly. I saw my breath. The moon made steam from our mouths.

Under the sound of dirges from the women, Kyrios Elias sat and sighed. Now and then he patted Martha's hand and uttered the same words that Ioannis had uttered, but with a gentle voice.

The music of death had overtaken us. We were split apart from each other. Everything was the music of these dirges, punctuated by the sounds of mundane things.

Ioannis returned. Martha sat up. She arose, shivering. Her eyes were swollen and red. Her face was yellow. Her hair was matted. She pulled her red dress over her shoulders. She beat the dust out of the silk gabardine suit that Ioannis had brought. She put on the skirt, but it hiked up in back. The blouse was short-waisted. She was a ridiculous figure in the black suit. It was altogether too small for her. It was full of pretension, whitened out, stuffed out by her body. She looked like an organ-grinder's monkey decked in unbecoming finery.

"I ought to have black stockings," she said. "This is terrible," she interrupted herself in grief, calling her father again. But she never faltered. She let the grief pour out in strident song as a part of the finicky preparations and tacky dress.

She looked at me sternly. She pointed at me and said to Ioannis: "In the morning she is to come. She is family. It is her uncle who has died. She is part of the morning ensemble."

What did it have to do with me, I thought. My relative? Incredible. I had never even met Barba Ioannis.

"The last words he said were: 'Say greetings and good night to Daphne.' " Thinking of the words, Martha put her face in her hands and went sobbing down the stairs.

When Martha and Ioannis disappeared, I stood on the porch a long time. In the silence I looked at the moon. I thought of nothing. The music of typhoons, dirges and death had overwhelmed me.

Inside Kyria Katerina pottered around. She held blankets in her hand. Kyrios Elias moved a kerosene lamp. They went into the back room. Kyria Katerina moved sacks of potatoes, meal, oranges, nuts and other stores to make a bed for herself and her husband. She laid the blankets on the floor.

At one o'clock in the morning Ioannis returned. When he came up the stairs he looked at me. In his light green eyes there was a flicker. He came close to me and took my hand.

"What you have seen tonight," he said. "What you have seen! When I took your hand . . . you remember?"

I did not answer.

"You remember, when I took your hand? When the wind was just coming. You remember? I took your hand?"

"I remember."

"I was afraid," he said. "All the way that you have traveled. All the world that you have seen. Ioannis Ekonomopoulos, I said, what have you done? Were you born and grown up in a house to provide the death of Daphne? All the way you have traveled, all the countries that you have seen, to travel to Greece, to travel to Hora, to arrive at the house of that Greek farmer, that fool, that *vláhos,* Ioannis Ekonomopoulos, to die?"

I seized his hand and began to laugh.

He liked me to laugh. He seized upon my laughter as I had seized on his hand.

"All the way you have traveled to come here to Hora to die in the house of a fool? Imagine? What would I have felt like?"

"Ioannis . . ."

"Shh-h. *Ákouse.* Listen. In another way I was glad. I liked it. Ever since I saw you I loved you. I thought: I am going to die. We are all going to die. We are going to die together. So I took your hand. In front of everybody. We are going to die together, I thought. And now, listen to me. Do you know what?"

"What?" I asked.

"Now, because of that typhoon, because I stood and I held your hand to die together in my house . . . you having traveled half a world to get here, to hold my hand in a typhoon of death . . . because of this, you are my sister. Do you understand that? You are my sister. I am your brother."

I tried to unloose my hand.

His pale green eyes were angry, imploring, but above all fierce.

"You do not understand what I say, but some day you will. You are my sister. I am your brother. You will understand that some day."

XI Sleep made me forget that any such thing as the typhoon had happened. When I wakened I remembered. The sun was high in the sky, pouring down through the roofless beams.

Ioannis was sitting in the kitchen waiting for me. Everything was a mess. A gigantic, littered, untidy, heaping, junklike mess.

Kyria Katerina began to clear out the storeroom next to the kitchen. She and Kyrios Elias would have to sleep there until the wall could be rebuilt on their room. There were bags of garlic, oranges, walnuts, tangerines, and almonds hung over the backs of chairs. Piles of sheets and blankets were stacked. A box of powdered milk labeled GIVEN BY THE PEOPLE OF THE UNITED STATES sat on the floor. In the corner of the *trapezaría* was a sack of unmilled flour, an empty gasoline can, three *paplómata* sewed by Kyria Katerina, unused, three old dresses, a pile of rags, a pistol, three pens and countless pencils with the lead broken, a three-legged, crippled table with a burn in its top, a heap of empty boxes, one of which said CAMPBELL'S SOUP on it. Kyria Katerina swept the room.

"Catastrophe," said Ioannis, his eyes merry.

Kyria Katerina stopped sweeping. "*Kakó pou páthame!*" Her eyes snapped shut; then she opened them, wagging her chin conspiratorially. She pursed her lips secretly.

"*Éla do,*" she said. "Look. Look."

She waved me to come. I followed her grunting, waddling body to the outer room.

The room was broken. The wall had toppled down, leaving only the floor. It was like a balcony. Bits of plaster were crumbled on the floor where the wall had torn off. I looked down in the courtyard below. The wall lay below crumbled into a thousand pieces. Yet in the cellar the horse and the goats had been unharmed. Inside, the room was a hodgepodge. A rain-soaked mattress was turned up in halves. Junk was piled on the bed. Chairs blocked the passageways. They were piled high with cloth, boots, underwear, string, all the household objects imaginable. Kyria Katerina had been going through an ancient wooden chest where she kept her valuables, linen mostly, to see if they had been wrecked.

Ioannis stuck his head in the door.

"Good balcony. We can take sun baths here in the spring."

I wanted to laugh. But for their sakes, I put on a long face. It did not work.

Kyria Katerina laughed. Ioannis burst out. The thing was so great in its destruction that it was wonderful and delightful. Today no one would go to work. Today was the day for assessing the ruin, for appreciating bodily survival. It was a litany, repetitious and triumphant.

"You know where my father and mother sleep?" Ioannis asked.

"Where?"

"There in that bed." He pointed. "Stones were piled three feet high on that bed."

"Whoooo!"

"You know what time the typhoon came?"

"What time?"

"Nine o'clock."

I shook my head.

"You know where my father and mother would have been last night if you had not come?"

"Where?"

"In that bed."

I looked at Ioannis.

"If you had not come, my father and mother, typhoon . . . kaput!" He clicked his finger across his throat.

"*Dóxasi o Theós!*" muttered Kyria Katerina, wagging her head. She crossed herself. "*Poh poh poh.*"

"Like Barba Ioannis," grinned Ioannis. "Kaput."

XII We abandoned the wrecked room. We went into the *trapezaría* and made coffee. Kyria Katerina opened the drawer of the table and brought out goat cheese and olives.

"*Na fagí. Na fagí.*"

We began to eat.

"Can you fix that room?" I asked.

"*Vévea*. Next summer I will build it up again. The first thing is the roof."

"Will it cost much?"

"Who knows? Maybe there will be an adjustment." I did not understand. "The government. Maybe the government will give *leptá*." Ioannis rubbed his thumb and forefingers together to signify money. "Tomorrow, maybe the day after tomorrow, they will bring ceramic tiles to Hora. Who knows? *Píos xéri?* This has been declared a disaster area. Three people killed."

We began to rehearse the details of the storm. The gossip and the stories.

"There was a woman . . . *epáno*. *Epáno*, where Maria lives. The wind came like this . . ." Ioannis circled his finger above the table and zoomed it down in spirals, jumped it up and zoomed it down. "The wind came and picked her up. She was sleeping in bed. It picked her up in the air and blew her in the sky for a half a mile. All that was left after that was bones and bedsprings."

We began to laugh madly. The old woman shook her head.

"*Dóxasi o Theós*. The poor *gynaíka*. The poor *gynaíka*. Who else was killed?"

"I don't know for sure. Maybe another one besides this woman and Barba Ioannis, they say."

"What was this storm?" I asked.

Ioannis explained what it was. It was a spiraling wind borne from the sea. He called it a "*typhón*." I translated that to typhoon. But it was really a twister, a tornado, a cyclone which had originated from the sea. A rare thing in Greece. It had followed the range of mountains. But it had not touched the *chtíma* below, the sharecropper's cottage where I had lived with Daddy. It had not touched the villages of Roumanou, Petrahori, or Kephalovrisa. It had wreaked its vengeance only on Hora. Then it had whistled up the mountain and dissipated itself there, affecting one small village afterwards, when it was blown out.

Kyria Katerina was still thinking of the woman who had been blown up in the air on her bedsprings.

"You say there was nothing left of her but bones?"

"Bones and bedsprings, *Mána*."

"Terrible. Terrible." She heaved with laughter. She wiped her streaming eyes.

XIII Kyrios Elias appeared below. He was in a hushed mood beneath which lay ebullience at his own survival. He had just come from the coffee shop. He had brought the newspaper *Akropolis*, published in Athens. He was dressed up in his best suit, a blue pin-stripe. The cloth was thin from wear, but it was pressed neatly from lying under a mattress. He was so thin that he shambled in it, but he looked very elegant. He wore a beautiful gray felt hat and carried a well-worn, shiny stick-cane. He took off his hat and hung it on a nail on the post where the horse's saddle hung.

"You should see it outside this morning," he told us. "Two rooms were ripped off Christos' house. They have set up hospital at the *pharmakíon*. There is a long line of people waiting for bandages. There is one doctor there from Gargalianos. Last night the hospital truck came from Pylos, but it could not pass through the road below Kato Rouga. There were too many cypress trees blocking the way. The Gargalianos Red Cross truck tried to get in, but it was the same thing on the other side of town. There was no doctor and no medicine until seven this morning. Ach ach, I recognize nothing. Everything is *gremizméno*, ruined. An evil hour has fallen on our town."

An article appeared in the *Akropolis* newspaper, one column on the front page. It said:

A typhoon struck the town of Hora in Trifilia, Messenia, last night at 9 P.M. Three people are reported to have been killed, but these reports are not confirmed. Of nine hundred houses in the town, five hundred are reported demolished. Two hundred more are damaged.

"How do they get these figures," asked Ioannis, "when the people of Hora don't even know?"

" 'Losses are estimated at six hundred thousand drachmas. Most of this loss is in crops,' " I read.

"They say the Red Cross is coming in from Athena. A woman who speaks English, a Canadian, she is coming. You can talk to her," Kyrios Elias said to me excitedly.

This prospect seemed ridiculous and marvelous. Three days at

Hora, I had lived three years. The prospect of talking English again excited me.

"Bravo! Bravo!" Kyria Katerina clapped her hands excitedly. "You go talk in English gypsy language to the Canadian. Think! A direct line to the horse's mouth. You go talk to her. Bring back two dozen packages from CARE." She said "CARE" in English unself-consciously. She thought it was a Greek word.

"Katerina! *Koutamáres!* Foolishness!" reprimanded Kyrios Elias. "She is our guest to go begging for us!"

Kyria Katerina ignored him. "Tell the Canadian there is old woman. All her underclothes flew away to Athena with the typhoon. Tell her that." She clapped and laughed vociferously.

"Katerina!" Kyrios Elias was scandalized.

Kyria Katerina nudged me. "You don't have to really do that. I make *astía.*"

"Jokes."

"*Koutamáres!* Nonsense!" Kyrios Elias waved her woman's foolishness away with a frown. He turned to another subject. "I have another news. They say the Queen is coming!"

"Frederika!" I chimed.

"Vasílissa Frederika. Yes! When all the church bells ring that will signify the moment she arrives." Kyrios Elias' elegant Greek came fastidiously through his toothless mouth.

"Ah ha ha ha!" yelped Ioannis. "The bells will ring. Ding, ding, ding. All the people will ride donkeys up to town. Everybody will go. You, Kyrios Elias, I. Even Kyria Katerina." Ioannis built his vision with powerful description. "We will put Kyria Katerina like a fat mountain in the cart of the motorcycle. We will drive her up to the church of Agios Ioannis so that she can stand up and bow to Queen Frederika. Kyria Katerina can kiss Queen Frederika's hand. All the people will bow. They will all kiss the ground, and then they will beg the Queen for alms and for help. See how beautiful! Queen Frederika will be there. She will wear diamonds. She will drive in the back of a big black Mercedes car. She will have two soldiers to drive her, and the *megáli,* the big shots of Athena, will sit in the Mercedes with her. She will lift the black window-shades of the car. She will peep out of the car for three minutes, maybe five. Then she will get out and stand on the church steps and look at the ruins. She can't stand on the balcony because no one will know whether it is safe or not. It might crumble under her."

"Then she will be buried in a pile of rubble . . ." I egged him on.

"Yes! Her diamonds will break and her dress will get dirty. She has to stand on the church steps. She will say: 'My people! You are my people! I am sorry to see the losses you have suffered. You are a national emergency. We will have to do something. I bestow my sympathy on you.' Then she will get back in her car. All the children will hop alongside it like dogs. Then she will drive off to Gargalianos and we will load *Mitéra* back into the motorcycle and all of us will return to our *spítia*."

"You don't like Frederika?" I asked.

"Oh, she doesn't know any better. She is just a queen. She can't help it. Frederika is all right."

"The *Englézi*. *Englézi* put her in," said Kyrios Elias. "The *Englézi*, they were our good friends. Ioannis does not know his history. And yet, queens . . . queens, what have they to do with *Elláda*? Queens know nothing of the people."

"These kings and queens are Germans," I said.

"Philippos," said Kyrios Elias. "He is a cousin to Frederika. He was born on Kerkyra."

"In Kerkyra they have a palace and two battleships in the harbor," said Ioannis. "Frederika and Paul go to look at movies on the battleship when they aren't playing badminton in the palace."

"I am dying to see Frederika," I said. "Do you really think she will come?"

"Listen for the bells."

"Will you go see her?" I asked Ioannis.

"Of course I will go to see Frederika. Frederika comes to Hora, I will go right up to Agios Ioannis to see Frederika."

"Frederika," breathed Kyria Katerina. "I will go in the sidecar, just like Ioannis says. I will be the queen of Hora. I will greet Frederika."

"Frederika comes, everybody will feel good. The catastrophe will be worthwhile," said Ioannis, rubbing his hands.

XIV It was eleven o'clock, time to go to the keening. Kyrios Elias was to take me.

Kyria Katerina put six pomegranates in a bag. Pomegranates are the ancient blood of death. Pomegranates were used in the ceremonies of funerals in Nestor's time. Kyria Katerina gave me the bag. While these preparations were being made Ioannis was laughing.

"Go and see," he said to me. "You will laugh."

"She should wear black," said Kyria Katerina. "It is a disgrace."

"I have no black dress," I said.

"That's all right, *Mána*. She has no black. She cannot wear black. What does it matter if she is not in black. After all, she is *xéni*."

"She is not *xéni*. *Xéni* to us, but not to Barba Ioannis. She is of the Athanasopoulos family. Her name, it is Athanasopoulos, isn't it? Ach, what a disgrace. She doesn't know anything. Well, go, go," she told me. "Go with Kyrios Elias. When you get there don't do anything. Just sit down. Be polite. And give the paper bag to Thea Ioannou."

"You will laugh," said Ioannis, beside himself with the prospect of imagining me at the keening.

"Why will I laugh?"

"Because you will hear this: *Ay ay-ay-ay-iay!*" He made a sound like the howl of a dog. "You'll be all right. Watch everything. Look at everything. You will see now the *vláhi* live. Then come back, and write everything you see down on your machine."

Kyrios Elias stood up. He selected a silver-handled cane from the junk pile in the back room.

"Pay no attention to them," he said in a dignified voice. "They are both good, but full of *koutamáres*. Come, *paidáki mou*."

Kyria Katerina and Ioannis hovered over the railing as we descended, anxious and vying, as if we were off on a pilgrimage to the other end of the earth.

XV The freak storm had left a viable presence in the town. The roofs of all the houses had flown off. It was like seeing a congregation of people with dismantled heads. Tiles were everywhere, whole, cracked, splintered, terra cotta filling the street. The roof of the schoolhouse was gone, but the walls stood solidly. The ground was strewn with glass. All the windows had blown out. A man stood in the road throwing rocks to the edge to make the way passable. A house stood sheared in half. In the second story a room was revealed complete and total, its wardrobe, pictures, and beds untouched. The mud wall from the broken house had fallen into the street. A shoe peeped out of the debris, brown, cracked and empty.

When I saw the wreckage my holiday mood vanished. Kyrios Elias pointed to the broken town with his cane.

From one house came the sound of a woman's wailing voice. It pursued its timbred, almost melodic cry and then stopped. There was no sign of anyone about.

We passed a pump. A donkey slowly ambled over a pile of mud. On the back of the donkey a woman sat side-saddle. A man walked beside her. The woman's leg was encased in a huge, dirty bandage. She looked at us, but with no sign of recognition. The moment she looked at us, she broke into a series of whimpering sobs as if she were in pain. But the moment she had passed us she was silent again. Her eyes were a blank, yet sullen stare. Misery and accusation.

Three children, a man, and a woman stood in the mud yard of their house. As we passed they nodded. They said "Good morning" with expressionless voices. Their faces did not change. They had a mournful air, almost self-conscious. They turned their heads away. This motion seemed exaggerated. It seemed as if they wanted to proclaim that they had lost faith in words. So they would declaim by understatement and only turn their heads.

A man walked jauntily toward us. His manner was in precise opposition to the mournful attitude of these people. He was a young, lean-fibered man with a black mustache. He said "Good morning" gaily to the people in the yard with patent disregard for their laconic moodiness. Then he approached Kyrios Elias. He took off his hat.

"Good morning."

"Good morning, *paidí mou.*"

"Terrible *prágma,*" he said. But it seemed as if he withheld a smile of excitement, even delight. He licked his lips and bowed his head very hypocritically. I caught his secret delight.

"*Mistírio,* a mystery," said Kyrios Elias, shaking his head mildly.

"A mystery is the word. Do you know they found a tin cooking pot seventy-five kilometers beyond Gargalianos. The wind had gone there, you know. It had wrapped the cooking pot right around the telephone pole. Just like paper. Imagine that! A Hora pot!"

"You don't say so!" said Kyrios Elias, impressed.

"Hora has never seen such a bad day. Stories will be made this day."

"True. True."

"Who is that?" asked the man, pointing at me.

Kyrios Elias changed his tone. He said in a subdued whisper, "She is an Athanasopoulos. *Amerikanída.* Athanasopoulos . . . of Barba Ioannis. Family. Cousin."

"You go there?"

"*Málista.*"

"Barba Ioannis. My sympathies." The man stared at me intently. "Barba Ioannis. *Dóxasi o Theós.* Ach. Oooooh. Barba Ioannis . . . in such ways the old go to their grave. There is a revolution on this earth."

Conspiratorially, excluding me as salient, they spent the minute bestowing a prayer. Then the man, reassuming his jauntiness, like stepping out of false darkness, bid us "Good morning" and went on his way.

"He is a donkey," I thought I heard Kyrios Elias say. "But catastrophe makes people act in many different ways."

The sun was hot. The air was cold. The downpour after the typhoon had bogged the streets. Mud ran up to the edges of our shoes. The sun sparkled on the brown water in the pools. The ragged town all around us shone dazzlingly in its new, stupendous wounds. But its blood was brown, the color of mud. This ostensibly seemed dull. It was not. The sheer outrage of the daily routine hid the festivity of tragedy. Whether people were mournful, suffering, hypocritical, or dazed, they all felt it. There was dizzy laughter hidden in the cracks and in the silence.

XVI

Daddy's sister's house formed the fortress for the small Athanasopoulos house just beyond it where Barba Ioannis had been killed. Except for the roof it appeared undamaged.

Thea Panayota stood out in the yard. Her hair was white, neat, grim. She was dressed, as always, in black. She bowed, but she did not speak. She followed us with her eye as we passed around the corner by Daddy's house.

The site of the Athanasopoulos house was a muck. There was no vestige of the house except for the basement. The rain had jellified the wreck and made a bog around the foundation. It was impossible to imagine that yesterday a house had existed. It looked like a quarry.

A donkey was tethered to a bush against the wall of the foundation. A pregnant goat grazed off some leaf niblets near the doorway. The corpse of Barba Ioannis was inside, in the cellar of the house.

We went down a pathway. It was hilly. The pathway was lined with chairs. Some of the chairs had been dug out of the ruins. These were slightly wet and brown with mud. Other chairs were donated. Thea Panayota had lent five chairs. The chairs did not sit up straight as the way was hilly.

Men sat on the chairs, perching on the edges of them because they were so crooked. Kyrios Nikos was ensconced in the most comfortable chair. He ruminated out of bloodshot eyes, smoking his cigarette in a holder, drooling brown juice onto his white mustache. Above the chair-lined pathway five cypress trees broken at half-mast made pointed V's in the air. Their not-yet-dead fir rustled in the brisk breeze.

There did not seem to be much organization to this keening, but there was. At first glance there were more men than women. That was because the women were inside, clustered around the corpse in the cellar.

One woman presided. As Kyrios Elias and I descended from the road, she came forward to greet us. Kyrios Elias took off his hat. I shook hands with her.

"Sit down," she said.

All the chairs were taken except one. Kyrios Elias ordered me to take it. He sat down on a bleached stone. He placed his hat in his lap and leaned on his cane.

No one spoke. The men stared at me, and I at them. Then there commenced whispering as to who I was and what relation I was and why I was here. Several men who were smoking flipped their cigarettes end over butt into the brush grass where they smoked and died.

It was very boring.

I wondered where Martha was. I wondered whether I would be let in to see the corpse of Barba Ioannis. I did not know the proprieties.

Women of the village do not smoke. They do not think it appropriate to smoke. There was nothing I wished to do more than smoke, but because of this rule, also because it was some kind of funeral, I refrained. The chair was very hard, and because of the tension of doing nothing, being a cynosure, and wondering what was about to happen, I got up, walked around my chair once, and sat down again.

Finally the woman who had greeted us came out with two small glasses of cognac. She gave one to Kyrios Elias and one to me. Kyrios Elias drank his in one gulp. I savored mine. I drank it in sips. It was very warm. It made me light. I felt the dazzling sun and the cold air, and the spirit of wonder came on me.

At last I drew out a cigarette. I lit it. Everyone stared at me but without expression, without opprobrium. I savored it with the cognac, and when I had smoked it to the last drag, I placed it on the ground and pressed it out with the heel of my shoe.

There was triumph in the men's faces. This action had somehow broken the ice. At once a man rose to offer me another cigarette. Across the mournful line of his shining teeth, I saw a glow of human excitement. I refused his cigarette asking for a rain-check. He, satisfied with his move, preened himself in the sunlight and sat down again.

Vaguely perceptible sounds rose out of the cellar door. I stood up again. It became apparent that under the guise of this purposeless waiting was hidden the mad elegiac of death in an inner sanctum. People went in and out of the cellar door as if on call. There was a vagueness on their faces when they went in and when they came out. It was like watching people going in and coming out of a movie which one has waited to see. You look on the people's faces coming out for some sign of its effect, for some notion of what it was like. But the people's faces are expressionless. They look very much the same as when they went in. It is perfectly obvious that they have been through an *experience*, yet coming out, they seem exactly the same as when they went in. This is incredible. One says to oneself: 'Surely, if he has been through an experience, he should be transformed.' What one wants him to be, one is not sure. One would like him either to have a light shining from his forehead, or ethereal and hollow eye pits. That would be proof. Since he does not, the blame must lie with the person himself. Clod he went in, clod is the composition of his soul, thus clod he comes out. 'But if I went in, if it were I who had that experience,' one says to oneself, 'I should be transformed both from within and without. Within me is the ability to transcend the human cloth.' So it is with any orgy, whether of joy, of wisdom, or of death. There is always the shock of recognizing the human being in his own flesh, a vessel, not an augur.

There was a great crudeness in this exterior precinct where we sat. People yawned. They stamped out their cigarettes. A woman came out and whispered with two men. The conversation was about which priest was going to perform the funeral ceremony. There was hurried and conspiratorial gossip. The priest of Agios Ioannis was going to charge 300 drachmas. It was outrageous. He had refused to do it for less. So the little priest of Agios Georgios had been decided on. He was the poor man's pope. It was a comedown, but who were the Athanasopouloses to put on like the *megáli*, the big shots?

Suddenly someone shouted: "Andreas is coming."

Andreas had come from Athens. As he walked down the alleyway his bald head was red from the sun, and his eyes were full of tears. Two women came out and embraced him. Three men got up from their chairs. People wiped their eyes. Men kissed Andreas on both cheeks. Andreas broke into sobs. He broke away from them. He mopped his face, his eyes, and his nose with a large handkerchief, sniffing. He made his way to the corpse inside the cellar. But he stayed there only a moment.

Kyrios Elias stood up.

Andreas came to me. He put out his hand. There was a feeble, tenuous smile on his pink face. Over his mustache, through his grief, he looked at me curiously and urgently.

"When I received the telegram," he said, "I telephoned Theo and told him you were safe."

"Thank you," I said. "That was very kind of you." But I thought: 'Daddy would never think I was dead.'

"You are to go in there now," said Andreas.

Two women escorted me to the cellar door.

XVII It was very dark in the cellar. Slivers of sunlight speared through the stones and cracks of the flooring above. Because the doors were closed and the sun had poured down overhead all morning it was as hot as a furnace. The earthen floor was packed dry and hard, contrasting with the muck outside. The roof was held up by splintery wooden beams. Saddles and bags of onions hung from posts. In the nether region stood a pile of wood. Chickens clustered around this woodpile. Whenever there was a motion they shivered, cackled wildly and ran among the women's feet. The women clapped their hands at the chickens and kicked at them wildly so that they would not run over the body of Barba Ioannis.

The conditions of Barba Ioannis' lying-in-state reminded me of stories of Christ's birth. The assembly was the same. Only the Three Wise Men were missing. The Agios Georgios *papá* would be the Wise Man. In America where we are addicted to petite images of the crèche we always leave out the stink of goats. Here the stench was everywhere. They stank, but they created the religiosity.

Barba Ioannis was stretched out on some boards borrowed from the lumber pile. The boards were propped on sawhorses, one at the top, one at the bottom. A sheet covered the boards, making a sparkling white platform. The sheets were embroidered with handmade lace.

A dozen women sat around the figure of Barba Ioannis. They were all dressed in black. They all wore black scarves around their heads. Only their faces were visible, dark, stare-stricken, streaming with tears and wild impassioned grief. They looked like human crows. They were seated closely in a rectangle around the corpse.

The sound when I entered was overpowering. The cellar was a cave of singing screams. The screaming was so violent that it made me tremble. I wanted to laugh. I set my teeth in a vicious grin to keep myself from collapsing immediately.

The song they were singing was a ritual song. It had an actual melody: Mi mi mi mi mi mi re re, mi re re, re do do. Sometimes it was sung in unison. Sometimes by only one woman. Some of the women had forgotten the words. But Theo Ioannou's sister, Thea Stavroula, was perfect in the words. All the women followed her lead. The words of the song said: "Where are you now? Where are you? What will become of your wife, your wife; what will become of your children, your children?"

There was a spirit of competition in the singing which led to its unbearable crescendoes. The object was to sing as wildly as possible to show the most grief. Thus, at any given moment it was to be expected that some particular woman, Thea Ioannou, Martha, or any one of the immediate family, would begin this song. It would be joined by others who tried to outdo the first. The manner of singing was yelping. The singer beginning the song would begin to screech. She would forget the corpse. She would look right up at the rafters and rattle wildly to God. She would careen, break off, throw out her voice. If she went too far, so that she could not sing any more, if she broke into howls of insane grief, the other women took her by the arm, fastened her down among them, patted her shoulder and admonished that she must calm down. They comforted her and commiserated with her and told her that it was impossible to break the barrier between her and God.

The singing was made ludicrous by the presence of flies. The whole cellar swarmed with flies. Flies lighted on people's hands, stockings, and noses. Between the notes of the song, the women slapped their hands at the flies. As I stood there, I saw a fly light upon an old woman's cheek. The cheek was sticky and salty. As her tears flowed out the fly was washed down toward her mouth. At last, she took a gnarled finger and with a snap batted the fly out into the air again.

As I became accustomed to the darkness and peered over the women's shoulders, I saw the figure of Barba Ioannis. His head was bald, just like Daddy's. It was furred with a rim of overgrown white hair which grew in tufts like fungi, beside his ears. His face was dead gray. There was stubble on his chin. Dried blood matted his ear. Cotton had been stuffed up his nostrils and into the bloody ear. Except for this, there was no sign of wounds. A blue-checked dish rag was tied around the jaw and knotted at the back of the head to keep the mouth shut. This gave the corpse a rag-bag mien, like a beat-up idol. I looked at the nose to see if it was like Daddy's. It was. It was long and dipped down over his mouth toward the blue dish rag.

As an entity, the corpse was worthless. It cost me much pain to look at it. Its soul was obviously absent. But as prey, as meat, as animal food, as the recipient of ritual, it was hypnotizing.

He was dressed in a gray double-breasted suit which was too big for him. It was of the style of the 1930's. It was dusty, for it had been retrieved from one of the chests buried in the rubble. His hands were tied together at the wrists with another rag of blue-checked material. His hands held a tin cross which had been bought (it seemed) from a dime store. It was an ornate cross. The edges of the tin had been punched to make curlicues. Under the cross was an icon of Jesus with a hollow mournful face and a yellow halo. Bits of candy and some wildflowers were laid in a pile by the icon on his stomach. The candy was made of the sludge of grapes and was fecal-colored, in the shape of a hot dog. It contained almonds. It attracted the flies. Flies buzzed around the icon making a zinging sound. One fly flew exploratively at his nostril buzzing curiously at the cotton wadding and dried blood. Thea Ioannou, who sat at her husband's head, flapped the fly away. Thea Stavroula patted the stubbled cheek. Other women bent down to kiss the hands of the dead one, laying more candy on the stomach. At the doorway some women made a cross of laurel leaves.

"Oh, *Theé*, where have you taken our Ioannis?" sang Thea Stavroula.

"Where are you now, my husband, my Ioannis?" screamed Thea Ioannou. She did not seem very different, despite the circumstance, from the first time I had seen her boiling the macaroni in the pot at Koryphasion. She flapped a fly off the cotton in the nose. She dissolved into wails of grief. Her face was scrunched up like the mask of tragedy. Tears rained down her cheeks. Every now and then she stopped her noise and mopped at her face with a handkerchief. Then she applied herself to her keening again, pulling her hair askew and screaming to God.

"Where have you gone, Ioannis? Where have you gone, Ioannis *mou*? Where are you?"

She stood up. She threw it beyond herself. Just at full crescendo, screeching, breathing fast, begging, she was pulled down by the others.

There was an object in this. The questions of the song were addressed, in spite of herself, to Barba Ioannis. When he did not move from the chains of his blue dish cloth she began to pound the air, as if she wanted to pound the body, to pound him back to a bodily existence.

Where was he? Was he in the clay corpse, or was he somewhere above the roof? These were the only two places people could look for him. It was a toss-up. You veered between grasping the life of him which the clay of him would not give, and hunting up toward Heaven which was up over the roof.

The beams of the ceiling were a barrier to this conception. The women who hunted up there and reached their arms up there ready to snatch fistfuls of the buzzing air just to get at Barba Ioannis, had the impulse to rip off the roof, just as the storm had already ripped off the house. Because of this the whole atmosphere was unbearably close. The sound of the singing made it even more stifling.

You could not bear the closeness of the cellar. But even if the ceiling had not been there, if the sky had been the limit, you would have drooped like a melting candle or a wilted flower.

The sky is too big. You would be confronted with the smallness of yourself. Especially in the Greek sky. The Greek sky is so dazzling clear, so infinite, that if Heaven is beyond it, you know that you cannot make it so far. The sky will fill you up with infiniteness, you Earthling. You are small, and it is big. The sky will make Barba Ioannis fade away. The vision of him will disappear, the clay of him will be ridiculous. So you are left with him as only a speck, not as Nothing, but as a speck, a Miracle, because of its being a Memory. This is too mysterious. You will never get the answer. The only significant thing is that for grieving the place has got to be confined, a cave, a cellar, or a barn. Better to have flies, chickens, and donkey droppings. These are the evidence of life. Take it outside, with the sky above you, you have the diminution of the question, the road to the metaphysical. As a living human you can sometimes have your pulse quickened by an indulgence in metaphysics. You can glory in your heart's creations and feel that you are blood brother with the spots in the sky. But as a griever for the dead, it is better to stick with earth's oozings, with blood, fingernails, and excrement. Then you can cry for the lack of them in the bereaved. You can demand them back. You can demand the evidence, just because you don't know what to demand *for* him. For Barba Ioannis. For the soul.

XVIII I account it very peculiar that I was let in on such grief. But not only was I let in, it was demanded of me that I be witness. It was not demanded that I be griever or mourner. I did not have to tear my hair, but my presence was demanded.

I was family. But I was more than that. I was family from across the ocean. I was stranger family. I was unGreek family. In me, to them, lay mysteries covered over by my silence. I was as mysterious as an idiot or a child before he can speak.

Furthermore, it became common knowledge that I was to have met Barba Ioannis this very morning, picking olives at Megambelia. Now I met his clay, confronted with their own screaming demands to know where he was.

It became common knowledge that I had come across an ocean. Two days after I had arrived the typhoon had visited the town and wreaked vengeance. There was no hint that there was meaning in that. But I had lived through the typhoon too. I had been whirled into the bosom of their rack. To these archaic Greeks, their rack is their existence, their suffering is their bosom. The catastrophe was outside. It was something that had happened to all of us. So now I was in their bosom. They had me for better or for worse.

"You are not *xéni*, are you? You are not a stranger? No, you are of us. You are ours. *Étsi den eíne?*"

XIX Martha was sitting next to her mother by Barba Ioannis. She was not a crow to me, because I knew her. But her face was quite unrecognizable because of the grief and the singing. Red, puckered, her eyes were bulbous with tears. Her hair was matted. Her best black suit was dusty and so ill-fitting it was ludicrous. It jacked up over her knees and her black stockings puckered. Her fat, buttery legs ended in pointed shoes encrusted with mud. She wailed, tooting off like a suppressed dervish taking the air.

"Where are you now, *Patéra? Patèra?*"

She looked at me, without expression. As if she did not recognize me.

When she finished the song, she wiped her face with a dirty man's handkerchief. She breathed a sigh of relief. This action, though coarse in itself, she accomplished with a backhanded grace. Yet her very attendance to these physical excesses made her grief appear suspect. I suspected everyone's grief in that cellar. I suspected Martha's. But having been in common with her one of the saved, I felt allied with this death. It was imperative, a source of the highest curiosity in me, to fathom how, if grieving, she could give out with such theatricality.

She looked at me once more. This time she recognized me. She sent a woman to me to tell me to sit down. She pointed to the chair. She whispered my situation to the others. She explained that I knew nothing and that I must be told what to do. Then, nodding her head, she coaxed me to sit in the chair. I sat down. Whereupon she began her song again, praying, squealing, shrieking and rending, interrupting it only now and then with a sharp, overseer's look at me to be sure that I was doing well.

Think, I told myself. Can they have been doing this since twelve midnight? Are they not tired to the point of exhaustion? Will they not collapse from this excess of grief?

Entombed for an hour with this wailing my first shock wore off. The music seized me. It took me along. It was so monotonous that I thought I should certainly scream or start wailing and singing along with it. At the same time it was so demanding that if it had stopped I could not have borne it. Tears came welling to my eyes. My hands grew sweaty. My throat constricted to keep down the laughter now grown tight in a theatrical paroxysm of pity. The pitch of hysteria had risen to a point where I did not know how to distinguish between anguish, laughter, pity, or ludicrousness. Such is the strength of a keening. The only pure and subdued part of me was a calm wonder standing like a ghost at the side of a lake, breathing to me a kind of superior wonder that such a performance should make me exhibit any emotion at all in connection with an ineffectual old man whom I had never met. At last, looking at the bits and pieces of rotten candy on the corpse's bosom, I felt ravenously hungry.

I stood up. A fly buzzed an instant before my mouth and flew off toward Martha as if it were a small carrier pigeon.

She looked at me questioningly. Then, elegantly, like a queen, she inclined her head. It was the period to the end of a sentence.

On the way to the door, I stopped behind her, placing the bag of pomegranates in her hand.

"*Apó* Kyria Katerina," I whispered.

For a moment she looked at me expressionlessly, as if she were far away. Then I thought I saw a flicker in her eyes. It denoted a calm, inevitable triumph. As if she had said: "So you are finally one of us after all. Sealed by pomegranates, red blood and death." But she said nothing.

I walked out the door with the same expressionless face as all the others. The sun was blinding, high in the sky.

XX No bells rang. Frederika did not come.

The greetings in the street had now changed from "Good morning" or "Good evening" to:

"Terrible."

"Catastrophic."

"*Poh poh poh.*"

"Misery."

"God only knows."

Or "*Ti na kánome?*"

After these obeisances and lip-scraping and genuflection to the agreed situation, the gossip began, spirited, confidential, conspiratorial, endlessly exciting. The reason was that there was all kinds of news to tell. After the news was told complaints began. Tales of feuds. And stories of scandal.

Troops were sent into the town. The arrival of fresh squadrons was expected daily. Two bulldozers were sent in with the troops. The people were excited by the troops. But they were possessed to Dionysiac rapture by the bulldozers. They stopped in clusters to watch them plough old roofs, plaster walls, shoes, mud, and broken cement sinks into huge piles in the streets.

"*Vlépeis to booldozaire,*" they chortled significantly, pronouncing the English word with French pronunciation, as though it were a Greek word.

"To booldozaire eíne i oraióteri michaní apo óles!"

"Ti oraío prágma! Poh poh poh."

With the rash of soldiers came rashes of tents. U.S. Army tents appeared overnight in the rubbled yards of the houses which were being demolished. Squabbles began about who had better tents. Some tents were white with sail-like patches in them. These were the inferior tents. The others, with the grim black stamp of USA on their regulation khaki sides, were the best. The USA tents stood up dauntless in the night breeze. In the daytime sun they collected suffocating heat from the sun. They expanded. They became hot-boxes. The heat in them lasted way into the night when the winter dews covered the ground. At midnight they grew very cold. The town looked like a broken Bedouin camp melanged with an American bivouac, all erected in a mountain of broken teacups.

The noises of buzzings and sawings filled the town. Greek soldiers in baggy Eisenhower jackets and dirty knee boots crawled like flies over the wreckage. They chopped up broken floors. They hammered down remaining walls. They pulled demented roofs off with ropes. They backed up trucks. They jawed and jammed motors. They burped forth fumes, gunning their truck motors. They threw bed-steads, mattresses, dirt, bags of rotten oranges, strips of corrugated tin, masses of terra cotta tiles and heaps of mud and rubble into the backs of trucks. They laughed at work. They whistled to each other. They shouted through the scream of the bulldozers. They filled up the restaurants and ate fried fish with their hands, spitting out the bones. They drank gallons of retsina. They played cards at the tables. They filled the *kaphenía.* They chittered, hollered, gasped, laughed, whistled, flirted, clapped, danced, gambled, and burped at their jobs. They were full of brawn. They all wore English commando berets, some red and some green.

Where the town's wound was fresh and raw the day after the typhoon, several days of subsequent working over by the army gave it a ground-over aspect. It was like a chocolate pudding after a child has mushed it with a spoon.

The rain made every road muddy. New mud was manufactured by all the adobe houses that had fallen. The rain reduced these to their original form. What roads were not already mud were now streaming soups. Houses popped up on each side of the road with patched doors, improvised stone walls, rag windows, and hastily canopied porches constructed of ripped-out rooms. You could not walk up the road from the school to Agios Ioannis without boots. The mud was ankle-deep. I walked it, but I had no boots. Sometimes my shoes were sucked off five times in one walk. Once I got stuck. Two people had to pull me out. This felt very ignominious.

One of the greatest games in the town was comparing news on which roads were more walkable. Every road became an obstacle course. The road by the Agrarian Bank had shoulders that were hard but ruts that were slithering pools. It was a better bet than the road from the school to Agios Ioannis. You could walk on the hard shoulder.

All the donkeys in the town went around with dirty feet. The donkeys were responsible for beating the road into mire. They punched the road up into periods and commas. Their feet sank lower than human feet. When they retrieved their feet from the mud it was with sounds of gigantic squishes. Mud groaned. Wheels of carts became flying windmills of shooting mush. Every time you saw a cart coming you were forced to hide or be showered with specks, droplets, and strings of ooze. When the sun shone and the donkeys' feet dried out, they entertained a perfect crust of dried mud on the fur of their ankles.

Another peculiar feature of the town was the roofs. Every roof had blown off in the typhoon. Tiles were scattered everywhere. If the mud had hardened, it would have been mud reinforced with terra cotta. What tiles were not already broken from the typhoon were now stamped by people stepping on them, carts banging over them, donkeys beating them down, and children throwing them. The earth took on an orange tinge. The roofs, denuded, looked like stripped ribs. The sight of the whole town was a warp and woof of skeletons. It gave one a hollow feeling just to see it. Beams crisscrossed everywhere and not an element to cover them. God's fingers could have poked right into each house and played skitter-mouse with the people inside.

Two days after the typhoon, truckloads of tiles were brought to the town. The trucks carrying them lurched, skidded, mired and ground into the mud, rooting out the punctuation marks of the donkey tracks and substituting drunken parallel lines. The new tiles were piled up in key places at the four corners of the town.

The moment these tiles arrived, the news circulated. The people left their houses and scurried to the spots where they were piled. Crowds were in the streets. Crowds gathered at the piles. Tiles were allocated to each family in the town. They were free. There was much cheating and complaining as to who got how many and who got more than another. Mathematics was the subject of the day. Every man in every household was seen outside his house with his finger pointing at his roof wagging one, two, three, estimating square feet. Minds went click click. Everyone caused his quota of demanded tiles to inflate. With the tile inflation were born new and fantastic dreams. Everyone began to plan little *spítia* out on their farms, additions to their houses, outhouses in their back yards, to be built with the free tiles. They did not bother about where to get the materials to hold up these projected new roofs. If they got an extra roof, they figured that fate would surely see to it that they got walls somehow to put the roof up on. They did not worry about that. The typhoon had knocked their habits to pieces. From the broken pieces of their habits burgeoned these new dreams. Out of typhoons . . . disregard their *miserere nobis*es . . . new, great, good things must be born.

The new tiles were a different color from the old ones. The old ones had reddened and rusted with age. The new ones were a lemon color, dashed with white. From the loading spots donkeys carried tons of tiles. People carried them on their shoulders, five at a time. Women carried them on their backs. Children carried them in their hands, one in one, and one in the other. Carts drove up to the piling spots, loaded up, and took off, creaking through the ruts. The whole town became one huge, swarming, moving mass of people carrying tiles. It was like an ant hive with the ants transporting bread.

With the carrying of tiles came the resurrection of the roofs. On every roof, in rain or shine, men crawled. The ants had moved from the streets to the roofs, playing with their lemon-colored toys.

Tiles are very heavy. I could not carry more than seven at a time. They are also very rough, like cement. After you have carried one, your hand is covered with the powder of terra cotta dust, refined mud dust. It covers your clothes if you are working with it. It fills your nostrils with the pungent odor of dried earth and sunlight. It has archeological smells in it, biblical and Homeric, of barren caves, dried mountains, and desert herbs.

All the roof beams in Greece are laid to fit the proportions of the tile. This requires minute, precise measuring. The beams for the tile are made of bamboo. In the better houses they are of pine-wood.

The laying of tile is exacting work. It is also delusive, because if you lay tile perfectly you can leave it for fifty years. It will protect you with no leakage. But it is prey to any high wind. Thus it is necessary to cement the tile. Cementing tile is persnickety work. The trick is to start correctly. You have to start from the top ridge of the house. All tiles are crescent-formed. The first tiles you lay with their stomachs to the elements. Over these, staggered, you place a second layer with their backs to the sky. Rain drops on the backs of the sky-tiles. Any water which drips through the spaces between these falls into the stomachs of the inner tiles and is brought to the eave safely without leaking into the house.

Ioannis got double his quota of tiles. He hauled them down the mud-stricken alley in the sidecar of the motorcycle. He gunned the motor. The noise bounced off the sides of the houses like a siren of triumph. It took him nine trips. We piled them into rows of hundreds in the yard.

"We will build a little *spíti* at Váges, my farm. Then in summer we will sleep out there with only the moon for a companion. I will get two cows. Cows can make money in Greece."

Along with the tiles, the tents, the soldiers, and the dreams, there sprouted another new thing in the town. Two days after the typhoon all the children came out in a rash of blue jeans and Hopalong Cassidy suits. All the blue jeans were spine-clean and whitened with age and starch, and all the Hopalong Cassidy suits were beat up, faded, and clean. The letters of HOPALONG CASSIDY were printed in English on the backs of the shirts and on the chest pockets. Escalloped frontier cowboys under shaved-flea heads. To see these Greek boys as sudden Americans, spouting their bubbling Peloponnesian Greek, was very peculiar.

As threatened, the Red Cross had made an influx into the town. The Canadian woman never showed. It was suspected that she didn't show because Frederika didn't show. But packages by the thousands ground into town on trucks from Gargalianos. The bulk of these were CARE packages. Most of them came from Canada.

The CARE packages were dumped into the church of Agios Ioannis where they were put under the protection of the *papádes*. Immediately this was done, there arose an underground stream of dissension in the town. Everybody knew that the *papádes* were fat hogs who would paw the stuff over, take half of it themselves, and give all the best to their cronies. The dissension was so strong that the *papádes* immediately banded together and deployed some of the army as a twenty-four-hour guard over the CARE packages.

The run on the CARE packages began. Everyone lined up at the church of Agios Ioannis.

"Go up there," Kyria Katerina egged me. "You see, I can't go. I don't have feet. So you go."

Kyrios Elias went.

Night, noon, and morning there were crowds. There was a suppressed excitement in the crowds. There is nothing so exciting as getting something for nothing.

The first day he went Kyrios Elias brought home a package. He put it on the *trapezaría* table. Kyria Katerina got scissors to cut the string. She breathed with bated breath. She crackled the paper as she opened it. Within was a pair of patent-leather Sunday shoes for a girl of ten, a bunny suit for a baby, two pairs of three-inch spike-heeled I. Miller shoes, a maternity outfit, and a ratty fur coat from the Evans Store in Chicago, fashionable in 1925.

I opened my mouth to howl with laughter, but I caught myself in time.

Kyria Katerina pawed through avariciously. Her face fell.

"I am going to wear these shoes to church?" she asked. She turned to Kyrios Elias. "What have you brought us!"

"Eh!" he said, throwing up his hands.

Maldistribution was legion. Old ladies received diapers and blue jeans. Old men received plaid skirts for junior misses and women's court pumps. Houses with eight children received men's overcoats and women's girdles. Young girls received old men's union suits and boys' baseball caps. Pregnant women received cowboy suits. Rugged men received knee socks, baby bonnets, and lingerie.

The town immediately became a trader's paradise. In every house the goods were talked over, wrapped up, unwrapped, displayed, and traded. When people were not working to fix their roofs they were busy trading.

A soldier spent every night on the steps of Agios Ioannis to see that no one broke in and stole. Rumors flew. The *papá* of Agios Ioannis, it was said, had removed twenty CARE packages to his house. He had distributed them to his friends and relations.

"It is a crime!" swore Kyria Katerina.

"*Poh poh poh,*" said Kyrios Elias.

"What are people?" asked Ioannis. "No better than beasts. You see what Greeks are. They are avaricious. They are liars, cheats, and thieves. This is what you learn in Greece. Now you do not lie, you do not cheat, and you do not steal. To be a Greek you must learn these things. What a university! This is the real test." He tapped his finger on the edge of a plate of goat cheese. "To be an Onassis. Not to be a Chara Lampis."

XXI Chara Lampis was a half-wit of the town, a self-made mendicant. Whenever he passed by people would laugh and cluck and sigh and giggle. "Poor Chara Lampis," they said. "What a character! What a king!" Chara Lampis was fat, burly, and dirty. He had a huge, yellowish white beard, like a large goat. He dressed in burlap and his white hair flowed dustily down his neck. He wore no boots but went barefoot, even in the November mud. The only article of clothing that he wore besides burlap was a black leather belt with a brass buckle that he strapped around his middle. When he traveled down the street the stink of goat manure and donkey traveled with him. His beard and hair were stuck with sticks, straw, and dead leaves.

He had a very commanding air. He was an old lampoon Saint Nicholas. He stopped and wagged his head to everyone and filled them with the grandeur of his poverty. Wherever he went he always carried a burlap sack full of grasses which he had picked for his one possession, his donkey. And he always carried a huge, beat-up, knobbed cross which he used like a staff. Whenever he stopped to talk to someone he held this cross up in the air and inveighed at them, preaching some gobbledygook about the Lord Jesus Christ. When he spoke it was in a very musty, toothless way, yet his voice had the timbre of the ocean and his eyes smiled benevolently and with voracious eagerness. He had the wonder of the world in his poverty, and a tick upon a dog interested him no less than the mayor, an urchin no less than the grandest *papá*, the *papá* of Agios Ioannis. He was illiterate, but that posed no problem to him as he always believed that he was communicating.

He lived in a ratty old cellar *epáno*, above Maria's house. He slept on a pallet on the dirt floor. The donkey slept beside him upright on its four legs. Whenever Chara Lampis trudged and weaved his way through town, dogs and children followed him. He never had any money, but he would always sit down in the *kaphenion* until someone offered to buy him a cup of Turkish coffee. He lived on the offerings of households which he solicited for a few greens, a bottle of oil, and crusts of bread. Sometimes sympathetic women even brought him a hot dish of rice with a couple of bits of meat in it. In return for these kindnesses which he continually expected, he offered only his existence and his presence. He did not pray or preach or bestow particular blessings. He was very free with any of these, but not in return for particular kindnesses.

The day after the typhoon he appeared on the street as usual, and his vagrant, smiling, grand, idiot face betrayed no sign of recognition that any unusual thing had happened. People passed him crying, groaning, and dazed, but he smiled at them and wagged his beard and mumbled his words as usual.

"Hey, Barba Chara Lampis, did you see the typhoon that hit us last night?" the children asked.

"Typhoon! Eh. God bless you all," he answered.

"See how the roofs flew off!" They pointed. He followed the direction of their fingers. He looked at the ribs and bones of the roofs, but it did not seem unusual to him.

"Kyria Mandroulis brought me some greens last night. They were good, God bless her. Warm and with much oil. Smack. Smack," he said.

"Do you know what a typhoon is?" they asked, trying to tease him out of his grand stupidity.

"The kiss of God, maybe?"

"Kiss of God! What a fool! Ha ha ha!"

"My children, you may laugh, but I felt the kiss of God last night. His breath was right on my face. Does that surprise you? I thought it was a dream. I thought I waked up and found the door open. There were a few drops of water on my face, and it was raining outside. But I was awake all the time. I had just been visited by God. He had breathed in my face and shed tears on it too. I never knew God's tears could be so cold, but all the elements of heaven are cold . . . or they feel cold to us because blood and living are warm and misleading, whereas all that is heavenly and pure is cold." He seemed to take the visit of God very matter-of-factly. He added: "I could not see Him, it was too dark. But He was a great presence. He will visit you too, *paidákia*, if you are good boys."

"Oh you idiot!" cried a little boy called Yannaki. "I will die laughing. That was a typhoon."

"Yes. Yes. You may call it so, but that was the visit of God. By whatever name, it will mean as much."

"Aren't you a fool, Barba Chara Lampis. Don't you know that a typhoon is evil? And evil does not come just by ones either. They say that the town of Hora has proved to be evil and that is why vengeance has come on it." The boy began to speak lower and his eyes grew bigger and Chara Lampis concentrated on what he was going to say with a look of excitation and pity. "Two more things must happen to Hora. Evil strikes in three. A second typhoon will come and it will kill hundreds. And then a third one will come and they say that it will destroy us all."

Chara Lampis looked completely baffled. For a long time he did not say anything, and then quietly, as if pondering and preoccupied, he whispered: "Don't be afraid," and walked off with a dazed face.

In the afternoon he was completely changed. His face had got a red glow on it and his eyes danced as if with a revelation. He walked into a *kaphenίon* and raised his knobbly cross for attention.

"Listen ye. All. I have found out about the kiss of God. You should not spread fear and lies among your children either. I have had to ponder it a long time, and I sat down by my donkey and wondered, but I have figured it out, and I came at once to tell you. A great change is coming. Don't ask me what. I don't know. How should your fool Chara Lampis know any more than you? But though it is true that evil comes in threes, this is not evil. It could not be, since I myself had the tears of God on my cheeks. Therefore, I bid you all, do not look forward. Take these signs of God in a quiet spirit. Take them even with rejoicing. That's what I do and you see why I am happy."

"Don't listen to that blather-head. He doesn't even know what a typhoon is. He has nothing to lose," said one man whose house had been ripped apart.

"He thinks he is Diogenes," said another.

"No, I know who I am," Chara Lampis said in a very dignified voice. "All I want to do is calm your fears as to evil. Some beautiful change is about to appear." Settling himself down happily, entranced by his own evocation of the beautiful change, he sat at a table and waited for someone to order him coffee.

All the men, still dazed from the catastrophe, did not pay much attention to him. Finally the farmer Volokis automatically ordered him the coffee. And despite what he had prophesied about the change, his very presence and his very idiocy seemed an innocence among all the huge wounds of the typhoon. They did not think of it, but they treasured him in the backs of their minds . . . that he was too idiotic even to recognize a catastrophe.

On the day when the first packages were given out, Chara Lampis appeared among the crowds at Agios Ioannis. He held his cross up high and smiled eagerly, but he did not appear to know why he had come.

"Hey, Barba Chara Lampis, did you come to get your cut of the Red Cross?" shouted a man.

"Bravo, *paidí mou,*" he answered eagerly, coming up to the man with one arm outstretched ecstatically. With the other he held the cross lovingly. "In all the time Barba Chara Lampis has carried this cross, not one soul in all this town has seen the true color of it. They say it was brown because Chara Lampis made it out of a eucalyptus tree. But see the blood streaming down it, Christ's own blood. I like to feel it because it is warm and it reminds me."

"Christ pity the poor idiot. He has the looks of Saint Athanasius but the brain of a donkey."

"Never mind the cross, Barba Chara Lampis. Get in the line."

"Wouldn't you like to wear some real clothes, like the people in Athena?"

"Don't you get sick and tired of your burlap bag, Barba?"

"Get in the line here."

"Here. Here. Put him in the line here."

Jostling, laughing, rolling, the men pushed the old idiot into the line, and then, with enthusiasm, they pushed him into the first place.

"Let Barba Chara Lampis receive the first goods from Canada! Let him be the first, not only because he did not even know the typhoon struck, but also because he lost nothing, having nothing to lose."

Barba Chara Lampis nodded and wagged his head. He had no idea why he was in the line or what would be bestowed upon him when the doors to the church opened. Nevertheless, having been pushed forward like this, he whaled his porpoisian sackcloth frame with infectious enthusiasm. He was a great stinking dignitary.

The door opened.

The big-nosed *papá*, proprietor of the goods, received into his bosom the stench. A sense of ceremony began. Barba Chara Lampis bent his head.

"Give me a blessing on such a great occasion, *Papoúli mou,*" he intoned in a nasal voice.

There was a burst of laughter. The *papá*, playing to the crowd, held his big nose between his thumb and forefinger and began singing a psalm. Everyone began making speeches in loud, good-natured voices.

"He is the unofficial *papá,*" said Kyrios Pavlos, one of the Ekonomopoulos tribe. "He mirrors the greatness of the Church like the monkey mirrors man."

"Thank you, Kyrios Pavlos," said the big-nosed *papá*. "I am glad to see that you have such respect for the Church."

"Give him the package. Give him the package!" insisted the crowd.

The big-nosed *papá* turned around in his robes, licked some papers, bammed a stamp, fiddled with some ropes, and put a small brown-wrapped parcel into Chara Lampis' arms.

The effect of this was tremendous. The old man blushed. His chin waggled with sentiment, and then a great fire came out in his eyes and he turned from being overwhelmed by emotion to great, uninhibited, doglike heavings and overtures.

"I want to kiss your cheeks, Papouli!" he yodeled. "In token of my great appreciation."

"Never mind the kisses. The *papoúli* doesn't want to trade lice. Open the package!" came yelps from the crowd.

Some of them hustled Chara Lampis away from the *papoúli*. Others grabbed his place in line. Still others encircled Chara Lampis and began breaking the strings.

The first sight that met their eyes when they broke open the package were three pairs of Dacron panties with flared flutings for an oversized woman, bought from Belk Leggett in Atlanta, Georgia.

"What are these?" asked Chara Lampis, holding them up in front of his face with a dazed look.

"It is a mistake," said Yannaki Stavros, a fox-eared boy with a tumultuous grin. "They were made for Kyria Papadopoulos." The boy seized them, jumped out of the welter of guffaws and flying hands. He ran to an aged, fat lady with hair on her nose. He put them in her hands and then escaped to shocked "*Poh poh poh*" sounds, blushings, screamings, and laughter.

"*Panagía mou!*" said one woman. "What insolence. What is the world coming to? A typhoon and now this!"

"They have air holes through them" said another woman, about the pants. "What good are they?"

The women shook their heads with small, sly grins. They crossed themselves, taking such actions to prophesy the coming of the second typhoon, in preparation for the third. Yet they turned to Kyria Papadopoulos, for they were not sure exactly what article of clothing they were. In Greek fashion, they felt of the material with their hands. Some murmured that these pants were parts of a bathing suit.

Under the pants in Chara Lampis' box were two treasures. The focus of attention turned back to Chara Lampis, for these two treasures were the envy of everyone. One was a ten-gallon hat from Dallas, Texas. The other was a beat-up leather camera case which had no camera. People pulled the ten-gallon hat out of the box and set it on Chara Lampis' head. The camera case was extracted and examined. No one knew what to do with it. They decided to sling it about his neck, as they had seen tourist cameras slung. But the act of getting it over the brim of the ten-gallon hat led to a tangle. Someone finally removed the hat and the camera case was slung over his head. The hat was replaced.

Chara Lampis was transformed from a fifteenth-century bearded prophet to a burlapped wild man of the Western plains, complete with a holster for his cross. It was he who thought of this use for the camera case. He raised his cross on high and set it in the box of the case, just like a soldier with the colors. Only this time it was the cross, and the ten-gallon hat suddenly gave majesty to it and a third dimension to the myth of Christ.

With misty, triumphant, dreaming eyes, he ambled around the church, facing all with the cross. In a reflex, entirely unconscious way, every person in the church responded to it. Hands flew and a thousand signs of the cross were made. Chara Lampis had stolen the day even from the *papádes* themselves.

From that day on Chara Lampis wore this holster for his cross, and wore his ten-gallon hat. His steps became bumpier and more exalted than ever. His voice became louder. This lasted for a month. And then, because he wore the hat in rain and shine and sleet and hail, it weathered. It broke its creases. It wilted.

Then, instead of having a firm brim, his ten-gallon hat drooped. It was more suited to the style of his burlap sack and his bare feet. Whereas he had been ridiculed before with his yellowed beard, his dirty feet and his unholy sackcloth, he added to his immeasurable ludicrousness the value of this huge wilted hat, like a sodden sunflower, ten gallons wide, more sensational than beardless Mortimer Snerd had ever dreamed of. From triumph he grew pathetic. His pathos had ten gallons and many inches to flap with.

He attributed it all to that kiss of God.

XXII Two days after the death of Barba Ioannis, the funeral was held.

Mourning made the death seem ancient history. It also made the typhoon seem as if it had happened long ago. Women baked bread, cooked meals, and served continual coffee and cognac to the mourners. The mud walls of the ruined house were trampled. It seemed as if no house had ever been there.

Elias and the other stepsons of Thea Ioannou gathered rocks together from the broken underpinnings. They built a wall against a hump of earth. They laid boards and tin wreckage over it for a roof. They used this shack that they built as a kitchen. A fire was kept burning within at all times. Wreckage was used as firewood. All the salvaged household goods were piled up against the wall of this shack. They provided insulation against the cold.

At the same time as the keening went on, women spent hours shaking out cloth, dresses, and rugs, saving precious household treasures from the wreckage. They found a small household icon made of wood. They washed it up and hung it in the new shack and lit a *kandíli* before it.

It was very dark in the new shack because there were no windows. It was continually filled with smoke from the fire because there was no chimney. The shack became the headquarters for the Athanasopouloses. Here they cooked their meals, ate, and spent the days. The children spent their days sitting on the earth at the fire. They were dirty and ragged children, and also very spoiled. They were scolded and petted alternately, as the youngest descendants of Barba Ioannis. They did not understand what was going on and were continually eating crusts and olives and funeral food.

The pomegranates that I had brought were for a purpose. They were used in the funeral food. The basis of the funeral food is *kólliva*—boiled wheat. The tradition is ancient. Wheat is life itself, Perpetual Hope. Around the corpse, at the graveside, all the people eat it, imbibing the staff and body of life. It is kernels of wheat unbaked into bread. It has escaped identification with any ethic or any body, such as Christ's, so that it is communion in its broadest sense. If you are eating kernels of wheat you can only know that you are eating kernels of wheat. If you have raised the wheat from the ground, you know how it is sowed, that it grows, that it matures, that it is reaped, and that it is replanted, and so on. The entire cycle. If it were baked into bread, it would run the risk of being thought to be some body or other, and then Christ or some other saint would get into the picture again, with ethics and messages, taking your mind off the simple cycle of sowing and reaping, living and dying.

The making of the funeral food took all the women's hands. First the grains were sorted. The kernels are put on a wire frame and examined, every one. With a little stick they are sorted into good piles and bad piles. It is an immense and never-ending job. For a funeral you have to look over so many grains of wheat. All the women did it. Sometimes they wept; sometimes they gossiped. Their fingers were so nimble that they escaped the eye. They spotted bad grain in a twinkling. During the sorting it seemed as if the grain came alive, twiddled, rolled, poked, and piddled with by those expert sticks and fingers. When the grain was sorted, it was dumped into a box. It was astonishing, such intricate work in the depths of grief. Yet it was one of those jobs at once eternal, because you were handling life itself, and at the same time reflex, because you did not have to think while you did it. You were free to weep and sigh at the tragedy of life while you were handling life. Very strange. There was something greedy yet pitiful in this concern with the grains of wheat while the corpse lay in the cellar.

As soon as the grain was sorted, it was put into a tub of water where it soaked for twelve hours. The tub was a huge wooden rectangle with sloping sides. The grain looked like muck. Good grain sinks but bad grain floats.

When the grain was soaked and ready, it was boiled; then drained, till all the remaining water had been carefully dripped out of the tub. The grain dried, and yet remained moist. The real process of making funeral food began. Other ingredients were added to the grain. Cinnamon, currants, scrapings of almond nuts, and pomegranate seeds. The pomegranates bled juice. The earthen floor became covered with it, sweet, red and sticky. It attracted the flies. Teams of women cracked almonds. Others cut them up. The almonds made punky, white nut scrapings, like soft fingernails. Cinnamon was poured in streams over the wheat. Sugar was poured. Countless hands, like flying swallows, mixed the substance. Currants were flung in. Women from time to time tasted it to see if it had the right sweetness and tang. Powdered sugar was added at the top so that the sweetness of it became even sweeter. The powdered sugar coated the top like dusty flour. The whole mass of this food did not cohere. It lay upon the fingers like wet sand and pebbles.

With the funeral food two things were done. A cake was made of it. And the rest was put up in bags to be presented to each member-mourner.

A funeral cake is not a cake at all. It is a patted-together mound of this grain, molded in a form on a silver tray. The grain is heaped upon the tray. It is patted into a huge, fat, hard heap, oval-shaped like a bas-relief egg. On top of the heap powdered sugar is poured. Like snow. It is covered in a blanket of sugar. The sugar is smoothed out over the grain until it has the perfection of a mound of snow or a minutely perfect and whitewashed burial mound. At this stage compliments begin to come in on the beauty of it, and there is a feeling of excitement, as at the creation of a work of art.

The decoration of the cake begins. Round, hard, silvered candies are used for the decoration. These are stuck like a thousand winking eyes into the sugar.

Martha made the decoration for her father's cake. She made a necklaced silver cross in the center at the top. This was mute and eloquent in its grief. Below the cross on the outer face of the mound she made the initials of Barba Ioannis, Iota Alpha. On the opposite face she laid the Byzantine sign for Christ of God:

Χ
Θγ

This was still eloquent. But then she began to border the mound with a necklace of the silvered candies. What had looked like testament teardrops now turned into hysterically sad sequins. The whole white mound-cake with its white balloon shape now took to turning and quivering under its winking globules like a shaking white belly-dancer teasing her fake pearls. The round silver candies floating in sugar became ten-cent-store items, cheap and glittering. Yet it was this teasing, glittering border that brought the enthusiasm of all the mourners to a high pitch. They clapped their hands together ecstatically murmuring:

"Ti oraía! Éxoha!"

A tinsel folly.

The mass of opinion or of enthusiasm dictates. You cannot hold aside some stern ideal. The Greeks have execrable taste. You can shout vinegared groans into the honeyed air, but they will waste away unheeded. I resented the pity I felt for this folly. The depth of tearful gratification that streamed out of Martha's eyes at this exhibition of her greatest talent in behalf of her father was stunning when you considered the cheap jewels that elicited it. I melted with pity. But I could not swim away out of that clink of cheap, phony, glittering, tuneful, winking tin-foil.

It was best not to do so. The tinsel was born of the union of the primitive and the Byzantine, instrumented and adorned by the mass-production technique which knows how to spray silver paint on hard candies and still have them taste good. Whether they tasted better because of the silver paint was the crux of the matter. The Greeks thought so.

The funeral became cheaper and more rococo by the minute. It was bewitching. Four candles were stuck into the belly of the cake. They were to be lit in the church, in the dark, perfumed stone chancel amid the chattering of gossips and the whining of psalmists.

The rest of the funeral food was prepared. For this purpose two hundred small white paper bags had been bought at the store. On each paper bag was engraved in fading green ink the sign of the cross smelling of death. The grain was shoveled into these tiny bags. The tops were twined. They were set out in rows. Each paper bag was peppered with a final powder of sugar before it was closed. Endless commentary began. Who would get the bags? Who would not? It turned out there were far more bags to be handed out than there were mourners, so we all began to eat the extra bagsful even before the ceremony. The food was excessively sweet-tasting and gluey. The pomegranate seeds squirted juice when you got them between your teeth. The whole business of the day was munching and spitting pomegranate seeds. After a while your mouth became so sweet with the powdered sugar and the moist cinnamoned grain that you sought some more definite substance. The sweetness lingered through the whole day of the funeral. Your mouth became as full of incense as the church. There was nothing that would wash it out except the bitter taste of Turkish coffee or the harsh elixir of cognac. And once you had drunk these as an antidote, you went back to eating the perfumed grain, the cycle being continued until you became a living example of the sweet and sticky taste of death.

Maria returned from Athens for the funeral. Her return was both desired and deplored, for her presence at the funeral meant much more grandeur, and much more furor. She had two strikes against her from the beginning. She had not gone through the catastrophe. All the slave Athanasopouloses sniffed at her from the cradle of their superiority.

She came to the grounds of the corpse with the lordly air of a patroness. She had brought a black wardrobe back from Athens with which to clothe Martha. This was the main subject of her conversation. She, herself, wore a new slag-shouldered fall coat of dusty blue. Her hair was newly dyed with the proper color of henna. She wore new shoes, black-and-white court pumps whose two-inch heels sank into the mud with a faint soughing sound.

She played games mistress, governess and chaperone to Martha. And Martha came into prominence among the mourners by Maria's presence. Martha sobbed, and Maria, with a feigned air of tenderness, ordered her to show her grief within the limits of propriety. Fresh from Athenian sophistication, she made it clear that she regarded these country carryings-on as backward.

"After all, I am your mother now and Nikos is your father," she told Martha, stroking her hair coldly.

Martha spread out her hands like an eagle his wings, but she did not protest to Maria's face. Only later, to Ioannis, she repeated this offer of parenthood with an eloquent and stricken indignation.

"She should be my mother! Nikos my father! *Pateráki mou,* where are you? I now live among strangers!"

By protocol Maria's advice was sought on all the arrangements. It was she who decided what Martha should wear. It was she who tasted the funeral food and decided when the kernels of grain were soaked enough. The old matriarchs, Thea Ioannou, and her sister Stavroula, sniffed gruffly and servilely in her presence while they talked against her behind her back.

"She tells us this. She tells us that. As if she knew! It is laughable. And the grain was not ready when she said it was. It is lucky we paid no attention. The great *gaïdoúra,* she-ass. We are always forced to be so hypocritical to her. But what can we do? Maybe we can get fifty drachmas out of her. We need more powdered sugar."

It was beautiful, the revolving of servility, hatred, sneaky jokes, grief and tinsel baubles. The funeral was one teeming with vicious hatreds, feuds, laughter and love, all plastered over with the gluey ritual of grief.

Mourners wandered over the muddy precincts. Two tents were set up. One was the dark khaki variety painted USA. This one was large. Six beds were installed inside, a chest, and some chairs. Thea Ioannou covered the floor of the ground with Spartan rugs. This gave the tent a feeling of opulence. You had to duck low to go through the opening. You entered a new world where your footsteps sank silently in the rugs and where the canvas rippled and soughed in the breeze. The tall tent pole soared through the middle like a mast. The beds were covered with hand-woven spreads, dark red and brown. All was speckless and clean and dignified. The mourners sat in this tent taking coffee which was boiled on a small table. The air was filled with the buzzing of the flies and the somnolence of the day. The flies came in during the cold nights, attracted by the lingering warmth of the day and the light of the kerosene lamps. In the morning they tried dizzyingly to get out, but they could not find the small aperture. So they clustered on the canvas, crawling sleepily against the threads, craving the sifted light and the heat of the sun which made the canvas warm.

The funeral breads were made in this tent. Tubs, flour, and oil appeared. Women beat the dough, pounding it in the wooden tubs with their fists, their dress sleeves rolled up to the elbows. They rolled the dough on a naked table-top. They stretched it, heaved it, rolled it to get it to cohere. Then they cut it in squares and filled the pans.

The area of activity then shifted to the *foúrnos.* Children were made to collect wood. Fires were built. The temperature was tested with a newspaper. When the sparkling Fourth of July holes burned through the paper, the *foúrnos* were ready. The smell of baking bread rose over the grounds and drifted up the hillside. Everything was almost ready.

The coffin for Barba Ioannis was made at the carpenter shop of Byros. It was a plain old pine box, very splintery. A wreath of laurel was adorned with a tin cross of a thousand curlicues, grandiose, pretentious, and cheap. A child had also made a cross out of cypress fir and stuck some prickly holly leaves in it. Maria brushed against it and cursed because it made her nylon stocking run.

The bread was ready. Its sweet smell permeated the area. Everyone grew hungry. A most marvelously embroidered white sheet was placed in the coffin. Barba Ioannis was hauled off his platform in the cellar and placed upon the shroud within. The cross of cypress fir was placed upon his bosom. Men began to hammer the last nails of the coffin to seal Barba Ioannis in.

A ripple of excitement waved across the crowd. Women began crying and moaning once more. In the large landscape of the mountains the crowd seemed small, bedraggled, and antlike.

The young men brought the coffin out of the cellar. Andreas, Elias, and the others groaned under the weight of it. Their eyes streamed with tears. It lurched as they lifted it onto their shoulders. A man shouted. They moved their legs and shifted its weight.

The *papá* from Agios Georgios lifted his arms and placed his embroidered chasuble around his neck. He uttered a prayer. Maria shepherded Martha into line behind the coffin. A sheep got loose from its tether behind the cellar and scrambled against the mourners, butting a woman. She screamed. Someone laughed. The sheep was caught and tied up again.

In the funeral procession the immediate family is supposed to follow the coffin first. Then come the cousins, aunts, uncles, nieces, and nephews. After them come the friends. My position was directly in back of the immediate family. Martha, her eyes streaming once more, pointed to me where I was to walk. The crowd stared at me because I did not wear black, and because I was a stranger.

The tin cross was placed on top of the coffin. Someone made an embarrassed motion to begin. The *papá* raised his cross. The men holding the coffin began. The black-veiled women followed. The mourners brought up the tail of the procession. The funeral song was begun, but in hushed tones as we entered the street. Some women cried very loudly, but as the procession started through the street there was a terrible, cold, infinite, and embarrassed silence.

The reason for this was the condition of the street. It was such a rutted, unwalkable mass that it was difficult to negotiate. There was a hypnotizing and all-consuming obsession with the coffin because everyone was afraid one of the pallbearers would fall, and the coffin drop into the mud.

People stood in their yards watching. The grief of the occasion was almost annihilated by the curiosity. Gnarled, brown faces of women and men watching in silence. Dumb beasts' eyes bespeaking cold misery.

The atmosphere of the day contrived misery. It was gray. There were a thousand coned clouds in the sky passing along each other like dirty, trailing hands. They were low upon us, almost touching the tops of the hills. The mountains were obscured by them. All the world was a sauce, floating in a greasy scum of rain. The broken cypresses wept drops of water, forgotten limbs of devastation. The atmosphere was cold and raw. The crying breaths of the mourners made steam in the air. There was no escape from the weather, neither inside nor outside. The procession seemed pitiful and small compared to the vast darkness of the glowering sky. The day had started fine enough with sun over the mountains. But by the time of the procession it had become rainy.

The church bells of the town began to toll the funeral knell. It was a special toll. Bum, bum-bum. Again. Bum, bum-bum. Death. This bell made an overweening, lost, gone silence forever. It was formidable. One could only try to think of the living, pulsing hands that were pulling the ropes, to think of all the living, the blank, reedy faces at doorways watching us pass. And yet it did not seem possible, even though you knew that they were living, to extricate them from this panorama of death. This was Death's day. The bell, the fact that the procession was so pitifully small, gave Death a grand and empty might. All life surrendered to it. Even the clouds were death. The whole grimy, blundering sky built Death over us. The mountain tops were obscured. Drops of rain wept.

A donkey met the procession halfway to the church. It was in a narrow lane. There was confusion. The men with the coffin lurched to a stop. There was no room for the donkey to pass. It paced broadside heavy with two wicker baskets of olives. There was a wide puddle in the road which the men could not enter and which the donkey refused to enter. Someone spoke. The man on the donkey's back lowered his head. "Sssss-s-s-s!" he hissed. The donkey moved its forelegs but balked at the puddle.

A woman sighed loudly.

The man took off his hat and again urged the donkey forward. The donkey, swaying, creaked its baskets against the side of the coffin. There was a scraping sound of wood. A few splinters from the coffin caught on the baskets as it moved on. The procession stared fascinated and aggrieved. Then the men carried the coffin on again. It seemed to float jerkily above the miry road.

The church was gray and greasy in the half-light. A dull benumbing sense of propriety overtook the procession. In this hollowness it seemed as if God had removed His presence from the town and as if the only thing people had any confidence in was liturgy. Ostensibly, there was something melodramatic about the rotten, dirty weather. But it was far worse. The atmosphere was pure emptiness, unnatural and unbearable.

I moved my red, raw fingers. I should have preferred to think that somehow this funeral would have the flagrance of melodrama mixed with ludicrousness. But even the coffin's adventure with the donkey could not riffle the hoary dullness.

The funeral cake was carried by a woman in the middle of the procession. It held as much fascination in its way as the coffin did, for it had the advantage of promising a future life for the mourners. It was to be eaten. When the first heavy drops of rain fell there was a gasp of horror. Then an umbrella bloomed over the cake to save it from the downpour. Other umbrellas came out. They flowed and jiggled like so many attendant bats, ballooning as an extension of the people carrying them. Like familiars taking shape and giving a supernatural hue to the silent and deathly hollowness. The procession took on a floating aspect. The coffin floated. The white cake complete with candles floated. The umbrellas floated. It was hypnotic.

Maria bobbed along in her blue coat. Through her nylon stockings you could see the hairs of her legs. Her nylons, already ruined by the cypress fir cross, were now bespattered with squelching mud. I was delighted, for it seemed the only human thing in the procession. Actually, Maria was spurned and criticized for not having worn black. It was regarded as an insult, and evidence of her maniacal vanity. But though I was rapidly joining in the servile hatred of Maria, I was pleased. Her crustacean wickedness added salt.

Inside, the church was dark. Hot perfume and tinkling bells filled the smoky air. There was a pale, depressive light shining in from the window. The psalmist began to sing. People stood milling about the coffin. The others stood in the aisleways watching. In a Greek village church no one sits down, except dignitaries in thronelike stalls along the side walls.

Four candles were lighted in the sugar cake. For the first time I could see the enchantment of cheapness. The candles lit up the baubled necklace of candy. It sparkled like a thousand winking, shivering eyes enticing the gloom away. The mourners all went to gather candles, and lit them. The faces of Jesus and the Panagia jumped in their brass frames. Songs of bereavement and harsh weeping filled the air. These sounds were punctuated by the smacking sounds of kissing as worshipers and mourners planted their lips against Christ's toe in the church icon.

I wanted the darkness to come, as if that would fill the hollow void of the world. I wished that the frail, sharp, tenor voice bumping endlessly through his monotonous trills would blossom into a full-throated bull choir replete with harmony to vaunt body, to give another dimension to Death.

But nothing stopped and nothing continued. The service was short. There was no eulogy. Only the mass for the dead. When it stopped the whole world was dead again. The candles everyone held were the orange beeswax kind. They filled the church with flickering. They spat. The wax hissed and spilled. The church was filled with fragrance. The mass was over. Everyone blew his candle out. The light ceased suddenly, and the air was filled with the tiny puffs of smoke from a hundred dead wicks. It was over.

Andreas, Elias, and the other pallbearers stepped forward to take the coffin again. They hauled it up on their shoulders. This, I thought, is how people are led from event to event. First Barba Ioannis had to die. Then he had to be laid out and wailed over. Then he had to be boxed. Then he had to be celebrated in church. Now all that was left was for him to be buried. The half-light darkened into gloom. We left the church.

The procession moved quietly to the little church of Agios Georgios. It stood foursquare and whitewashed upon a hill overlooking the valley of the mountains. The grass was dark and wet, it blew in the gusty breeze. The gravestones of the cemetery were toppled, weathered and riddled with age. The procession gathered at the graveside. It was a rooftop on the world. A bush rattled in the dark, cold wind. The men lowered the coffin into the grave. They grunted. The *papá* threw a token of raw earth in. And the others threw the first clods upon the box, filling up the hole. Four men worked silently with four shovels. When the hole had been filled the mound of earth lay high. It contrasted strangely with the white mounded sugar cake at the head of the grave. Like a birthday cake. It sat on top of a little chimney which secreted within its bricks an icon to be lit with a *kandíli*.

Thea Ioannou tore her hair. She cried:

"Ioannis *mou!* Ioannis *mou!*"

The keeners started. Martha cried aloud. The black-bodied women formed a crow-society around the grave. The noise of screams, rending, and wailing was loud.

But all the sounds on this hilltop flew away into the dim silence of the sky. We were so high up, the valley was so far below, that the earth echoed only its rainy silence to their cries. The wind blew upon the bush and the grasses sighed.

The old, frail, beadle-eyed *papá* knotted his hands and snorted into the wailing. A woman tried to throw herself upon the mound as if she wanted to claw the clay of the earth itself into living.

"*O Theé! Theé!* O, Ioannis *mou,* where have you gone?"

The wind could abide such screaming, because it was bigger than the human cries.

A woman lighted the candle in the little chimney. People gathered around the sugar cake. Each arm reached out. Each person received his portion of the wheat. Each hand lifted the grain to his mouth. Each mouth tasted the thick, gluey sweet. Each face was dusted with powdered sugar.

XXIII After the ceremony, we sat in a group in the kitchen hovel in the Athanasopoulos yard. Thea Stavroula was cooking greens for a token supper. Night was beginning to fall. Martha sat on a little stool before the fire. Ioannis was perched on a chest where the forks had been laid out, ducking his head because of the lowness of the corrugated tin roof. The fire hissed sparks, and the drops of rain bleated above. Once in a while a rivulet leaked through the covering of tin and spat upon the fire. I sat upon a wooden board set against the side wall like a settee. Thea Ioannou, wiping her nose with the edge of her black *mandíli,* trimmed the wick of the *kandíli* before the icon of the Panagia and made it burn more brightly. Yannoula and Boulis, the children, dozed like hypnotized puppies at Martha's feet. When Thea Ioannou had finished with the *kandíli,* she threw another log on the fire. It spattered and smoked. We could scarcely breathe. Tears watered our eyes from smoke. Then the new log caught fire and cast a jump of pulsating light upon us all.

"*Mána,*" listen. Listen, everybody," said Martha in a whisper. "Listen, Daphne. Do you remember what the calendar said the day you arrived?"

"If you lose a father, you gain a sister." I remembered. But I was silent. Martha repeated the verse in occult, meaningful whispers. Her voice caught momentum. It lowered down to an electric, fathomed, beating sound. "Do you remember . . . last summer . . . so long, long ago . . ." She trembled as if she would break down weeping. "When Theo first came, and we sat around the fire in the *kámpo* that night, and he told us the story of Hermes. Do you remember what Elias said?"

"*Koutamáres!*" snorted Ioannis from his perch. "Superstitions!"

"Ioannis *mou, chrisé!*"

"Fit only for women's mouth. Ignorant." Ioannis got up and

spat out the doorway. When he came back he forgot to duck his head. He bumped it against a low beam.

"Be careful, Ioannis. But listen. For it comes true. It comes true!" Martha was admonishing, but only half-heartedly, for she was possessed by the spell. "It was predicted. Elias saw the three women, remember? One was fat and short and decrepit! Ioannis *mou, chrisé*. You remember what he said? 'A great wind will come. You will lose a father, but you will gain a sister.' Twice it was predicted!" Martha's voice hung in the air. A gust outside riffled the roof to punctuate it. "O *patéra* is gone. She is here!" Martha pointed to me.

A sob escaped Thea Ioannou. Then she raised her head and gazed at me with ravaged awe. She lifted her hand and crossed herself. "*Dóxasi o Theós. Dóxasi o Theós!*" she moaned.

Ioannis wanted to laugh. He cracked a whip-smile at me, mocking. He shrugged. He pointed his forefinger to his head and screwed it to indicate that Martha was peasant-crazy and baying like an occult dog. And yet the edges of his green eyes were wild. And when Martha's eyes came back to him, he dropped his and looked silently, even angrily at the floor.

The significance of this was incalculable. Martha began crossing herself, giving herself up to an echo of her mother's prayers. I felt strange. It was as if an arc of light had shone upon me and I was sitting on a throne in a new firmament of meaning, trying to pierce the darkness all around me. As if I were the center of a new mass. I caught myself thinking: 'What a strange thing. And wouldn't it be stranger still if I flirted with this significance?' And yet I did. It was inescapable. For Thea Ioannou had dissolved into grateful, straw sobs and was clutching at me with new light in her eyes. And Martha was dream-lighted, striving with her arm to catch Ioannis, and looking at me with raving love.

XXIV The next day I received a letter from Daddy from Athens.

"Did they throw coins into the grave?" he asked. "That was for Charon. He is taking Barba Ioannis across the River Styx."

VII Easter

I A BLANKET OF SNOW covered the olive trees and the oranges and the hill where the typhoon had come. It was almost Christmas. It felt like Christmas. The *keramídia,* the tiles, were dovebreasts of snow. The oranges looked like oranges faces peeping out of their blanket of white and green. The tents in which people lived were sagged with flakes. Over the mudholes which were the streets was knitted white cross-stitching. Hay flakes were white. And the saddles on the donkeys' backs, carrying burlap sacks, were covered like beds.

There came an inevitable day after the typhoon when I had to decide whether to stay or not to stay. "Am I a burden?" was the question. The opposing question: "Do you ditch the sinking ship?"

"You stay. You are ours. If the house was kaput, like Barba Ioannis' house, if we had to live in a tent too, if there were not room, if you had to sleep with the donkeys, if we had no bread . . . then it would still be yours, as much as ours. For you are ours. But if all these things were true, it would be better for you to go, for maybe you would get sick. But we have our house; it is yours too. How different our *tíchi,* our *míra,* our fate, our lot! For us it is poor. For you it is rich. For some it is better, for others worse. But you, of all foreigners who have ever been to Greece, you experienced everything with us. Now you are ours. Now all that we have is yours for as long as you want."

Silence had settled over all this part of the Peloponnesus and over the white fields with the snowy bamboo fences I could see the *thálassa*, gray, with a white-dim light under the heavy sky.

I made myself a hybrid breakfast of tea with sugar, black bread toasted over the wood fire, and olives. I was suffering from a cold in the stomach. That is the disease of Greece in the winter. Terrific stomach cramps, mixed with a fever and a feeling of helplessness and ecstatic inspiration.

It was phenomenally cold. It was early morning and everyone slept but Ioannis and me. Today there would be no picking of olives. The snow covered them all. Ioannis said everyone would be kaput if they went out.

"This is the day to sleep," he said. "To be in Athena and to sleep all day. To get up in the afternoon and go to see a movie, and then fifteen drachs, to eat, drink, and then back to sleep."

I slept on my bed of straw, under a *páploma*, a comforter, and two rugs.

The sun was beginning to peep out now. There was a *mangáli* in the kitchen full of burning charcoal from the cooking house. Ioannis put a half lemon in the coals. This was supposed to keep the smoke from giving him a headache.

"This is the day to go out to the mountains and shoot birds with a shotgun," said Ioannis. "To splash in the snowy puddles. *Plátsa-ploútsa!*"

II In that winter of Greece, with the snow on the ground, I suffered from guilt. Should not I, who had money in the bank, hand it over at once to the proud starvelings who offer me a cut of their raw eggplant to munch? If I am theirs, are they not mine? To me, once, poverty seemed a matter of injustice, not of fate. To these poverty is a matter of fate. A despicable notion. Medieval. I would have despised them once and thought: 'I am not that. I am different.'

Now that I do not despise them, and now that I do not think I am so very different, I have nothing to say to them except:

"When summer comes, the sun will shine and you will not be cold. If you go to America now, why you will not laugh over nothing. You will work, and you will be alone too. You will be a low midget among thousands and you will not know how to compare, for you have nothing but myths to compare with."

That winter in Greece, I was always cold and always hungry. But most of all, I was thirsty.

"No! No! Do not drink water!" they said, dashing a glass from my hand. "If you drink water in the winter, you will get a cold in the stomach. It is very bad."

I was almost beginning to believe that what they said was true, as if Greece indeed were a different planet, as if their rules of health and of civilization were the only real ones. As if their climate were the only one.

Helpless and inspired, I degenerated into a world of my own. Love had come up over me with the typhoon; it had risen about me ever and ever increasingly, like the very cold which gripped the countryside. I had the gush of love like a disease. I felt them mine as they claimed I was theirs, all born of holding hands in a typhoon. I felt sweepingly beholden because all the beholden feelings aer born of love.

I was the submitting American. I was the treated one, the protected one. I thought I had no answers. I was given this set situation into which I stumbled all innocent. Love born of a typhoon which ripped the guts out of the established milieu.

"We have lost one, and we are given one," Martha said. "It is you who are to take his place."

I bought even this. It was like being born again. Greeks are so good at making phoenixes. But with the exact same question one grows to ask when one is first born: What for? And: What should I do?

I was involved in a partisan love, because I held their hands in a typhoon and because they took my hands and put them over their fire. They had given me *trachaná,* meal cereal, first when they had only *trachaná* to eat. They made me *koúkla,* another cereal, in the morning because they knew that I liked it. And they had taken me into their house and did not want me to go.

I felt the most perverse obligation to take from them, as if that proved my love. It was their tenet: 'If you do not take the half I offer, then you do not love me.' That was the love that had risen around me.

What should I do? Give them money? I say that I was given this situation, and I was. I could not upset it with a moral social-work program. Their gods as long as I remained there would be mine . . . not progress, and not belief. I would sing: *Ti na kánome,* along with them, endowed as I was with my three skirts, three blouses, and two sweaters. And if I had had one thousand dollars suddenly to hand to them, to become their god myself, I do not think I would have given it. For what had they to compare with that? Who was I to be their god? I could not undertake. I could not undertake. I could not.

III In the evening we all sat around the *mangáli* to keep warm. The fire smoked. The cut lemon sizzled in the coals and kept us from getting headaches. We ate at nine o'clock.

After dinner Kyria Katerina brought a handful of chestnuts from a bag in the back room. She chewed a hole in each one with her two teeth and laid them in the fire to roast. With her half-open eye she winked. She groaned her way up.

"I must see what the weather will be tomorrow."

She went out the door onto the rickety porch to consult the stars. She stuck her licked finger into the air. She wagged her head and returned to the fire.

"It will be fine tomorrow," she said. And then she pulled the roasted chestnuts out of the fire, peeled them, and handed them around. But she always said it would be fine.

This is how Kyria Katerina became known as the *Prophítis.*

If the weather was sunny in the morning she was hailed as a good *Prophítis.*

If it rained, Kyrios Elias said:

"She told a lie! She is a bad *Prophítis.*"

She looked like a true *Prophítis,* good or bad, with her balled, mounded hair, her drooping eyelid propped open with plastic tape, her toothless hole of a mouth and her wagging fingers. But she lied as much as she told the truth. So the hag-oracles live still in modern Greece.

IV The *Prophítis'* fascination with my *michaní*, typewriter, did not abate. I was hard put to get her out of my room in the morning when I wanted to go to work.

As it grew colder in January, I used to take my typewriter out to the broken room. It was like a private porch now, with its wall gone. There I would station myself on a chair in the sun. I borrowed the *Prophítis'* stool, and there I placed my typewriter. I used to write my stories and articles dazed by the blasting heat of the day and influenced by the sour glory of retsina from the noon meal. I could look from the busted wall out over the fields to Nestor's palace and down to the sparkling sea. But I did not look. I had my mind on my work. It was very warm in the sun. I could roll up my sleeves. Inside the house and in the shadows it was about thirty degrees cold.

At five o'clock in the afternoon, when the sun was beginning to make the cold shadows long and brilliant, I wrapped up my work and took it in. And then I went to the post office, which had moved itself downstairs in its sheared building, and set itself up in a room which still containcd four walls and a ceiling.

One day when I returned home from the post office, I found a paper in my typewriter. It said: "3dM7izxcvy b&8'½½¢@sDVEm 4., ii mfop pooksa MyNforEveha ha."

'Somebody has been poking around with my typewriter,' I thought. But the answer did not occur to me then.

One night three weeks later as we all sat around the *mangáli* eating the sweet chestnuts with wine, the *Prophítis* stated:

"Your machine has *grámmata*."

"Yes, it has many letters," I said.

A sly look covered her face. She winked with glinting eyes. And then I could see that her elephantine frame was wiggling with delight and heaving with suppressed laughter. At last she controlled herself.

"I can write on your machine," she said in a sleepy way.

"Ha ha," spoofed Kyrios Elias. "The *Prophítis* does not know one letter from the other. She can write on the machine!"

"Talk, rotten dog," she said to her husband. "I know what I can do, because I did it!"

I pointed my finger at her.

"It was you!"

She folded her fingers gracefully in her lap. She leaned back her head and laughed long and smokingly. Then she raised her head and gazed at us all with her twinkling eyes.

"I wrote on the machine," she said. "Tak-a-tak-a-tak!"

"But *Mána mou*," said Ioannis, "you do not know one letter!"

"I do. I know two letters. But I did not have to know any letters to write on the machine . . . although not as fast as you," she added to me. "So fast, taka-tak-a-taka-tak! *Ti ordia* for those who know how to go so fast!"

"What letters do you know, *Prophítis*?" I asked.

"I know alpha and omega," she said.

"Indeed, she knows," said Kyrios Elias with a smile as delicate as frost. "She knows much if she knows alpha and omega."

"Ignorant I may be," retorted the *Prophítis*. "Without eyes I may be. Without feet I may be. Without teeth I may be. But I know of alpha and omega."

The kitchen room was filled with laughter and the lemon sizzled.

V Attendant upon my stay in Hora was a great predication. This was the fact of Maria.

Her romance with Daddy having gone down the drain, she was left not with ashes in her mouth, but with poison. This poison was very rich and syrupy. In any other circumstances, in the city with a fast pace of life, this poison would have died a simple death, smothered in other ires. But the simplicity, the freedom, even the boredom of long, unfed hours in Hora gave ample opportunity for embroidering her discontents into a work of art.

The day after Barba Ioannis' death, when the women were gathered to make the funeral grain cake, Maria arose. She began a twenty-minute defamatory speech about Daddy. This would not have been unusual except for two things. (1) It was a funeral. (2) I was sitting not more than three chairs away from her.

Her charges were: (1) Daddy had demanded a *kotópoulo* (a chicken cooked with rice). Although this charge was stale, she used it. (2) Daddy spurned Horaites. (3) Daddy treated his sister, Théa Panayota, like a stranger. (4) Daddy boasted. (5) Daddy had not brought any gifts to his relatives. (6) Daddy did not take care of his daughter and allowed her to stay in a house with strangers, and (7) Daddy was an undoubted liar—he claimed that he was a banker and a lawyer, but there was no evidence of any money in his hands, and besides that he was tight-fisted. That meant he either had money stashed away like a miser, or he was making up a whole pack of lies to explain his forty years in America.

In the course of this peroration, Maria tried to enlist the sympathies of Thea Panayota. Thea Panayota played it cagey. Though she had her own feud with Daddy, she was not going to allow Maria to cut in on it, or to ally her just because she had other grievances. While Maria was speaking Thea Panayota stole sly looks at me.

This annoyed Maria.

"You don't need to be afraid. The *korítzi* is *koutí*, stupid. Completely stupid. She understands nothing." Maria came to me, smiled tenderly, and put her hand under my chin. "Do you, my little *papagálos?*" She winked in a sly, enticing way.

My usual answers to Maria were either Yes or No. I did not indulge in conversation with her. Today I listened very carefully and said, "*Nai*" (yes). This was such a complete *non sequitur* that Maria turned about with a dazzling smile, shook her hands out and announced in triumph: "Eh! So what did I tell you. She has the brains of a sheep." She turned to me again. "Congratulations, my little parrot. You say '*Nai*,' eh . . . because you can't say anything else. '*Nai, nai, nai*,' just like a little goat, eh?" She laughed with delight.

Under the sound of this laughter I was very silent and meditative. It was true that I did not understand everything that Maria said. But on this particular subject I knew the subject, I knew the object, and I knew the word "*kotópoulo*." So I figured it out quickly. I was surprised that she really believed I was that ignorant. At the same time I wanted to laugh. I saw the possibilities in allowing her to believe that I was a dummy. I was not angry that she would take such liberties both with me and with Daddy. I only became angry later.

To the funeral guests this situation was perplexing. They searched my eyes to see if I had understood. I looked back at them so straight that they could not believe that I had not. It became clear to them that either Maria was being duped, or I was. They became embarrassed. They became furtive.

Suddenly I smiled a beneficent smile upon them. They dropped their eyes at once. They became convinced that it was I who was duped. They were ashamed of themselves for having believed in a chimeric intelligence within me when it had become so suddenly obvious that there was not a shred of wit in my soul. For no girl would smile at her Daddy's expense. Thus it was with relief that they saw my smile. They were sorry for me, and disappointed that I was not fair game.

This sport could not go on forever. It seemed as if I had never received so many sun-stunned glances as I received in Hora. People were forever casting the blaze of their eyes upon me, stunning with curiosity, depthless, precious, vulnerable curiosity. Did I know? Did I not know? They grabbed at my silences. They seized on my smiles. It was a delightful and fearsome game, born of my inability to talk well. I was their live-motion idiot.

The day after Maria's obloquy, the grapevine carried the news. Maria wanted me "out of town."

Her plans grew daring and full-fledged. With Daddy outside her orbit she turned on me. She studied me very carefully. She took cognizance of what I wore, what I ate, how I walked, and what I did.

"Why do you keep her in your house?" she asked Ioannis. "The *papagálos* eats too much, just like her father."

"I know," answered Ioannis, egging her on. "She even makes eyes at me. But what can I do?"

"Makes eyes at you!" breathed Maria, surprised that she had not thought of the possibility of this new development. "What does she do?"

"She combs her hair in front of me and puts on lipstick."

"And what do you do. Tell me," said Maria slyly.

"What do I do? I do nothing," said Ioannis with mock innocence. "She does not appeal to me."

"She is too thin," nodded Maria in agreement.

"Yes. I prefer my women fatter."

At this, one of those long conversations began regarding the features of Maria's figure, particularly her large bosoms which Ioannis praised and appraised with a brazen smile and loud laughter bellowing in his heart.

He decided that this was the perfect opportunity to take the bull by the horns. He proposed marriage to Maria. Actually he had proposed marriage to Maria three times before in order to force her into a position to offer him a larger dowry for Martha.

"Marry you!" sniffed Maria. "Why should I marry a man who is inferior to me? However, we have been over that subject a thousand times before. Don't get me off the main subject. About the *papagàlos* . . . after all, she is eating you out of house and home. You have admitted it. If she is making eyes at you, so much the worse. She is causing extra trouble. Why do you not send her straight away?"

"That is just the trouble," said Ioannis quietly. "I can't."

"You can't? What's the matter with you? Aren't you the master of your own house?"

"It's my father," admitted Ioannis, rubbing the side of his face. "The *papagálos* is just like that with my father." He put two fingers together. "And you know that old man. He is as pure as the driven snow. Next to Christ there was no man born with such a sense of goodness. . . ."

"He is the world's fool."

"Just the same he would give the shirt off his back to the nearest beggar. . . ."

"He is a fool and a mule, too. Oh yes, your father, parading around reading the *Lives of the Saints*. I know him! You remember when he tried to take over the monopoly from Nikos! Good man, your father. Always spouting French. Never did know which side his bread is buttered on, and hasn't the wit to find out."

"Of course. But what am I to do with the old dog? He loves the *papagálos*. He says she is to him as his own child. Well, *télos pándon*. He insists that the *papagálos* is to stay as long as she wants. Of course, I could order her to go, but in that case, well, I would hate to contemplate it. The old man would go too, or else I would have to spend the rest of my days sitting under that gentle glance feeling guilty. To sum it all up, there is nothing I can do."

For five minutes Maria was thinking of this problem. Then sly, slowly, in a whisper, she said: "I have an idea."

"What?"

"You say she won't go. You say your father loves her like his child. Well, the answer to this is to make her want to go."

"Bravo, Maria. Brilliant. What do you propose?"

"Well, it is a well-known fact that Americans hate to be uncomfortable, is that not true? They cannot stand it."

"Yes?"

"The roof!" said Maria, standing up in ecstasy. "The roof! Think, Ioannis! The roof!"

"What about the roof?"

"How much of the roof is gone from the typhoon?"

"Most of it. *Poh poh poh*. What a loss!"

"Well, don't you see! When you fix the roof back up again, fix it up. But leave one hole. One hole. Right over her bed. It will rain in over her bed every night. It will blow cold air in from the winter. It will snow. She will not be able to stand it!"

Ioannis contemplated this plan.

"But you see, Maria. The difficulty is this. Of all the places that the roof flew off, it so happened that it did not fly off right over her bed. Thus, even if I fixed the whole roof, or did not fix it, for that matter, it would be no good. For the place where her bed stands is whole and neat and protected like a bird's nest."

"That is easy, *búffo*," she said, drawing near to him. "Are you *koutós*? It is so simple. Move her bed. Move it under the biggest hole in the roof. Never fix that hole the entire winter long."

VI "Why do you play her along?" said Kyrios Elias to Ioannis. "Why do you lie and agree with her, *paidí mou*? Why do you deal in such *koutamáres*?"

"All I'd have to do is move my bed," I said scornfully.

Ioannis was double-dealing with Maria. In return for certain jobs (the hauling of her grapes in the motorcycle, a pledge to spade the fields in the spring, a promise to burn her dead grapevines to make charcoal), he had got Maria to promise him a steady supply of wine for the winter. Ioannis' household supply of wine had gone bad. It had a deficiency of resin, and the gnats had gotten into it. But Ioannis knew perfectly well that he would receive his supplies of wine in driblets. She would make him dance and beg for each bottle. So he decided to supplement the supply that Maria was going to give him by stealing. Martha figured in his plans. So did I.

Under his father's disapproving eye, Ioannis set up new rules. Everybody was to be joyous, flattering and enthusiastic in Maria's presence. I was not to let Maria know that I could understand Greek. I was not to speak it lest she find out I knew it. I was never to let on that I knew how to write it. And I was to answer all her questions wrong so she would keep on thinking I was a fool.

Every evening before dinner, about seven o'clock, we all gathered together at Maria's. We sat in the common room where *to Paidí* slept. At a certain time Martha would leave, and while Ioannis diverted Maria's attention with flattery, she would steal one or two bottles of wine from the extra hogshead in the cellar. She would hide these bottles in a secret place under some burlap bags beneath the stairway and then return. Later, when I departed to go back to supper, I picked up the bottles from their hiding place and carried them down to the *Prophítis*. It was very exciting and very successful.

Nevertheless, it was necessary for Ioannis to rationalize the game of stealing, for it was only a small part of a much larger intrigue, his relationship with Martha. He was playing Maria along to get money out of her . . . Martha's dowry. If any of us insulted Maria we would be forbidden the house. What would be the result of that? Would we care? No. We could do without wine. But Martha would suffer. Martha would be cut off from me, her cousin. She would be cut off from Ioannis. She would be beaten, scolded, cuffed, and humiliated. Better stealing and hypocrisy than honesty and schism.

"But what good is it this way?" I asked. "Martha should leave since she is so ill treated. Why doesn't she leave? She is over twenty-one."

"You do not understand," said Ioannis. "How could you understand? This is Greece. Should she go to Athena? What could she do? All she can do is cook and make clothes. Martha is *koutí*. You must understand that. She is not like American women. She can barely read and write. She never went to school beyond the second grade because Maria would not allow her. What should she do? Should she walk the streets of Athena? What would happen to her there? She is dumb. She is religious. She prays every night. And then, you must understand her attitude toward Maria. She hates Maria, yes, she hates her. But also she feels sorry for Maria. Martha is like Kyrios Elias, good, and dumb. If she left, she would not know what to do."

"Better the hardships you know than the hardships you do not know."

"That is right. Bravo," said Ioannis.

Beneath this game floated a huge, silent sea of pity. It is over this sea that the sea gulls dip, wing, and die, taking care that their feet do not trail the water too long.

"Obligation, that is the chief reason for the corruption of Greece," said Ioannis. "We do not use money. We use goods. We trade goods and we trade labor. At the basis of all evil lies obligation."

"Ach, ach," said Kyria Katerina. "*Anángi* causes it all. One becomes obligated to another, and then all the lying and cheating and stealing begin. You—" she turned, pointing an accusing finger at Ioannis—"you are the greatest cheat of all, because you have no conscience. You do not believe in obligation. You get yourself obligated in every way. And then you do not live up to your obligations."

"If I lived up to my obligations," said Ioannis, "then I would be a good man like my father, and poor. So I am a cynic. If the world is to be bad, then I will be the most vicious person in it. But, then, I am soft-hearted too, so it adds up."

I sat down on an old wooden stump and stared at the bubbling pot of greens upon the fire. Kyrios Elias lighted his pipe with a burning stick. He sighed.

"Eh, eh. The soul of *Ellás*. Made of a fabric of lies, cheating, and stolen goods."

"When you steal," said the *Prophítis,* "you have to laugh." She stood up and spooned in the pot. "You cannot sigh like the master!"

"Hear the *Prophítis!*" mocked Kyrios Elias.

"Think how many barrels of Maria's wine we have drunk this winter. I estimate at least two and a half barrels. Oh, *poh poh!* If Maria ever found out!" She laughed gleefully.

"*Phantastikó!*" echoed Kyrios Elias.

"At least half a barrel each! On the face of it we appear to Maria with our hands out and say like little slaves: '*Dóse mas,* Maria. *Den échome. Den kánome típote. Dóse mas pou den échome!*" All the while we sit down here guzzling. Wonderful! Not to stint ourselves! Do we ever say 'No, we had better have only one glassful tonight so we won't have to steal so much!'? *Óhi. Panagía mou.* We know there is always more where this came from. All we have to do is steal it! *Ti oraía!* Heeheehee!"

"But we should be modern, *Mána mou,*" said Ioannis. "We should reinstitute Nestor's conduit."

"What is that?"

"You know how Nestor got the olive oil down to his slaves in the field by the *chtíma.* He laid a pipe the three miles down the mountainside. Since Maria is above us, it would work perfectly; dig a hole right under the barrels, and lay the pipe, right down by the Agrarian Bank. When we wanted the wine, all Martha would have to do is open the tap."

"That's beautiful. That's beautiful!" hooted the *Prophítis.*

"Bravo!" said Kyrios Elias in laughter. "From the heritage of our ancient ancestor Nestor, implemented by the mass production system, the modern Hellene can at last make his contribution!"

"Greeks are all fools and liars and cheats and thieves," said Ioannis to me. "Nothing is real here. Therefore everything is beautiful."

VII It was the *Prophítis* who finally put Maria down.

Early one morning she came to see the *Prophítis.* I was in the yard, washing my hair. I leaned over the tub of hot water. I rubbed my head with a big cake of olive-oil soap.

The *Prophítis* ushered Maria in through the portal gate and pulled her up a chair. Maria sat down. For a long while she was silent. Then she began a speech.

"See," she said, pointing to me. "Eating up the soap. Wasting it. See? It is in the water now, melting. This family is consistent, has been for twenty years, like grasshoppers. Taking, using, eating, wasting, and never a return for your money. Not that I blame the girl I don't. How does an American know the ways of a Greek? How does she know anything but to sit around in a kitchen with the electric stove doing all the work, wearing high heels and stockings and smoking cigarettes?"

"Mmmmmm," said the *Prophítis* in an acquiescent, yet noncommittal way. She took the sticking plaster off her eye and let her eyelid close to disguise the expression in at least one of her eyes.

"Doesn't she eat your food?" demanded Maria.

"Mmmmm," said the *Prophítis.*

"Besides, what is she doing in your house anyway? The house of a stranger. Why, she is not even of your family!"

"Mmmmm," said the *Prophítis.* "But Panayota's husband Ninos was the second cousin of my aunt by marriage. . . ."

"Yes. By those rules I am related to the Archbishop Makarios," answered Maria scornfully. "*Télos pándon.* I am sick of going on about it. To tell the honest truth, Kyria Katerina, you are being fooled by someone. Here she is, eating you out of house and home, and now she's using your soap up too. Well, we all know where that soap was made, don't we?"

"And we are very grateful, Maria," said the *Prophítis* between her teeth. "I tell Ioannis every day: 'You must never forget the *anángi* we owe to Maria.' "

"Yes, yes. Ioannis. A lot else may be said in his favor. He is a very wily man, but he doesn't take his obligations as seriously as he might. 'Ioannis *mou*, Ioannis *mou*,' I say to him very gravely. 'You are so impetuous, you are such a creature of force, you are also so very curious and crooked in any whim which you have, you will be the death of all of us who love you. Particularly of your parents, you know. . . .' "

"But Ioannis is a good son," mumbled the *Prophítis* angrily to the stones on the ground. She could not say it directly to Maria, but she felt: 'I may criticize my son, but don't you presume!'

"Well, what is this business?" demanded Maria pointing to me.

"She is very *morphoméni,*" faltered the *Prophítis*.

"*Morphoméni* she may be. Cultured she may be . . . too much for your good, I warrant. So cultured she doesn't know what wasting soap means."

"*Ti na káno?*" Kyria Katerina gave up. She yawned loudly in Maria's face and stuck out her hands. "Kyrios Elias loves her. That's all I know. They sit together every night and discuss England and France."

"Two birds in the same roost!" snorted Maria.

"He is my husband. What am I? Only a woman. What can I do? He says she is to stay. There is nothing I can do about it. I am a good wife. But you don't know how it is. You have been preserved from the state of marriage."

With this barb, the *Prophítis* began to feel better. She decided to put on her sticking plaster again. Her eye began to twinkle.

"*Christós kai Panagía mou!*" swore Maria, getting up. She tipped the chair over backward as she did so, and it fell into my tub of water with a big splash, spitting soap into her mouth and eyes. "To think that I should come over here to do you a good turn and should be insulted to my face! Well, that's enough for you. I am sick and tired of the whole pack of you, and I leave you to rot in your own waters of extravagance. But you needn't expect my co-operation any more!"

Kyria Katerina shuffled up and tried to placate Maria all the way to the portal gate. But when she had left, she forked the stick against the gate.

"*Poh poh poh,*" she muttered, waddling back to her chair. She sat down upon it, put her hands in her lap, and laughed fit to kill, wagging her eyes to heaven.

In the end Maria gave up in her attempts to make me leave Ioannis' house. Her threats were as idle as her promises.

VIII Two months passed. It was almost Easter. I grew restless. It was time for me to go. And yet I was so entrenched in their lives and the life I had found myself there, that I contemplated leaving with difficulty. I felt as if I must rip myself away. A part of me would be torn for them to keep. Like the calendar.

Martha and Ioannis held on to me. They said: "If you must go, you must go. But this is your home too. If you must, then go. But you cannot leave until Easter."

I wrote to Daddy in Athens: "I am staying in Hora until Easter. But you may expect to see me directly after."

He wrote back: "Good. You will see the greatest hypostasis on earth. The transformation of a Jew into a Greek. But it is utterly without ideals. Do not be fooled."

IX Sitting around the table after our supper, the *Prophítis* asked me: "Were you baptized?"

"What did you say?"

"She asks were you baptized." Ioannis held up his hands, plopped them in imaginary water and played the sign of the cross on his forehead.

"No. I wasn't baptized."

"Eeeeh!" gasped the *Prophítis*. But she controlled herself immediately. She pretended that she had heard wrong, or that I did not understand.

"Not at all?" she intoned in a low voice toward Ioannis.

"No, not at all!" I answered enthusiastically.

Her consternation grew greater. Her eyelids sank down, even the one with the adhesive tape. She whispered to Ioannis:

"Not baptized at all? Then she's not a Christian. Then what is she? Is she an *Evraía*?" she continued in darting, lethal whispers. After all this time to discover that I was an infidel! If this were so, then I must be as the snake in the Garden of Eden. All the more awful because they loved me. I had suffered with them. I was innocent and did not know that I was such a snake. What should the house of Ekonomopoulos do?

Ioannis girded himself. He took a long breath. He was about to launch into a peroration, and I could see that he was going to utter some loud and publicly embroidered lies. Before he had a chance, I said:

"No, I am not an *Evraía*. I am a Protestant."

Ioannis changed his tactics. He prompted me in a loud voice:

"You were baptized in the Protestant church, weren't you?"

"No."

He ignored this. He opened his mouth, but the *Prophítis* butted in:

"What is Protestant? What is Protestant? That is not *Kathóliki*, is it?"

"No. Protestant is another thing, *Mána*."

"The Protestants hated the Catholics. They ditched the Catholics because they didn't want the big Roman pope in Rome," I said delightedly.

"Good," said Kyria Katerina in approval. "But I never heard of this Protestant. Italy and Gaul, they are *Kathóliki*."

"But the English, the ones who settled America," I told her, "they are Protestant. For four centuries they have been Protestant because they had a king who wanted eight wives. But the Pope wouldn't let him have them, so he kicked out the Pope."

"The Protestants have eight wives?" said the *Prophítis*, shocked.

"No. No, *Mána*," shouted Ioannis.

"But she said—"

"That was long ago. In America we have everything. Protestants, Catholics, Greeks, *Evraíi*. But mostly Protestants."

"Protestant is Christian?"

"Yes. Yes, *Mána*. It's Christian. Like Greece."

"They have the Father, Son, and Holy Ghost?"

"Yes," I said.

"You are sure they are Christians?"

"Yes, *Mána*. Yes."

"*Poh poh poh*. Just think of it . . . all over the world such different things!" She was relieved, but insistent on getting back to the subject.

"So you were baptized in the Protestant Church?"

"Yes, yes," said Ioannis, butting in before I could answer.

"But she said—"

"She didn't know baptism was that." He turned to me. "You were baptized in the Protestant Church, weren't you? *Baptizméni*," he repeated, showing his teeth, and making the plopping-in-water motions.

"Yes," I said with glazed resignation.

It was due to this conversation that I was excluded from the necessity of fasting in Lent. Ioannis was also excluded, but that was because he insisted on it. There was an element of artificiality in my exclusion. I had been through the typhoon with them. Easter's significance this year was inextricably bound up with that catastrophe. Every ritual took on a new significance. So that when I was excluded, it was as if, through me, they were escaping both the martyrdom of Christ himself and the opprobrium visited for nineteen centuries upon his killers.

On the other hand, this was not a respectable emotion. Kyria Katerina served me two fried eggs with absolute delight. It was vicarious. She poured on double the usual amount of oil.

Kyria Katerina was in the vanguard of the fast. She was blatantly sneaky, as if backhandedly beckoning me to notice her virtue in not eating any oil. She even began to confide to me the wicked details of the fast, which foods were allowable and which were not. I listened wickedly too, abandoning myself to the discussion of these taboos while eating with great relish the two eggs which stared insinuatingly at me from their pool of oil. On Sunday Christ would rise. There would be magnificent feasts. Feasts to equal Nestor's before Christ had ever been born. Kyria Katerina knew it. And this was the paradox.

x Lambs and kids, innocent, bleating, symbols of Christ in animal flesh began to appear in the marketplace. Kyrios Elias and Ioannis went to survey them as the farmers brought them in for sale. But they did not buy any, because they had two young kids themselves, and they had already hired a killer for one of them.

The kids hallooed, frisked, and jumped in the stone courtyard below the rickety porch. They nosed out morsels of food from Kyria Katerina. They kicked the hens around, unaware of what their fate was to be. This fate was even more significant, because only one of them was to be killed. The other was to be spared. The choice lay in a board decision of Kyrios Elias, Ioannis, and Kyria Katerina. Both the kids were black. But one of them had white fur above his hoofs, and a white nose.

"Which one is to go?" I asked Ioannis.

"That one," he said, pointing to the totally black one.

The *Prophítis* emitted a long sigh and shook her head tragically. Ioannis looked wicked. He threw back his head and in the same tone he had used to talk about Barba Ioannis, he said: "He didn't know he was to be born for that, eh?" He cut his throat with his forefinger. "See how he laughs and jumps!"

"Why don't you kill him yourself?"

"Because," he said almost boastfully, "that is a professional job. It takes patience. You get dirty. You have to get the right guts out, throw the right guts away, chop up the hoofs in the right manner. . . . It would take me five hours. Mandroulis can do it in one. Besides, this kid affects me even more than the Italian I captured in the war. The kid is innocent. But the Italian, he got down on his knees and hugged my boots . . . we weren't supposed to take prisoners . . . they were a liability, you understand? More mouths to feed. Anyway he begged, and cried, and sobbed, and I kicked him away. Finally he took out the photographs from his wallet. These are my *bambini*, my wife . . . *nine bambini*. Save me. There was a major watching me. I kicked at him again, whispering at the same time: Run. Run away. He kissed my boots, and I told him when I kicked him again that he was to get up and run. I kicked. He ran away, and I immediately shot at him and missed. But the kid, see, he is not a person: he has not lived a long life. He is an animal, and he is aware of nothing."

"You purposely missed!" I cried.

Ioannis play-boxed with the goat. "See, he is innocent. Innocent," he said. "But, ah, you see. When his head is sitting on the table, and we will be privileged to eat this very eye that is winking at me now, oh no, we won't think of the little kid. We will stuff ourselves and burp, and say *Christós anésti*. And that is the way of the world."

"*Dóxasi o Theós*," said Kyria Katerina. "It is true."

XI *Megáli Pémpti* (Great Thursday instead of Maundy Thursday) had an air of suspense. It was suffocating, broken only with whispers as people did their daily work. They did their work as usual, yet everything was different about it. They did not pay attention to it. Christ's death and the feeling of crime hung over, stifling the importance of everything else.

At noon Kyria Katerina said: "This was the day Christ was killed. He will be killed tonight again."

Ioannis said: "You go. You watch everything in the church." His words were almost the same that he had used the day of Barba Ioannis' funeral. "Christ will be killed tonight. Just a little before midnight. The psalmist will sing of it. The funeral bells will ring."

"It's not so far away. Isn't it strange!" I said to Ioannis.

"Only over there . . . just a few hundred kilometers away." He pointed from the porch toward Navarino. I followed his finger and translated it to a boat in space chopping over the waves of the Mediterranean, like a silent movie, hitting the coast of Israel, where it became transformed into the Sunday School slides of a Christ dragging the cross. The reality transmogrified the blues and tans of the Sunday School picture into gray-green rocks, lime dust, dirt, and the hot merciless sky of the Middle East.

"America is very far away from Christ getting killed or the place where He was killed. But this is near. Near!" I said. "This is the same climate."

"It was only nineteen hundred years ago," said Ioannis.

The gorsed rocks, the igneous mountains upheaved, turned topsy-turvy the scale of time and eclipsed centuries. "Keep your eyes on the big-nosed *papá*," said Ioannis. He is the most irreligious, money-stuffing *papá* in Hora, and he will sing the story of Christ. You just keep your eye on him. If he had Christ in his hands today, he would kill Him. Instead he sings of Him. You will see."

XII The night was crisp. The moon hung out over the streets of Hora. It had the same aspect of merciless beauty that it showed when it had lighted the destruction after the typhoon.

Ioannis left me at the entrance to the church. His cigarette burned and curled in the moonlight. He said he was not coming in. I turned into the doorway and he walked moodily up the street toward the *kaphenía*.

The church was crowded. The light inside was an orange glisten. It seemed to have blood in it, in contradistinction to that transparent, white, cold-heat in the eye of the moon. All the candles were lit. The people held them, spitting. The perfume smelled purple. It was myrrh and some frankincense. Very heady. The candles were lit in the golden candlelabrum. They glistened and made the mahogany-colored throne-seats on the side walls shine mellow-hued.

When I entered I spotted Martha. She was standing in the center of the church in a press of women. She was staring at the psalmists, engrossed in their chanting of the Passion. She made a place for me. She gave me a candle and lit it from her own. Maria sat like the Queen of Hearts on a throne-chair above. She nodded to me with the expression: Off with her head. Nikos was sitting in a king-chair on the men's side, dribbling off the end of his mustaches, his bloodshot eyes rolling.

Outside the town was still a broken town, still unreconstructed. And here were the people, having arrayed themselves in the best clothes they had been able to salvage from the mud and wind. They chittered. They glistened in the golden candles, enclosed in the whitewashed walls, with God watching them from the ceiling from a purple eye, while they walked along a certain muddy path and over certain hills, embodied in the sound of bare footsteps, punctuated by the quivering *pee poh pah* of the Byzantine music, enunciated in trills which could have been sobs. Were they the people or the Christ? Whose crime did they think it was? Theirs or somebody else's? Did they carry the cross? Or did they watch it being carried? Were they going to die like Christ and Barba Ioannis? Or were they going to kill? Or were they going to watch? Or were they merely going to hear?

I began to be sucked into something. I did not understand what it was, because I understood nothing that the four psalmists were singing in their music. The *Kyrie eleisons* were periods in harmony with each canticle of the service. It was like exhorting God to watch, as if He did not know that this was the day He was killed in the body of His son.

I was nowhere near Christ's dragging, foundering walk under the cross. And I protested that the same phenomenon was going on that had happened in classical times when the people gathered around the long tables to hear the sound of Hector's body being scraped in the dust behind the dishonoring horses. Also Socrates had lived since then. Everything was backward.

Christianity, I thought, is a trolley-train running from the second century to the present. People never have the choice of being born or not born in Christianity. Some board the trolley. "Hey, Christians, what have you got there? What are you carrying?" "We carry the ancient laws of the Jews, the prophecies of the Persians and Jews, the rites of the pagan Greeks, and the ethics of the classical Greeks." Most people are born on the trolley and they fill it up with their goods, chattels, and descendants. Birth and death all the time. And coveting. Coveting of one element of Christianity above another. Revolutions and reformations.

The bundles of Christianity have changed their aspects in the passing air and light of ages. Some people have spent their lives in the trolley scrabbling over bundles to find the real and true Christianity. Every pronouncement of the true Christianity has brought followers and dissenters.

But choices are inevitable. What a grab-bag! The present is always more important than the past. If the present is good, it consumes the people and lights them with a light so strong that it makes the vision of the future dim.

The psalmist strung his notes, biting the air.

All of a sudden the church bell began to ring. Bum, bum-bum. Bum, bum-bum. It was the funeral ring, the same that had accompanied Barba Ioannis' body in the box to the church below. But the moment I heard it, I sensed a heartbeat! It kicked. It boomed. It was arrogant, demanding, desperate. It was so loud that it spoke twice to each note, itself and its echo traveling a circuitous, strange route to the inside of the church. Two other church bells rang also. The deserted streets outside were whanging and echoing with the sound of these bells.

Prickled hair rose on my arms.

"He is dying," rose a whisper in the church.

The church-house became the gigantic flesh of Him. Every person was enclosed, struggling in the heartbeat bell, twitching. They were consumed in the death agonies. I had the impulse to get out of there. The candles were still flickering and above their lights I saw the stare-crazy eyes of all the black *mandílied* women. The men were electrified. There was not a breath. They cowered at the first sound (though they had known very well what would happen). They were actually thrown out of themselves and catapulted into the spasms of the bell. There was nowhere that Thursday night in all of Greece that Christ was not being crucified and paying out the last splurge of His vital life. It was no longer a matter of whether these people had done the killing or whether they were the Christ dying. There was nowhere to go.

At that moment something rustled behind a screen in the center of the church. Everyone turned to look. The screen was like a puffed canopy. It was decorated with pink crepe paper and showered with white flowers.

As everyone watched, Christ came out. He was nailed to the cross. He was an icon held aloft on a pole by the big-nosed *papá.*

"Look. Look!"

"It's He! It's He!"

"Oh Christ!"

"Oh my poor suffering Christ!"

The big-nosed *papá,* holding Christ up on the pole, led a chanting, trailing coterie of psalmists and parishioners from behind the screen. The appearance of this was ludicrous and demonic. For Christ though life-sized gave the impression of being gargantuan compared to the people and the *papá* below. He dominated everything. The *papá* beneath was like a microbe smiling.

"Oh my Jesus, Jesus, *Christé mou!*"

"Oh my God!"

The bell held up its steady wrack over these whispers. Each strand of its silvered, doomed sound became more distinct.

But there was a difference in the populace, for the bell was now different, having found its focus in this *externalized* portrait. One simply put that doomed heartbeat within the emaciated rib cage of the icon. The populace, having been scared into doing the suffering, with the bell clapping them like a dying martinet, now had the enormous sensation of seeing that Christ had done and was doing it for them. There was a crescendo of relief.

"Oh Christ, dear *Christé mou!*"

Christ had the damp, white, mildewed brow of medieval days. His hair was darker than the usual sandy, reddish tan. His arms were brown, toasted to the color of a paper bag by the sun. The blood dripping from His brow and His hands was black with the color of red, the same hue as those igneous droplets crystallized into stone on Petrazhori beach. And yet it was cartoon blood. His knee muscles were too liquid. With the bell beating out in spasms, they should have been knotted. Also, His face was too serene. Set-edged back of His dark, wet hair was a pumpkin-shaped halo with spokes like a bicycle wheel. His divinity came off these metallic spears in electric shocks, contrasting riotously with the liquid, milky droop of His head. His gaze fastened upon everyone. There was no one He did not watch. For He had been painted with those all-seeing eyes, hypnotically blue. I stared at Him. He stared at me, half smiling, half buried in deep and awful pity.

As the big-nosed *papá* moved, Christ began to tilt, sometimes backward, sometimes forward. He hovered over the people as if He could veritably embrace them, even though His hands were nailed up. Everyone's head waved mesmerized as each kept his eyes upon Him. A huge pity began to balloon up in church. It was a two-way telecommunication. It figured backward and forward in the total contrast to the booming bell. The bell seemed, in fact, to mete the pity out, like a metronome. This long, and no longer, will you be able to pity me, it seemed to say. Christ's pity for the people. The people's pity for Christ. Because the bell had just so long to ring, and then it would die. The big-nosed *papá* walked an ovarian arc across the floor of the church. Every minute particle in the populace was in conference with Christ's death struggle.

Martha uttered a shocked sob and fell to the stone floor on her knees. From this position she stared at Christ, perpetually crossing herself, and inveighing to Him. There was the noise of an isolated sob from the men's section. Handkerchiefs were stuffed up against mouths. Tears began to stream down the women's cheeks. Maria's lips twitched. Her marble eyes popped out of their sockets. Old Nikos on his king-chair drooled helplessly and wiped his eyes with a loud, white handkerchief. He wagged it as if he were surrendering.

My heart beat. I was transfixed. I knew that I was in something big. I could not escape it. The church around me was massive with belief. I was wrapped into its mass. I thought: "It's phony. It's phony," and "It's a picture. It's a worthless icon in a cross-shaped frame. In bad taste too." But I actually whispered to myself, feeling the dew on my forehead: "Yours not to reason why. Yours but to do and die." I was very pleased with this banality that I dug up from Tennyson. It fitted in. I had an equation in my mind: Banality plus banality equals profundity. I was quite vague about the general You used in the doing and dying. It was Christ who was so obviously dying. I could not deal in a petty embarrassment. I had to embrace the banality. It was like Barba Ioannis' funeral cake. It had to do with the typhoon. Christ was yielding up love. What did it matter who had painted it?

Not one drop of Christ's anguish escaped from me. The big-nosed *papá* twisted Christ and was proud of the reaction in the audience. He smiled a triumphant smile as if to say: "Witness me! This is Christ and this is me. And you know He would not be up here at all if it weren't for me. I hold Him! Hail to the glory of me!" I appreciated this particular blasphemy in the *papá* because it was true!

Lucky You do have the big-nosed *papá*, I addressed Christ. For who can afford to have taste in regard to You? Lucky You have the Greeks, unchanged from their pagan days. Too bad that You are not required to be unknown, I thought. Too bad that John, Luke, and Matthew existed to sing of You, to twist their fables, expound their ideas, and create their myths. Too bad that every hungering artist has created You. For there is not one in this church that does not know You. Even I do! How do we know that we know You right?

My heart was pumping and manufacturing all these thoughts to fight His eloquent silence, and to beat His duration. For He did not have very long. Better that He should have been like all the unknown soldiers, unseen and burning with only a flame. If ever He spoke words, too bad that He spoke them.

But He lives! He lives! I wanted to telegraph this out of the church at once to the far corners of the earth. It was a special message, and it was rhapsodic. I leaned down and put this in Martha's ear instead. She closed her eyes and her tears fell out in agreement. The beating of that bell was like the beating of pulses in hand on hand when we held hands in the typhoon.

It stopped.

The silence was terrible. It had an actual consistency. Some of the people blew out their candles. Smoke rose. A smell of beeswax, sweet and unstrained.

"He is dead," came the whispers.

XIII The next day, *Megáli Paraskeví* (Big Friday instead of Good Friday) was muted, for the mourning had a penance in it, the ghost of responsibility for the crime whose enactment I had seen last night. There were some who went to the church in the afternoon to see *It*. What *It* was I was not sure, for *It* was spoken of in whispers. I did not go to the church until the evening. I blocked the secrecy, the whispers out of my mind.

I went to the church late. The people were packed in. I found Martha. She had a severe expression on her face. It melted slightly when she saw me, and her eyes rained for one moment, liquid, black, pouring and intense, as if to tell me: "This is the same thing as the funeral for Barba Ioannis." Then she scowled and asked accusingly: "Why are you so late?"

I looked around. Maria had overheard and she smiled with satisfaction at Martha's annoyance. It showed her superiority to penance. She tossed her head like a horse and sniffed.

The dignity of the populace was overbearing. Everyone was dressed in black. This gave a lowering atmosphere distinctly in contrast to the light of the candles. The singing was heavy and monotonous. Everyone sweated under the black dresses and coats. The closeness of the crowd was proof-resistant. It appeared to be attentive, but the very mass of bodies, close, smelling, rigid against the sound of the music, hid some corrosive desire. What were they waiting for? What was it they had come to see all day? What had been whispered over? What was it? The bodies were pressed against each other so tight in the mob that it was impossible to see anything. I stretched my head. I spotted the screen in the center of the floor of the church. The screen was covered with flowers, all white, white lilies, white laurel. Flowers were strewn, heaped extravagantly on every table, around every candelabrum. I saw at once that the mask of foreboding, of righteousness, of pretended sorrow was hiding a sheer suspense at what was behind the screen. The crowd was not interested in what the *papá* was singing. They were not interested in the psalmists at the chancel. They were interested in the screen!

Suddenly the *papá* moved from the chancel. In wide, flopping steps, with a coarse tilting of his head, he strode through the crowd. They moved apart, titillated and gasping. They followed his footsteps as he headed for the screen.

He disappeared behind it. Tiny sleighbells began to ring. The church boys hauled at the screen. Martha gasped tightly, her mouth open. Maria's eyes began popping wickedly. As the screen gave way flowers toppled. The whole effect was as a prize wedding cake being razed. The big-nosed *papá* poked his head out as the screen folded. He uttered sonorous calls, prayers, evocations which sounded like warnings to the crowd. Lilies fell on the floor. Before our eyes the screen collapsed. The scene was transformed.

A coffin lay in front of our eyes. It was a bier upon a platform. An embroidered cloth with the figure of Christ was piled high with white flowers, so that only one half-closed, melancholy eye stared toward the ceiling lifeless and uncaring.

At the moment that the flowers fell to the floor and the bier was revealed, the crowd swooped forward. I saw arms stretched out. Martha hopped like a hen, pushing people out of the way, bent down, as if she were begging for a trampling by Christ's corpse. She snatched one of the lilies, half ground under the heels of the crowd. When she rose up, holding it, her eyes were filled with tears.

The crowd stretched out arms as if to capture the contents of that bier. Then bumbled, bounced, jounced, hemmed upon one another, they were catapulted into searing pain. The sight of the phony coffin, covered with the banks of living flowers was uncapturable. It was a pink-papered monstrosity which housed an empty kernel supposed to be Christ. In the midst of this sweating body, where was Christ?

I could not answer to whether this bier was satisfactory or unsatisfactory in this situation. I remembered the dying bell, that heart beat so loud that it swept the crowd and made them die with Him. Now these hasty, excited sleighbells made the bodied pack sweat in His spirit. But there was no image of Him to hang upon. Only the memory of Him deprived of life before. A ghost. Not even a clay Barba Ioannis. As the imitation pallbearers took up the caked bier resplendent on their shoulders, I could imagine dried bones batting from side to side in that fake box. So patent was it that Christ was not in that. His absence became unbearable now. Even offensive. One desired an even more gargantuan icon than before. One desired an icon so huge that it could not be gathered or held or supported or borne, even as the casket was borne. Desiring this image, the substitute, the casket in its bridal aspect was entirely ludicrous. Where was He?

"Come. Come. Now. It is now!" whispered Martha, taking me by the arm, pulling me.

A crowd began to form behind the big-nosed *papá*. The church doors were opened. Banners, lanterns, and religious standards were raised on poles. The psalmists formed in couples, the four of them behind the casket. "*Kyrie eleison! Kyrie eleison!*" they chanted.

The casket moved. Candles moved, disembodied by its side. The golden Byzantine crosses on the poles caught the light of the candles and winked and titillated them. The procession began. I held my candle in my hand. It spat and burned. Martha's candle caught the breeze from the doorway. It almost went out, but she shaded it with her hand just in time. The lily she had captured drooped in her other hand.

Maria's expression was almost as it had been when she followed the coffin of Barba Ioannis. She acted as if she were above these country proceedings, and yet it was evident, in her sauntering walk as she gazed back and forth watching the snaking parade and insisting on her place in it, that she was actually fond of every moment of it, and that she had got the gilt and glitter of extravagant mourning rubbed off on her.

"Come on. Come on," she hissed imperiously into Martha's ear. "Let us get up by the casket. That is where we belong."

"Yes. Yes. So Daphne can see."

That was Martha's rationalization. She pulled me along roughly so that she skirted the edge of the slow, snaking parade. Everything in the church was in disarray from the dismantling of the screen. Luxury was abandoned, wastefully, extravagantly cast aside all the tokens, the flowers, the paper, the candleabrum even tipping as people pressed against it and banged it coarsely in the pursuit of the empty casket.

The psalmists' *Kyrie eleisons* faded out the doorway as the casket was drawn out. The church seemed suddenly abandoned, though it was still full of people . . . exactly like a room in which a wedding had been performed, when all the people have fled outside to throw rice at the bride.

We got to the doorway. A breeze fanned. Everything was dark. Everything changed. Everything was changed.

Oh, it was large. The night was huge and it was cold too. The gigantic dome of black ensconced us and yet it led up to infinity. There was infinite promise. But there was nowhere you could touch, all the heavens were so far away, and farther still when you considered that the stars were only way-stations in one's imagination of greater space, and galaxies only reminders that there were unknown galaxies much farther. Unlike the night of *Pémpti,* there was no moon. There was no bright, tender, or merciless lucid thing to concentrate on or to compare with or to give its attention to the earth or focus it for our minds. For the moon is earth-oriented, and in Greece Greece-oriented, seeming to exist only to light the space before you and make you see: "This is the earth. This is Hora because the moon hovers above to tell you so." Yet it was breathlessly clear. All the stars were out, and it was they, in millions of glittering clusters, infinitesimal dust, at such a wide range that you could not take them all in at once, that gave the night its depthless quality.

All the bodies, the closeness, the sweat, the perfume, the incense smoke, the suppurating flowers melted away. The people became small. Words and voices became at once more distinct, but at the same time microscopic. Two boys ran before us to catch up with the casket. Their footsteps crackled and popped along the gravel of the street. Their breath could be heard in its passage from their throats and out between their teeth. Every utterance was dashingly clear.

The candles were an imitation of the stars. They were a procession, a human Milky Way. The thousands of little flares flickered, vulnerable, quick. We could see our breath in them. All the people holding them were indistinct, black and disembodied ghosts. The candles jumped the world up. Everything seemed to hover. Now and then a foot, a stone, a part of a stone wall was caught in the spell of light. Everything delusive and suspended. Because we could not see the town, broken and battered from the typhoon.

The parade was led by the bier. The *papá* followed, and then the crow-robed psalmists. They nosed down past the Agrarian Bank, past the police station, toward the elementary school which housed Nestor's relics. They held crosses up on poles and torches which spit light upon them. They chanted as they walked. The bier was held up on strong shoulders. Surrounded by the brood of torches it had a gay aspect, festivalic, a celebrated bed of death suspended in the torchlight, luminated grandiosely and splendidly in the darkness at ludicrous odds with death itself. What a difference from the funeral of Barba Ioannis that lowering afternoon! Now with night-lit infinity. And yet I knew that this bier was empty. Not even clay. "See Christ is not here!"

"They are coming. They are coming!" Martha uttered this and pulled my arm, pointing with streaming eyes to the crossroads before us.

It was the church of Agios Nikolaos, the thousand-candled procession waving down the road to meet the procession of Agios Ioannis at the crossroads in Kato Rouga. What we saw, ensconced in our own snaking procession, was the whole of their candle-lit procession, tiny little lights upon the mountain road. A spasm of excitement took us. Throats closed. Eyes closed and when they opened again they were flung with tears through which the candles refracted and multiplied. One could not contain the suspense of seeing a body of the town about to meet another body of the town. Long before we met we could see that Christ-bed, also empty, floating at the head of their parade, and the robes of their psalmists shining silver from their strange light, and their crosses, sparkling and military. Martha and I flung ourselves away from Maria and ran down along the edge of the crowd, our candles heaving, waving, suspiring, almost expiring, until we reached the casket and the psalmists. The casket from this point was like a great moving roof. Our candles grew big and threw a blossom of light against the bottom of the casket. Just at that moment the army of Agios Nikolaos met the army of Agios Ioannis.

The crosses clashed in gold. The footsteps stopped. The processions halted. The psalmists threw their heads in the air. The crowd opened their mouth.

The whole of the Hora world sang out "*Kyrie eleison. Kyrie eleison. Kyrie eleison.*" "O Father in heaven!" Addressing God because Christ was gone. A torrential, collective sob . . . because of the populace, all those gatherers, all that was human who had witnessed Christ die, gathered together in His absence, lighting up their thousand solitary candles as if to burn the blackness white to find a trace of Him. All these solitaries in congress, hearts and flames, could not penetrate the night sky above. There was such a sound as reached the stars. But the stars were silent. Christ ceased to have any meaning whatsoever, for he was drowned in that magnificent mourning. There was only an empty box, a decorated shell, like the shells of the broken buildings which were hidden all around us in the darkness punctuated only by the broken light of the candles. A thousand lonely people and a thousand separate lights suddenly confronted each other. They were attached to death by the marvels of such festivalic mourning. They were attached to life only by the feeble fires of their candles. But no candle was capable of lighting up such a total and infinite disappearance. The town was too small upon the hillside in his death. The night sky was too fathomless. Each human of us was too minuscule, too sharp, and too defined in the abstract limitlessnous of His absence.

Where was He?

XIV

The next day was very strange. The sun rose as if to declare that Christ had played a game with that festival for his death. He was in hiding. Hiding from us. To think one should know that Christ lived because He was hiding. He had become a Hora Christ. Right there somewhere if you could only find Him. A late Phenomenon, considering Nestor who had lived as far before Him as we were living that moment after Him. One did not need to repair across the sea to Israel, or re-create Him by means of Sunday School pictures. He existed, and one waited breathlessly, almost for the sound of His voice: "Allee Allee in free!" Or longed to shout to Him, the essence of earth and death having been confused, not knowing whether you were the kernel yourself, or He.

Everyone knew that He was going to rise on Sunday, and that He would live again. But how? Where was He now? Was He accustomed to being lost so quickly, and had He made another world so strong behind bush or leaf or grass that He had forgotten the earth's game? This knowledge of His impending Resurrection, instead of cutting down the suspense, only brought it to boil. Everyone felt the urgent necessity to find out and locate the death of Him. This took a myriad of forms. Most of them had nothing directly to do with death. They had in fact to do with life and quickness. It was a blind, scratching, fumbling on the side lines of the area of death.

Baking began. The town was filled with the smells of *kouloúria* and Easter breads. Everyone's *foúrnos* was lit, and the smokes rose, and the newspaper temperature-gauges were tried. Loaves, buns, rolls, sweet-breads. Thousands of eggs were dyed. All of them were dyed red. Red eggs stood on the tables of every house in town like comical jewels revealing the futility of discovery. Red eggs were inserted into the bread dough, and baked within the *foúrnos.* So the Easter loaves contained their quorums of red egg decoration. Goats and lambs were killed. Screams rose from the neighboring houses. Blood dripped. The hoofs were cut off. The guts were cleaned. The animals were skinned. Flesh was washed with water. Into the *foúrnos* went the first layers of meat.

The sun was brilliant. The day was warm. The bells rang out from the churches, reminders to the people that the great ceremony of Resurrection would take place that night. These bells had no relation to Christ's heartbeat. They were strangely earthly and warm, and without significance. Without any clue to His whereabouts.

I imagined him asleep in some tomb, like Romeo. In fact tombs were the closest estimate one could make toward His Death. Since Hora was rich in tombs, and since these tombs had a special flavor, being pre-Christian, the path to His whereabouts and discovery was irresistible.

That morning I went with Martha to a mill to pick up some flour which had been ground there from Maria's grain. The mill was above Maria's on the mountainside, over a stream which bordered a long meadow. In the meadow were twelve or thirteen round tombs, *táphi*, of the period of Nestor. Water rushed down from the mountain, and while Martha dealt with the miller, I went to explore these *táphi*. They were beehive-shaped, shallow and dank inside, rotten, and earth-smelling and unkempt. Dandelions danced at the entranceways, and the grass was brown and hard. In one of them I found some potsherds. I wrapped one in a handkerchief to show to Martha.

She spurned these *archaía.*

"Some boys have broken some jars in there," she said.

"No, they are valuable! They are ancient! They belonged to Nestor's slaves," I said.

"Eh!" She threw out her hands. "*Archaía* they are then. Valuable! Take them to America."

"You don't believe me!"

"Of course I believe you, my dear cousin. But does it matter whether I believe you or not? They are ancient. The slaves of Nestor used them. Take them to America, and remember me. Remember they are from Hora. Do not forget." She continued in a monotonous singsong to herself. "But you will forget. You will forget the typhoon. It came from another day, you will say. Ah, *Christé mou,* where are you? Father I have no more. Mother, she runs like a hen from morn to night, trying to keep life together. I live in the house of strangers. I work for stranger. Brothers and sisters far away. And you, my cousin, you are going far away. And who knows when I will ever see you again!"

This made me very silent. I simply whispered: "I won't forget. I will never forget anything."

Later, walking up from Kato Rouga in the afternoon, she turned pensive.

"Did you see how beautiful it was last night? Now you remember that when you go back to America. You remember how you saw this *Pascha Christós* die and how we mourned for him. Ah-ho-hmmmm. *Christé mou, Christé.* Why did You die and the world is still so bad?"

"Where do you think He is now?" I asked.

"I don't know. They say He was dead, right there in the tomb."

Above the road where we walked was the hill where Barba Ioannis was buried. The little church was orange with the sun, and the spokes of the cross were black against the blue sky.

"*Patéra mou, Patéra mou,*" she called, beginning to weep. "Are you in *ouranós* watching me? What do you say, *Patéra*? Can you still see our house which fell down on top of you? Do you grieve for us when we miss you so? Do you see me with Daphne walking by the hill where you lie? Do you grieve for us? Do you see how Hora is still laid upon the ground? Did you think before the typhoon that you would not be here with us when *Christós* was crucified? *Patéra, Patéra,* speak to me!"

"Do you think he is up there?" I asked, pulling her arm.

"I don't know, Daphne *mou*. Like the *Christós* . . . not exactly like Him, but I mean . . . they are both dead. I think he, *Patéra*, is up there, and if he is, *kakomíris,* I hope that he hears what I say. But I don't wish him to be sad because we are. Think of it. Four months and six days and five hours since he was killed. And now *Christós* is dead."

"But He is supposed to be around here, somewhere around here. Isn't He?"

She gave me a strange smile.

"Ah, that you should say that, *adelphoúla mou.*"

What did she mean? Now that His image, that donated Banality which had been brought out and erected in every eye, had got melded into the figure and memory of Barba Ioannis, the necessity to keep Him alive, or to re-create Him, became more poignant. When I heard the Agios Ioannis bell, I tried to distribute Him, beating. Martha actually jumped back on her heels. The desire to have Him get Risen became so profound that if wishes had had true effect, He would have stood in the road before us that moment, either Christ or Barba Ioannis, I don't know which.

It was as if Martha were prompting Barba Ioannis to get into communication with Christ in Elysium so that he too could get a vicarious Resurrection tonight. As if he had a personal ticket, and could seek Christ out of the hordes in the Shadowy Place, as Petrarch had gotten to Socrates. In so doing, he would get some of His immortality rubbed off on himself.

"*Ti na káno? Ti na káno?*" she suddenly whispered, breaking into sobs.

For the first time I could see the justice of asking that question. Since she was not dead and not There, she could not do this soliciting herself.

"Look around. Look at Hora," she said.

I looked at Hora.

What I had become used to for all these months, I now saw again. A rag doorway waved in the breeze. Three houses which had been shorn by the typhoon were now a heap of rubble complete on the ground. The army had demolished them and the people were living in tents in the back yard. Three tents in the back courtyard. A cypress tree stump stood by a rickety wall. The windows of the school were still boarded with wood. That was the extent of the repair job since the wind had smashed the windows in. There was also a tin door in place of the wooden one which had been torn to shreds. On this new tin door sat a shiny padlock. All the roofs were new and lemon-colored. But an old doorway still stood in a vacant lot where the house, demolished, had not yet melted into the earth.

I, knowing that I was leaving, could have shorn that vision right off the top of my mind. I could have imitated the typhoon, which, after all, had not come to Hora till I had come to it too. It took an effort not to do that. In such ways do people always make their departures before the actual leave-taking.

But there was too much unresolved. They had thrust Christ like a giant into the scene, crucified Him, hidden Him, melded Him, and faded Him. Now that there was left only this lone and denuded Hora, what had once been a nameless town, the town where my father was born, now my own town, now my town, not nameless, there was something demanded.

I honestly thought that Christ, the image, would be resurrected once they had made Him Arise that evening. Having wrested Christ from the Jews and from His own Words even (this they had done a thousand years ago, I was sure) and made him a Hora Greek, I was hung up on their resurrection of Him. That will be Greek. That will be Greek, I thought.

As I walked up from Kato Rouga with Martha, the afternoon fell. The chilly, down-swinging sun made the stones and the adobe all purple. The cool zing of the departing day frosted us. We were no longer lit with the feverish spring sun.

XV

I was aware of the physical attributes of the church that night because it had been dressed up. Everything was material. It seemed lighter than the night of *Megáli Paraskeví*. All the candles were lit. The flares burnished roseate. The perfume had a sensuous quality, like wine, beading and bubbling. The screen was covered with flowers as before, but now they were multicolored. Red roses and white lilies. Flowers were strewn, heaped extravagantly on every table, around every candelabrum. Women had donned their *skoularíkia* (earrings), bracelets, and rings. So that as the psalmists warmed up and cricks began in backs and straining neck muscles, as people moved restlessly, impatiently under the wavering necks, these pieces of jewelry moved with them, caught the light like cats' eyes and shattered the church with expectation. Everything was yeasty, like the fermentation of retsina. To think that all this had been housed in shoddy, splintered hogsheads, born of mud tracks, nursed in crumbling houses, picked, scrapped, saved in lonely trunks, had weathered a typhoon, and endured through the muddy, scurrilous, snow-pecked and suffering winter! They held their mouths tight and stern, for the hour had not come yet. And though *Christós* was sung, as before, there was not a trace of Him. Precisely because the scrimping, the saving, the donning, the very occasion screamed in its expectation. Only Martha wore black.

I accounted it as gross and childish hypocrisy. I longed for Christ.

I wanted the big-nosed *papá* to haul Him out on the pole. I leaned over a bracket gate which led to the throne-chairs and waited. This time Maria did not separate herself from Martha and me. She stood, in deference, I supposed, to the impending Resurrection. But she seemed bored. She yawned, putting her forefinger in front of her nose and stretching her neck toward the big-nosed *papá.* She pulled her beige coat over her shoulders and surveyed her lapels with her shell-eyes. At times she inspected the seams of her stockings. Then her eyes would rove over the standing congregation, and she would sniff, making wrinkles in her nose, to inspect the variegated perfumes around us, and put down in her mental black book who wore what scent.

Again Ioannis had not come. But he had whispered to me before we had left: "This night. This is the beautiful one. You will see. You put it down on your machine, like the typhoon. But yet I don't want to tell you anything about it, because something will happen that you won't recognize. And that's what the miracle will be." So I knew that he was somewhere in the town, hiding like a crusty, black goblin, ready to come out at the appointed hour.

Barba Ioannis had also disappeared. I strained for traces of him in Martha's eyes. She was in a faraway state. She looked at me from time to time and smiled with her black eyes, but she was in another land. She paid only a token attention to the hypocrisy around her. I could see the effects of it. She pursed her lips, she put up her nose, and then she discarded it. Though she was intent upon the psalmists, she was not in rapport with the service. She was quite hidden. Shadows were in her face and her expression was vague, almost benign. She gave me a candle and held one in her hand. I longed to shake her and rattle her again with questions. Where was Christ? Had Barba Ioannis accomplished his mission with Him in the Land of the Dead?

It was very boring. At last I yawned, being set off by Maria, and tears of impatience came to my eyes in the yawn.

It seemed to be a signal. There was a vague stirring in the crowd. People came to attention. The psalmists changed their yawning monotony. Different words leaked out of their mouths. The brilliant colors, the jewels, the eyes, the flowers came into focus. Under their overpowering effect was the first faint hint that across the centuries there was an answering stir in the tomb. The populace straightened itself. Each held his unlit candle fast in his hand. The robes of the black-robed, big-nosed *papá* began to tremble. In his face there rose, as if from some depths, a sneaky, curving smile, promising something. Exactly like a politician. The smile extended until his mouth was the shape of a Turkish delight.

"Kyrie eleison. Kyrie eleison. Kyrie eleison!" The psalmists' evocations grew sharp and excited, with the off-color shrilling of cocks' crows in the morning. And yet it was only a little before midnight. Maria checked her watch. Her powdered cheeks began trembling slightly. Tiny granules of powder sifted into her wrinkles. This vision of the powder, matching the color of the lilies, of the incense which the big-nosed *papá* now sent out from his silver censer swinging on its chain, covering the church with smoke—the powder, the smoke, the sweet smell, the texture of the flowers, the fleshed cheeks taking on blood and movement, the strains of perfume from the attentive bodies, the heads like a thousand pears, all so suffused the church with fullness, material fullness, that everything was caught up and overwhelmed by the physical *materiality*. Sweet and stifling flesh!

Suddenly the *papá* stopped singing. He held an unlit *kandíli*. He looked out over the heads of the populace for a moment as if something had gone wrong. He stared at the screen with a mesmerized expression. Everyone turned at once to look where he was looking.

There was a gasp. Before our eyes the screen collapsed again as if a thousand hands were wafting it away. The flowers exploded in disarray. They tumbled to the ground.

There was nothing there!

No body. No bier.

I wanted to laugh. But the people hooked their breath in their throats. I perceived a conspiracy with nothing. The church was still as death. Everyone was motionless. Only the last rustle of the last flower as it skidded to the stone floor.

The *papá* moved in the chancel. He bent over the altar fire like a witch, his sex disguised, his nose out of sight. He lit his taper from the altar fire. He turned around. His voice, hoarse from three days of chanting, came out in a whisper: "Come! Come receive the light!"

It was in a sense too simple. The crowd spasmodically lurched toward him. But he stepped forward awkwardly. One did not look at his face for it was not he they wanted, but the fire he carried which beamed small and bright on its tiny candle pole, a minuscule, pathetic imitation of the image of Christ, the icon bepoled. Is this how one caught at a resurrection? To hold a breath of earthly fire in which no face, no physical manifestation could survive? It was so simple and so soundless that one might have overlooked it entirely. Only thought: 'They are doing something. What are they doing?'

An old lady reached the *papá* first. She stretched out her candle toward him. He held out his candle and touched her wick. It was a kiss of fire. A transfer. Triumph lit up her wrinkles. She too held a new nodule of resurrected breath. But what was strange, this nodule of fire on her *kandíli* sprang her ancient materiality, her physical face shining into everyone's eyes. It was a Promethean act, but the breath of Christ sharpened her physically. She in turn held out her flare, spilling with generosity, and lit a boy's. "Receive the light!" she murmured.

The *papá* lit another woman's taper. In a second five *kandília* burned. A minute later twenty. This graduation of the resurrection in terms of fire increased the volume of triumph. It was punctuation in fire. It changed the church, for it grew lighter and lighter out of spurts and darts from the fire kisses. In being silent everything became emblazoned.

Suddenly above the churchbell began to ring. Bong, bong! Magnificent, extravagant, triumphant.

"*Christós anésti!*" the populace cried. "*Christós anésti! Christós anésti!* He is risen!" It was in the realm of the pure phantasmal. The church was emblazoned in glory. The cry of the crowd was a sound throwing wonder and triumph through the bong of the bell into the medium of fire.

"*Christós anésti! Christós anésti!*"

In absolute fact, there was nothing to say but "*Christós anésti.*" One looked for words to find to express this total joy. In searching, scrambling along the long tree of Greek language, one could only come to that one thing that the occasion was for. That Christ had arisen. Christ is risen. All their hypocrisy, their jewels wagging, fell off. Their arms stretched out. Physical materiality merged into embraces, the only consummation of the fact of crucified, demolished, impoverished, hidden Christ darting out of a thousand grubby hands to conquer the air. He escaped in flames. Every heart escaped with Him in each petty shoot. It was the conglomerate that made His Resurrection happen. The separate small lights made the brilliance so devastating inside that church house that not one person there could forcibly have kept his heart inside his body. Proof was irrelevant. Because the heart had escaped from the body, the image was surrendered to light.

XVI Later when Martha and I went outside the church, a firecracker exploded. I saw a strange thing. The town was transformed. Each hulk and shell of a house sported a holy thing. On each side of the road were arranged candle-lit niches, little tables with glittering white linen with lace edges (rummaged out of the trunks which had survived the typhoon) upon which sat holy icons of the Panagia and Christ Himself, glittering in the light of brass frames luminated by the home's precious candles. A broken balcony had become an altar. A crumbled window-ledge was a banquet table for someone's communion with God. A broken wall showed Christ's mournful face dropping love in candle-sputters. What had been a street of broken stone doorways and portal windows was now a plethora of open-window boxes, all lit up, dancing. The Panagia became fanciful. Floated. A separate little movie cut out of the darkness of the night. A thousand fairy-like panoramas. Inside the houses the candles were lit too, and the best linen was spread upon the tables, and the few articles of silver. The whole town was a series of these luminated boxes in which these dignitaries of Christianity sparkled and darted, eyelights of joy, crystallized in silver and spun in lace and set upon fine linen. It was delicate and transcendant. Linen upon stone! It had a miraculous flavor. A Raphael Madonna, delicate, looked down on our faces meaningfully.

People pouring out of the churches filled the street. Suddenly we wanted to laugh. For it was magic. We began to laugh, tinkling, majestic, dashing, we laughed. All the boys of the town began to set off firecrackers. Women pointed. Little boys gleamed at the bangs. The air was cold. Firecrackers spun crazily over the potholes in the road. Girls screamed as the wheeling, spinning shivers of light arced in the darkness and exploded in tiny pistol-shot pokes. Everything became unreal. The world manifested itself as a collection of transcendent toys; one had the hysterical desire to expire on the spot, to go up with the fire crackers and the *Christós anéstis* in one deliciously cold explosion into the night-happy dark. Every eye winked like a bead. Christianity had become a lit frost, a foam of tapers. All of this was a seizure, to snatch a fistful of the golden-whispered night to keep for immortality. That which Christ was supposed to have meant had come out of the body of Him and was literally exploding up into the airy night.

At that moment I saw Ioannis. He was standing upon a stone at the exact spot where the two processions of mourning had met last night. He sprinted off the rock and suddenly his head was next to Martha's and mine.

"All that glory and that miracle," he whispered. "And you know what Hora is!" His eyes hissed and sparkled splendidly and wickedly, just like a candle. He possessed the savagery of a conspiracy of joy. It was so, because under the splendor streamed a dreaming, liquid look, just like the day, under the sunlight instead of the starlight, when at Nestor's tomb he had said: *"I zoï den eíne tipote."* Life, it is nothing.

XVII There is an eleventh commandment which Boris Pasternak made up. I thought of it the next morning at that early hour when Ioannis and Martha took me to the bus. My hands were full of things. I had two newspaper-wrapped parcels containing red eggs. A bundle of fish. My luggage. A jackknife which Ioannis gave me as a present.

"You who are individual and alive must not commit against the confused and universal that which you do not want it to do to you."

I thought that it was profound. Because everybody does. They do. They do even when they do not know what reward will come to them.

There was nothing more to say. We shook hands. We were dignified. Our hands were very hard when we shook hands. Martha began to cry. Ioannis began to cry. I saw them last through the bus window in the early morning grains of light, their faces against the gray window of the *kaphenion*, like masks.

XVIII I ran to find Daddy at the Piccadilly when I arrived in Athens. He was there, sitting with some American Greeks at the marble-topped table.

"Farouk, some coffee. Hot. Be sure to make it hot!" he ordered. "So you're back. Well, what do you say. What do you say!"

I unloaded my packages on the marble-topped table, and all the men laughed.

"What did you see?" Daddy asked.

"I saw everything. Phew!"

"Their icons talked and cried," he said.

"And they sang," I answered.

"Tomorrow they will complain," he said.

"And also sing."

"Then next day they will fight, and the Panagia will curse Christ and Christ will curse the Panagia, and then they will kiss, and they will fight again."

"But they will always sing. They will always sing."